CALCULUS
GRAPHICAL, NUMERICAL, ALGEBRAIC

TEACHER'S GUIDE
WITH ANSWERS

D1232411

Prentice
Hall

Glenview, Illinois
Needham, Massachusetts
Upper Saddle River, New Jersey

Many of the designations used by manufacturers and sellers to distinguish their products are claimed as trademarks. When such a designation appears in this book and Prentice Hall was aware of a trademark claim, the designation has been printed in initial capital letters (e.g., Macintosh).

Prentice
Hall

Introduction

Calculus: Graphical, Numerical, Algebraic is a course that will prepare students to excel on the Advanced Placement examination. In addition to this *Teacher's Guide,* the accompanying supplement titled *Advanced Placement Correlations and Preparation* provides correlations, AB and BC assignment guides, worksheets, and sample tests that will help you prepare a course that is equivalent to a college calculus course. That supplement also includes a Pacing Guides for the AB and BC courses.

USE OF TECHNOLOGY IN STUDENT EDITION

The calculator graphs in the student text were generated on a graphing calculator and then smoothed out on a computer. Color has been used to differentiate graphs when multiple equations appear on one screen. The advantage of this kind of art is that students can see the mathematics of the graphs without being distracted by the pixel format produced by the calculator. The disadvantage is that the smoothing of the curve sometimes fills in points that are not on the graph, such as discontinuities. Students will need to be aware that a graph that appears to be continuous in the book may not be. Students should be encouraged to read the text with calculator in hand, actively reproducing any calculator screen that is shown.

This text is a balance of graphical, numerical, and analytical approaches. The graphs are used to predict and support analytic and numeric results, while analytic techniques are used to confirm or prove results obtained with technology. An important goal of the course is for students to be able to use all three approaches to gain an understanding of functions, limits, derivatives, and integrals, and to communicate their understanding in writing.

EXERCISE SETS IN STUDENT EDITION

There is a set of Quick Review exercises for every section. These exercises provide practice on prerequisite skills for the lesson and for the regular exercises. The Quick Review can be used in several ways. Sometimes you might want to assign it the night before a lesson. Occasionally, you might want to have students work a Quick Review exercise before discussing a particular Example.

There is a wealth of problems in this text. A suggested assignment guide is given in each section of this *Teacher's Guide.* Cooperative Learning activities are indicated in the student edition (designated by the phrase *"Work in groups of two or three"*) and are suggested in this *Teacher's Guide.* Other exercises may also lend themselves to group work. Exploration exercises often have students use technology to actively experiment and work with the concepts of the lessons, which is often an appropriate forum for group work.

After Chapter 10 there is a Cumulative Review that can be used to review the semester or the year. On page 100 of this guide, a correlation between these exercises and the appropriate section is provided.

The Selected Answer section at the end of the student edition contains answers to all Quick Review exercises, most odd-numbered exercises, and all end-of-chapter Review Exercises. There is also a Selected Solutions section in the student edition that provides complete solutions to representative exercises from each section.

The complete *Solutions Manual* provides answers to Explorations in the student edition, in addition to all the exercises. Most of the time we show exact answers using analytic methods. Teachers should encourage students to use graphical methods when they are more appropriate. The exact answers will provide a good check for the graphical solutions.

USING THE TEACHER'S GUIDE

The bibliography at the beginning of each chapter provides a starting point for finding additional resources for the course. In the section notes, there are Objectives, Key Ideas, Notes on Examples and Exercises, Common Errors, Exploration Extensions, and samples of Alternate Assessment. Also included are Teaching Notes, which include suggestions for starting and concluding each section.

Take it to the NET
www.phschool.com

- Self-tests
- Lesson Plans
- AB and BC Correlations
- Downloadable Calculator Programs
- Professional Development

CONTENTS

Chapter 1   Prerequisites for Calculus   1

Chapter 2   Limits and Continuity   11

Chapter 3   Derivatives   19

Chapter 4   Applications of Derivatives   34

Chapter 5   The Definite Integral   43

Chapter 6   Differential Equations and Mathematical Modeling   53

Chapter 7   Applications of Definite Integrals   63

Chapter 8   L'Hôpital's Rule, Improper Integrals, and Partial Fractions   72

Chapter 9   Infinite Series   79

Chapter 10 Parametric, Vector, and Polar Functions   90

Cumulative Review Exercises   100

  Answers   101

          Chapter 1   101

          Chapter 2   119

          Chapter 3   128

          Chapter 4   145

          Chapter 5   163

          Chapter 6   170

          Chapter 7   183

          Chapter 8   189

          Chapter 9   196

          Chapter 10   207

          Cumulative Review Exercises   223

          Appendix   225

Chapter 4   Beginnings of Banking

Chapter 5   Merchant House

Chapter 6   Gold and Holdings and Manipulation Avenues

Chapter 7   Rules and Obsolute Insult

1

Prerequisites for Calculus

Bibliography

FOR STUDENTS:

AP Calculus with the TI-83 Graphics Calculator. George Best and Sally Fischbeck, Venture Publications, Andover, MA, 1998.

AP Calculus with the TI-82 Graphics Calculator. George Best and Sally Fischbeck, Venture Publications, Andover, MA, 1995.

HiMAP Pullout Sections from *Consortium: The Newsletter of the Consortium for Mathematics and Its Applications.* COMAP, Inc., Published quarterly.

Precalculus: A Graphing Approach. Franklin Demana, Bert K. Waits, Stanley R. Clemens, and Gregory D. Foley, Addison-Wesley Publishing Co., 1997.

A Student Guide to the AP Calculus Courses and Examinations. The College Board, 1997.

FOR TEACHERS:

Advanced Placement Course Description: Calculus AB, Calculus BC. Educational Testing Service, Published annually.

Consortium: The Newsletter of the Consortium for Mathematics and Its Applications. COMAP, Inc., Published quarterly.

Teacher's Guide AP Calculus. Daniel Kennedy, The College Board, New York, 1997.

FOR STUDENTS AND TEACHERS:

Resources for Calculus, Volumes 1–5. A. Wayne Roberts, Project Director, The Mathematical Association of America, 1993.

Solutions AP Calculus Problems Part II AB and BC 1983–1997. Broadwin, Lenchner, Rudolph, Mathematics Olympiads for the Elementary and Middle Schools, Bellmore, NY, 1997.

VIDEO:

AP Calculus Videoconference. The College Board, October 1996.

Calculus in the Year 2000: New Ways of Teaching the Derivative and the Definite Integral. The College Board, New York, 1996.

TI-83 Basics and Calculus. Sally Fischbeck, Venture Publishing.

TI-86 Basics and Calculus. Sally Fischbeck, Venture Publishing.

Chapter Opener

The Chapter Opener introduces students to an exponential function that models radioactive decay. Students = should observe that only a small percentage of the toxic material has decayed after 5500 years.

Solution:

$y = m(0.5)^{t/24,000}$

$y = 435(0.5)^{1000/24,400}$

$y \approx 422.8165$

$y \approx 423$ lbs

1.1 Lines

Objectives

- Students will be able to use increments to calculate slopes.

- Students will be able to write an equation and sketch a graph of a line given specific information.

- Students will be able to identify the relationships between parallel lines, perpendicular lines, and slopes.

- Students will be able to use linear regression equations to solve problems.

Key Ideas

Increments

Slope of a Line

Parallel and Perpendicular Lines

Equations of Lines

Applications

Teaching Notes

One way to introduce this lesson is to discuss increments on a number line or a ruler. Since students are frequently intimidated by the study of calculus, it is nice to start with something easy.

The concept of slope is used to develop the point-slope, slope-intercept, and general linear equations of lines. A discussion of the slope of horizontal lines (zero) and vertical lines (no slope) should be connected to the discussion of parallel and perpendicular lines.

Throughout the text, we assume that each student has access to a graphing utility (grapher). Students are expected to know the impact that changing the viewing window has on the representation of a graph and should be able to adjust the viewing window as necessary to obtain a graph that suggests all the important features of a function.

Agreement on drawing graphs: The phrase *sketch a graph* will mean to use pencil and paper without a grapher; *graph* will suggest (but not necessarily require) the use of a grapher; and *draw a graph* will mean to use the method of your choice. This terminology is consistent throughout the text and should be used in your lectures, class presentations, and testing.

To summarize the lesson, Exercise 34 can be discussed in class.

Notes on Examples

- In Example 5, it does not matter which of the two given points is used in the point-slope equation. You can assign or discuss Exercise 41 to ensure that students understand this.

- Example 9 uses the "solve graphically, then confirm algebraically" approach, which occurs throughout the text. A graph can suggest any number of facts that we can then verify algebraically.

Common Errors

In calculating a slope given two points, students often make errors when substituting into formulas and in doing arithmetic calculations involving negative signs. Before students begin calculating slope using two points, have them plot the two points and visually estimate the slope, then compare the estimate with their calculated answer.

When solving problems involving regression equations, students will frequently obtain wrong answers due to excessive rounding in the intermediate steps of a solution. You can reduce the chance of this happening by showing students how to automatically paste regression equations into the $Y =$ window of a graphing utility.

Notes on Exercises

- Ex. 5–24 and 31–34 are traditional exercises involving equations of lines. It is essential that students are able to complete these exercises easily.

- Ex. 39, 40, and 47 require students to perform linear regression analysis.

- Ex. 48 is an extension of Example 8, dealing with Fahrenheit and Celsius temperatures.

Assignment Guide

Ex. 3–36 multiples of 3, 37, 39, 43, 49

COOPERATIVE LEARNING

Ex. 44–46, 52

ALTERNATE ASSESSMENT

Journal Exercise 48

1.2 Functions and Graphs

Objectives

- Students will be able to identify the domain and range of a function using its graph or equation.

- Students will be able to recognize even functions and odd functions using equations and graphs.

- Students will be able to interpret and find formulas for piecewise defined functions.

- Students will be able to write and evaluate compositions of two functions.

Key Ideas

Functions

Domains and Ranges

Viewing and Interpreting Graphs

Even Functions and Odd Functions—Symmetry

Functions Defined in Pieces

The Absolute Value Function

Composite Functions

Teaching Notes

One way to introduce this lesson is to discuss examples of real-world functions. Include some relations that are *not* functions (such as the relation between heights and ages of students) to help clarify the meaning of function.

It is a good idea to review interval notation. Students must understand the difference between open and closed intervals in order to write domains and ranges correctly.

Many graphing utilities allow the use of Boolean logic tests that can be useful for graphing piecewise defined functions like the ones in Exercises 31–34. For example, the function in Exercise 31 can be entered as $y_1 = (3 - x)/(x \le 1)$, $y_2 = 2x/(1 < x)$. We use division instead of multiplication so that the grapher will display the different pieces of the function in connected mode without drawing extra "vertical" segments.

Agreement on the domain of a function: If the domain of a function is not stated explicitly, then assume it to be the largest set of real x-values for which the equation gives real y-values. If we wish to exclude values from the domain, we must say so.

Exploration 1 provides an interesting way to summarize the lesson.

Notes on Examples

• Example 7 introduces transformations of a graph. Students should be able to graph this kind of function without the aid of a grapher.

Common Errors

When using a grapher, students sometimes forget to enclose algebraic expressions in parentheses when they are part of a radical, quotient, or rational expression.

Some students tend to assume that technology is infallible, so they do not recognize grapher failure when it occurs. Remind them to use their prior knowledge about graphs in order to make sure that the results obtained on a grapher are reasonable.

When writing formulas for piecewise-defined functions, some students will attempt to define the function on intervals that overlap instead of on disjoint intervals.

Exploration Extensions

Exploration 1: Repeat Exploration 1 using $f(x) = |x|$ and $g(x) = \sqrt{4 - x}$.

Notes on Exercises

• In Exercises 5–18, 29–34, and 55–58, students are expected to draw on previous knowledge in finding the graphs of various kinds of functions. It may be necessary to discuss what important features are expected to be shown in the graphs.

• Exercises 19–28 encourage students to apply their prior knowledge and intuition to determine whether functions are odd or even.

• Exercise 35 introduces the vertical line test for recognizing graphs of functions. This concept is further developed in Exercises 37–40.

• Exercises 51–54 are similar to Exploration 1.

• Exercise 67 introduces the sum, difference, product, and quotient of two functions.

Assignment Guide

Ex. 3–33 multiples of 3, 35, 36, 39, 42, 45, 49, 53, 57, 63

COOPERATIVE LEARNING

Ex. 59–62

ALTERNATE ASSESSMENT

Interview Ask students to explain their solutions to Exercise 63.

1.3 Exponential Functions

Objectives

- Students will be able to determine the domain, range, and graph of an exponential function.
- Students will be able to solve problems involving exponential growth and decay.
- Students will be able to use exponential regression equations to solve problems.

Key Ideas

Exponential Growth

Exponential Decay

Applications

The Number *e*

Teaching Notes

One way to introduce this lesson is to describe what happens to a population of 10 rabbits if the population doubles every week.

Radioactive decay is an important application of exponential functions. Students should be comfortable with the concept of half-life.

The lesson can be summarized by comparing the time it takes for an investment to double at an interest rate of 8%, compounded quarterly, and compounded continuously.

Notes on Examples

- Examples 1–4 all present real-life applications of exponential functions.
- In Examples 1 and 3, it is important to realize that the population is given in millions.

Common Errors

Some students may forget to convert interest rates from percents to decimals before performing calculations.

Exploration Extensions

Exploration 1. Graph the function $y = a^{2x}$ for $a = 2, 3, 5$. Compare your results with the graphs created in part 1. (**The new graphs are compressed horizontally by a factor of 2.**)

Notes on Exercises

- Ex. 11–14 provide review of the properties of exponents.
- Ex. 27–32 involve various kinds of compound interest. Students should have learned how to perform these calculations in a previous course, but you may wish to review this material.
- Ex. 37–38 require students to find and use an exponential regression equation.
- Ex. 40 requires students to use a graphing utility to solve the equation $x^2 = 2^x$. Note that this equation is a *transcendental equation* that cannot be solved algebraically.

Assignment Guide

Ex. 3–24 multiples of 3, 22, 25–29, 34, 38

COOPERATIVE LEARNING

Ex. 19–22, 38, 39

ALTERNATE ASSESSMENT

Project Have students look up population data for your state and either find an exponential model for the data or explain why an exponential model is not appropriate.

1.4   Parametric Equations

Objectives

- Students will be able to graph curves that are described using parametric equations.
- Students will be able to find parametrizations of circles, ellipses, line segments, and other curves.

Key Ideas

Relations
Circles
Ellipses
Lines and Other Curves

Teaching Notes

Example 1 provides an introduction to the lesson. You can help students to understand the concept of parametric equations by plotting points that correspond to various values of t. To illustrate the importance of choosing an appropriate value for t-step, you may wish to show how a graphing utility would calculate the graph for t-step = 0.5 and t-step = 5.

You can summarize the lesson by showing how to parametrize the ellipse $\frac{x^2}{4} + \frac{y^2}{25} = 1$ as $x = 2 \cos t, y = 5 \sin t, 0 \le t \le 2\pi$.

Notes on Examples

- Example 3 examines a parametrization of a line segment. It is worth explaining how the restriction $0 \le t \le 1$ affects the graph.
- Example 4 shows how to find parametrization for a line segment. You may wish to explore other parametrizations for this line segment.

Common Errors

Students will sometimes confuse the parameter interval with the values that govern the size of the viewing window. The scale factors of the viewing window do not have an effect on the way the graph is drawn, but the t-step does affect the way the graph is drawn.

Exploration Extensions

Exploration 1. Graph $x = 3 \sin t$ and $y = 3 \cos t$ using the parameter intervals $[0, 2\pi]$, $[\pi, 3\pi]$, and $[-\pi/2, \pi/2]$. In each case, describe how the graph is traced. **(Full circle clockwise from $(0, 3)$; full circle clockwise from $(0, -3)$; half circle clockwise from $(-3, 0)$)**

Exploration 2. Graph $x = 3 \cos 0.5t$ and $y = 2 \sin 0.5t$ using the parameter intervals $[0, 2\pi]$, $[\pi, 3\pi]$, and $[0, 4\pi]$. In each case, describe how the graph is traced. **(Half-ellipse counterclockwise from $(3, 0)$; half-ellipse counterclockwise from $(-3, 0)$; full ellipse counterclockwise from $(3, 0)$)**

Exploration 3. Graph $x = 2 \tan t$ and $y = 2 \cos^2 t$ for the parameter interval $(0, \pi/2)$. Explain what you see. **(You see the right half of the witch of Agnesi. The relationship between x and y is the same in either pair of equations, as one may demonstrate by replacing t with $\dfrac{\pi}{2} - t$.)**

Notes on Exercises

- Ex. 6 provides an exploration of translations of parametric equations for circles.
- Ex. 7–26 provide practice in relating parametric equations to Cartesian equations.
- Ex. 41 is a challenging exercise that further develops the discussion of the witch of Maria Agnesi.

Assignment Guide

Ex. 3–30 multiples of 3, 42

COOPERATIVE LEARNING

Ex. 33–36

ALTERNATE ASSESSMENT

Self Assessment Have students write a paragraph describing any difficulties they encountered while graphing parametric equations.

1.5 Functions and Logarithms

Objectives

- Students will be able to identify a one-to-one function.
- Students will be able to determine the algebraic representation and the graphical representation of a function and its inverse.
- Students will be able to use parametric equations to graph inverse functions.
- Students will be able to apply the properties of logarithms.
- Students will be able to use logarithmic regression equations to solve problems.

Key Ideas

One-to-One Functions

Inverses

Finding Inverses

Logarithmic Functions

Properties of Logarithms

Applications

Teaching Notes

You may wish to revisit Example 8 of Section 1.1 as an introduction to the concept of inverse functions.

Tables 1.11 and 1.12 point out in a very concrete way the relationship between a function and its inverse.

The symmetry of a function and its inverse about the line $y = x$ motivates much of the critical thinking about inverses. When using a grapher to confirm the graphical representation of a function and its inverse, enter the line $y = x$ with the two functions and use a square viewing window to allow easier recognition of the reflection about the line $y = x$. (A square viewing window is a window in which the x- and y-axes have the same scale. Examples of square viewing windows include $[-4.7, 4.7]$ by $[-3.1, 3.1]$ on the TI-83, $[-6.3, 6.3]$ by $[-3.1, 3.1]$ on the Casio 9850, and $[-6.5, 6.5]$ by $[-3.1, 3.2]$ on the HP 48G.)

Students should understand the relationship between the domain and range of a function and its inverse. They should also understand that the composition of a function and its inverse yields the identity function: $f(f^{-1}(x)) = x$ and $f^{-1}(f(x)) = x$, for x in the appropriate domains.

A discussion of a function such as $y = x^3 + x$ can enhance students' appreciation for parametric graphing of an inverse function. This function has an inverse because it is one-to-one, but the equation $y = x^3 + x$ cannot be easily solved for x.

You can summarize this lesson by showing how to find f^{-1} for $f(x) = 9 \cdot 3^x$.

Notes on Examples

- After presenting Example 3, you may wish to show how to calculate the inverse of the function $f(x) = x^2, x \leq 0$, in order to emphasize domain and range issues.

- Example 7 introduces logarithmic regression.

Common Errors

You may wish to discuss the notation f^{-1}, which represents the inverse function of f. Some students need to be reminded that the -1 in f^{-1} is not to be interpreted as an exponent. That is, $f^{-1}(x) \neq \dfrac{1}{f(x)}$.

Exploration Extensions

Exploration 1. Complete (a), (b), and (c) for the functions $f(x) = 2x + 3$ and $g(x) = 0.5(x - 3)$.

Exploration 2. Support the power rule by completing parts 1–3 for $y_1 = \ln x^a$, $y_2 = \ln x$, and $y_3 = y_1/y_2$ (for $x > 0$).

Notes on Exercises

- Ex. 16–21 can be used to emphasize the domain and range issues that sometimes come up when dealing with inverse functions.

- Ex. 41–44 require students to use the properties of logarithms.

Assignment Guide

Ex. 3–42 multiples of 3, 43, 48, 50, 54

COOPERATIVE LEARNING

Ex. 51, 56

ALTERNATE ASSESSMENT

Interview Ask students to explain their solutions to Exercise 54.

1.6   Trigonometric Functions

Objectives

- Students will be able to convert between radians and degrees, and find arc length.
- Students will be able to identify the periodicity and even-odd properties of the trigonometric functions.
- Students will be able to generate the graphs of the trigonometric functions and explore various transformations upon these graphs.
- Students will be able to use the inverse trigonometric functions to solve problems.

Key Ideas

Radian Measure

Graphs of Trigonometric Functions

Periodicity

Even and Odd Trigonometric Functions

Transformations of Trigonometric Graphs

Applications

Inverse Trigonometric Functions

Teaching Notes

One way to introduce this lesson is to review the values of trigonometric functions of angles such as 0, $\pi/3$, $\pi/2$, $2\pi/3$, and so on.

Students should be familiar with the decimal approximations of irrational numbers that appear frequently in evaluating trigonometric functions:

$$\frac{1}{\sqrt{2}} \approx 0.707 \quad \frac{\sqrt{3}}{2} \approx 0.866 \quad \sqrt{3} \approx 1.732 \quad \sqrt{2} \approx 1.414 \quad \frac{1}{\sqrt{3}} \approx 0.577$$

Note that the solid and open dots shown in Figure 1.45 are intended to simulate the display of a particular graphing calculator. A calculator display may give the appearance of having different types of dots, depending on whether or not the curve hits the pixel corresponding to the dot.

You can use Example 5 to summarize the lesson. It nicely ties together the concepts of inverse trigonometric functions and the periodicity of trigonometric functions.

Notes on Examples

- Example 2 provides a good opportunity to review the concept of transformations of graphs of trigonometric functions.
- Example 3 introduces sinusoidal regression. This feature is available on many, but not all, graphing utilities.

Common Errors

Students will need to pay attention to whether their calculators are in degree or radian mode. Remind them that almost all calculations in this course will be performed in radians.

Exploration Extensions

Exploration 1. Explain why the relationships you found in parts 2, 4, and 5 occur.

Exploration 2. Predict what will happen if you repeat part 3 with t-step $= 45$. Then confirm your prediction using your grapher.

Notes on Exercises

- Ex. 25–30 provide practice in using inverse functions to solve equations.
- Ex. 33–34 and 41 involve sinusoidal regression.

Assignment Guide

Ex. 3–30 multiples of 3, 32, 34, 38, 45

COOPERATIVE LEARNING

Ex. 33

ALTERNATE ASSESSMENT

Portfolio Have each student select an exercise that demonstrates his or her understanding of inverse trigonometric functions.

2

Limits and Continuity

Bibliography

FOR STUDENTS:

A History of Mathematics. Carl B. Boyer (Second Edition revised by Uta C. Merzbach), John Wiley and Sons Inc., 1991.

Graphing Calculator Calculus Workbook, an Exploratory Approach. Al Shenk, New York: Harper Collins College Publishers, 1994.

FOR TEACHERS:

Calculus, An Active Approach with Projects. Stephen Hilbert, et. al. (The Ithaca College Calculus Group), New York: John Wiley & Sons, 1994.

Learning by Discovery: A Lab Manual for Calculus. Anita Solow, ed., MAA Notes Number 27. *Resources for Calculus* Collection. MAA, 1993.

VIDEO:

The Intermediate Value Theorem. Jack Koumi, producer, Open University World Wide, distributed by Films for the Humanities and Sciences (#6352), 1986.

MAA Calculus Films in Video Format, Tape 1. MAA.

Chapter Opener

The Chapter Opener introduces students to the concept of Economic Injury Level for insect pests that attack crops.

Solution: $D(t) = \dfrac{t^2}{90} + \dfrac{t}{3}$

What is t when $D(t) = 20$?

$$20 = \frac{t^2}{90} + \frac{1}{3}$$
$$1800 = t^2 + 30t$$

$$t^2 + 30t - 1800 = 0$$

$$(t - 30)(t + 60) = 0$$

$$t = 30 \text{ or } t = -60$$

Since t must be positive, $D(t) = 20$ when $t = 30$ days.

$$\text{Rate of change } = \lim_{h \to 0} \frac{f(t + h) - f(t)}{h}$$

$$= \lim_{h \to 0} \frac{f(30 + h) - f(30)}{h}$$

$$= \lim_{h \to 0} \frac{\frac{(30 + h)^2}{90} + \frac{30 + h}{3} - 20}{h}$$

$$= \lim_{h \to 0} \frac{900 + 60h + h^2 + 900 + 30h - 1800}{90h}$$

$$= \lim_{h \to 0} \frac{90h + h^2}{90h}$$

$$= \lim_{h \to 0} \left(1 + \frac{h}{90}\right)$$

$$= 1$$

The population density is growing at a rate of 1 pest per plant per day.

2.1   Rates of Change and Limits

Objectives

- Students will be able to calculate average and instantaneous speeds.

- Students will be able to define and calculate limits for function values and apply the properties of limits.

- Students will be able to use the Sandwich Theorem to find certain limits indirectly.

Key Ideas

Average and Instantaneous Speed

Definition of Limit

Properties of Limits

One-sided and Two-sided Limits

Sandwich Theorem

Teaching Notes

The function $y = \frac{\sin x}{x}$ can provide an excellent introduction to the idea of limits. Using a grapher, students can see that this function approaches 1 as x approaches 0. This discussion is found on page 56.

The function $f(x) = \text{int } x + \text{int } (4 - x)$ has interesting properties which can lead to a meaningful discussion of limits.

An important goal of the course is to make students be at ease with technology for exploration, confirmation and interpretation of results, and problem solving. Graphing utilities are very useful in the study of functions, but they cannot be used for proofs. Stress the importance of confirming all graphical solutions by algebraic methods.

A more rigorous treatment of limits can be found in Appendix A3.

A discussion of Exercise 54 and the Sandwich Theorem is a good way to conclude this lesson. Students should understand the Sandwich Theorem intuitively.

Notes on Examples

- In Example 2, stress that an instantaneous speed is a limit. It is very important for students to understand the calculations in Example 2, since similar calculations will be involved in calculating derivatives. This example provides a link with the discussion of rates of change in Section 2.4.

- Example 3 provides important practice in applying the properties of limits.

- In Example 5, the table-building capacity of a grapher can be used for a numerical approach that will help students to develop an intuitive understanding of limit.

- Example 8 gives examples of one-sided and two-sided limits.

Common Errors

Graphing utilities sometimes connect the two branches of the graph of a function like $f(x) = 1/(x + 1)$, suggesting that the function is defined and continuous for every value in the domain, including $x = -1$. To avoid this *spike* or *phantom asymptote* in the display, you can use a "friendly window" or "decimal window" (that is, a window in which the pixels correspond to exactly 0, 0.1, 0.2, and so on), or use the dot mode format for the display of graphs of such functions.

Notes on Exercises

- In Ex. 21–22, the undefined values of x will show up as "holes" in the graph if a "friendly window" or "decimal window" is chosen.

- Ex. 31–32 are excellent exercises to present in class for a group discussion.

- Ex. 49–52 provide a strong foundation for problems to be presented in later sections of the textbook. They are important for students who are planning to take the Advanced Placement Calculus examination.

- Ex. 65 is related to the definition of limit. One way to solve these problems is to set Ymin and Ymax, then find Xmin and Xmax so that the function just fits in the window, corner to corner.

Assignment Guide

Ex. 3–30 multiples of 3, 32, 35, 39, 42, 44, 45, 48, 49, 55, 58

PREPARATION FOR ADVANCED PLACEMENT EXAM

Ex. 45–52

COOPERATIVE LEARNING

Ex. 63

ALTERNATE ASSESSMENT

Self Assessment Have students write a paragraph describing any difficulties they encountered while finding limits.

2.2 Limits Involving Infinity

Objectives

- Students will be able to find and verify end behavior models for various functions.

- Students will be able to calculate limits as $x \rightarrow \pm\infty$ and to identify vertical and horizontal asymptotes.

Key Ideas

Finite Limits as $x \to \pm \infty$

Sandwich Theorem Revisited

Infinite Limits as $x \to a$

End Behavior Models

"Seeing" Limits as $x \to \pm \infty$

Teaching Notes

A discussion of the function $y = 1/x$ provides a meaningful introduction to both limits as $x \to \pm \infty$ and infinite limits as $x \to 0$. You may wish to show a graph of the function in the window $[-100, 100]$ by $[-1, 1]$, using the *trace* feature to show how the values of $1/x$ approach zero as x approaches $\pm \infty$.

The mathematical meaning of the symbol ∞ should be understood in the context of the phrase "$x \to \infty$," meaning that in a function of x, the x-value increases without bound. Students should understand that ∞ does not represent a real number.

Theorem 5 is important but may be confusing for some students, so it is important to discuss several examples. Exploration 1 provides examples which will help students understand the theorem.

You may wish to discuss the end behavior of three types of rational functions, that is, rational functions where the degree of the numerator is less than, equal to, and greater than the degree of the denominator, respectively.

A discussion of Exercise 41 can be an effective way to conclude the lesson. Verify the end behavior models algebraically, and discuss why the function has a vertical asymptote but no horizontal asymptotes.

Notes on Examples

- Note that you can solve Example 1 analytically by dividing the numerator and denominator of the expression by $|x| = \sqrt{x^2}$. This procedure can lead to interesting discussions about signs and absolute values.

- An alternate method of solving Example 9 involves dividing the numerator and denominator by x^3 in order to demonstrate that the limit is 0.

- Example 10 illustrates the fact that $\lim\limits_{x \to \infty} f(x) = \lim\limits_{x \to 0^+} f(1/x)$ and $\lim\limits_{x \to -\infty} f(x) = \lim\limits_{x \to 0^-} f(1/x)$. Some students may find this example easier to understand if a change of variable is introduced:

  If $z = 1/x$, then $\lim\limits_{x \to \infty} \sin 1/x = \lim\limits_{z \to 0^+} \sin z$. The method used in this example will be used in solving Exercises 43–46.

Common Errors

Many students will have trouble with limits involving the indeterminate forms $\dfrac{0}{0}, \dfrac{\infty}{\infty}$, and $0 \cdot \infty$. L'Hôpital's Rule, a rigorous approach to evaluating these limits, is the subject of Section 8.1.

Exploration Extensions

Exploration 1. Let $f(x) = 5 + e^x$ and let $g(x) = e^{-x}$. Can we use the product rule to find $\lim\limits_{x \to \infty} (f(x) \cdot g(x))$? Explain. Does the limit of the product exist? **(No; yes)**

Notes on Exercises

- Ex. 1–16 require students to use the graphing and table-making capabilities of a graphing utility to estimate limits.
- Ex. 53 requires students to model data using cubic regression and quartic regression. This exercise illustrates the fact that regression models sometimes make very unreliable predictions.
- Ex. 54 can provide important insight regarding the limit of a product, where the factors approach ∞ and 0, respectively.

Assignment Guide

Ex. 3–48 multiples of 3, 54, 57, 59

PREPARATION FOR ADVANCED PLACEMENT EXAM

Ex. 47–48

COOPERATIVE LEARNING

Ex. 49–51

ALTERNATE ASSESSMENT

Interview Ask students to express their understanding of end behavior models in their own words.

2.3 Continuity

Objectives

- Students will be able to identify the intervals upon which a given function is continuous and understand the meaning of a continuous function.
- Students will be able to remove removable discontinuities by extending or modifying a function.
- Students will be able to apply the Intermediate Value Theorem and the properties of algebraic combinations and composites of continuous functions.

Key Ideas

Continuity at a Point

Continuous Functions

Algebraic Combinations

Composites

Intermediate Value Theorem for Continuous Functions

Teaching Notes

You can begin the lesson by using a pencil to trace the graph of a continuous function over any interval without lifting the pencil from the paper.

The definition of continuity must be understood by students if they are to be successful in this course. Be careful to distinguish between continuity at an interior point in the domain (which involves a two-sided limit) and continuity at an endpoint (which involves a one-sided limit).

Different types of discontinuities are discussed on page 76. It will be worthwhile to illustrate each type of discontinuity with a grapher or with a chalkboard sketch. Names for the different types of discontinuities should be used consistently throughout the course.

A discussion of Exercise 31 can be an effective way to summarize the lesson. The discussion should include algebraic combinations and composition of functions, as well as a reminder that a continuous function can have many points of discontinuity (outside of the domain).

Notes on Examples

- Example 1 provides a visual introduction to continuous functions. It is important for students to understand why the function is discontinuous at $x = 2$.

- Example 3 illustrates the notion that continuous function can have a point of discontinuity (outside of the domain).

- Example 5 is important because it shows how to use the Intermediate Value Theorem in a way that students may not find obvious.

Common Errors

Some students may have difficulty recognizing the difference between continuity at an interior point in the domain and continuity at an endpoint.

Some students may mistakenly attempt to apply the Intermediate Value Theorem to functions that are not continuous.

Exploration Extensions

Exploration 1. Repeat steps 1–5 for the function $\dfrac{x^3 - 3x^2 + x - 3}{x^2 + x - 12}$, using an appropriate extended function in step 5.

Notes on Exercises

- Ex. 1–10 provide practice in recognizing different kinds of discontinuities.

- Ex. 25–30 provide practice with removable discontinuities.

- Ex. 39, 40, 42, and 47 require students to use the Intermediate Value Theorem.

- Ex. 49 gives an interesting example of a function that is defined for all real numbers but is not continuous anywhere.

Assignment Guide

Ex. 3–30 multiples of 3, 36, 39, 42, 48

PREPARATION FOR ADVANCED PLACEMENT EXAM

Ex. 43

COOPERATIVE LEARNING

Ex. 31–34

ALTERNATE ASSESSMENT

Journal Exercise 45

2.4   Rates of Change and Tangent Lines

Objectives

- Students will be able to apply directly the definition of the slope of a curve in order to calculate slopes.

- Students will be able to find the equations of the tangent line and normal line to a curve at a given point.

- Students will be able to find the average rate of change of a function.

Key Ideas

Average Rates of Change

Tangent to a Curve

Slope of a Curve

Normal to a Curve

Speed Revisited

Teaching Notes

One way to introduce this lesson is to recall the results of Examples 1 and 2 in Section 2.1.

Most students should already have an understanding of slopes, so they should be encouraged to examine the graphs of functions to make sure that their answers are reasonable.

The average rates of change introduced in this lesson provide an application related to limits or rational functions. They are also related to derivatives, although we do not use the word *derivative* in this lesson.

You can summarize the lesson by showing how to find the tangent and normal lines to the curve $y = x^2 + x$ at $(-3, 6)$.

Notes on Examples

- Example 1 introduces the concept of average rate of change. You may wish to point out that the average speeds calculated in Section 2.1 are examples of average rates of change.

- Example 2 illustrates that average rates of change can be estimated from graphs, even if the function is unknown.

- In Example 3, note that Q is considered to be a "floating" point that can move along the curve, as opposed to a fixed point on the curve. The notation $\lim_{Q \to P}$ (secant slope) makes sense in this context.

Common Errors

Many students are prone to algebraic errors when calculating the slopes of curves. Encourage students to understand their own mistakes so that they will be less likely to make these mistakes in the future.

Notes on Exercises

- Ex. 7–8 require students to estimate instantaneous rates of change from graphs.

- Ex. 9–12 require students to graph a curve along with its normal and tangent lines at a point. Stress that the graph in a square viewing window can be used to visually confirm that the calculations were carried out correctly.

- Ex. 34 uses data to illustrate that an instantaneous rate of change cannot always be estimated easily.

- Ex. 37–40 introduce the concept of *vertical tangents*. You may wish to discuss this concept with your class before assigning these exercises.

Assignment Guide

Ex. 1–33 odd

PREPARATION FOR ADVANCED PLACEMENT EXAM

Ex. 25, 26, 30, 32, 41

COOPERATIVE LEARNING

Ex. 37–40

ALTERNATE ASSESSMENT

Portfolio Have each student select an exercise that demonstrates his or her understanding of lines tangent to a curve.

Chapter 2 Review Exercises

PREPARATION FOR ADVANCED PLACEMENT EXAM

Ex. 29, 41–42

CHAPTER
3
Derivatives

Bibliography

FOR STUDENTS:

Visualizing Calculus: Powerful Programs for Graphing Calculators. Clarence Hopper, Dale Seymour Publications, 1998.

AP Calculus, 6th Edition. Shirley O. Hockett, Barron's Educational Series Inc., Hauppague, NY, 1998.

FOR TEACHERS:

Calculus Problems for a New Century. Robert Fraga, ed., MAA Notes Number 28. *Resources for Calculus* Collection. MAA, 1993.

Work Smarter Not Harder. Debra Crawford, Mary Ann Gore, and Sam Gough, Venture Publications, Andover, MA, 1997.

VIDEO:

Calculus in the Year 2000: New Ways of Teaching the Derivative and the Definite Integral. The College Board, NY, 1996.

The Mechanical Universe #3: Derivatives. David Goodstein et. al., California Institute of Technology, 1985.

Chapter Opener

The Chapter Opener teaches students the importance of using the proper dosage of a medication.

Solution: $D(t) = \dfrac{750t}{t + 12}$

To find the rate of change (in milligrams per year), we apply the Quotient Rule with $u = 750t$ and $v = t + 12$.

$$
\begin{aligned}
D'(t) &= \frac{v\dfrac{du}{dt} - u\dfrac{dv}{dt}}{v^2} \\[2mm]
&= \frac{(t + 12)\dfrac{d}{dt}(750t) - 750t\dfrac{d}{dt}(t + 12)}{(t + 12)^2} \\[2mm]
&= \frac{(t + 12) \cdot 750 - 750t \cdot 1}{(t + 12)^2}
\end{aligned}
$$

$$= \frac{750t + 9000 - 750t}{(t + 12)^2}$$

$$= \frac{9000}{(t + 12)^2}$$

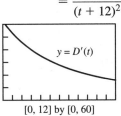

[0, 12] by [0, 60]

The graph shows that the shape of the graph resembles the growth rate of children. The rate is greater for younger children, and slows as they reach maturity.

3.1　Derivative of a Function

Objectives

- Students will be able to calculate slopes and derivatives using the definition of the derivative.
- Students will be able to graph f from the graph of f', graph f' from the graph of f, and graph the derivative of a function given numerically with data.

Key Ideas

Definition of Derivative

Notation

Relationships between the Graphs of f and f'

Graphing the Derivative from Data

One-sided Derivatives

Teaching Notes

An interesting way to begin this lesson is by presenting the graph of a function and showing how the slope of secant lines approaches a limit corresponding to the slope of a tangent line.

Students should learn to calculate derivatives using the definition. This can be done in two stages: first, calculate the derivative at a particular point $x = a$, then generalize the process to calculate the derivative at a generic point x. The different notations for derivatives should be discussed.

The lesson can be concluded by discussing one-sided derivatives. When discussing one-sided derivatives of a piecewise defined function such as the one in Example 6, emphasize that you are evaluating the left- and right-hand derivatives of a single function (not two functions).

Notes on Examples

- In Example 2, the derivative of $f(x) = \sqrt{x}$ is evaluated. The derivation requires the technique of rationalizing the numerator, which may be unfamiliar to students. Note that the formula for $f'(x)$ is needed for several exercises prior to Section 3.7, where the power rule for fractional exponents is proved.
- Example 3 visually demonstrates the relationship between the graphs of f and f'.
- Example 4 shows how to graph a function from its derivative.
- Example 5 shows how to calculate numeric derivatives directly from paired data. Students who solve Exercise 29 will learn how to calculate the data used in this example.

Common Errors

When calculating derivatives using the definition, students often make errors in evaluating and simplifying the numerator of the difference quotient. When $f(x)$ is a polynomial or rational function, h is always a factor of the simplified expression.

Exploration Extensions

Exploration 1. Use a pencil and paper to copy the graphs in Figure 3.3. Sketch a possible continuation of $f(x)$ representing the next 5 days. Then use the technique in Example 3 to graph the corresponding continuation of $f'(x)$. Use your graphs to describe what happened to the water in the ditch over the course of the 5-day period.

Notes on Exercises

- Ex. 7–10 require students to visually identify the correct derivative of a function whose graph is shown.
- Ex. 14 introduces students to the derivative of exponential functions, discussed further in Section 3.9.
- Ex. 19–20 involve determining derivatives from data. Some graphers have features that can eliminate tedious calculations. On the TI-83, the given data can be entered as L_1 and L_2, and slopes calculated using the command $\Delta\text{List}(L_2)/\Delta\text{List}(L_1)$
- Ex. 29 shows students how to find the data in Example 5. This exercise is meant for students who are familiar with probability theory.

Assignment Guide

Ex. 1–25 odd

PREPARATION FOR ADVANCED PLACEMENT EXAM

Ex. 21, 25, 26

COOPERATIVE LEARNING

Ex. 27, 29

ALTERNATE ASSESSMENT

Project Have students use the technique in Exercise 29 to create tables showing the probability that, in a group of n people, at least two people will have birthdays in the same month. Explain what happens when $n \geq 13$.

3.2 Differentiability

Objectives

- Students will be able to find where a function is not differentiable and distinguish between corners, cusps, discontinuities, and vertical tangents.
- Students will be able to approximate derivatives numerically and graphically.

Key Ideas

How $f'(a)$ Might Fail to Exist

Differentiability Implies Local Linearity

Derivatives on a Calculator

Differentiability Implies Continuity

Intermediate Value Theorem for Derivatives

Teaching Notes

You can introduce this lesson with an informal discussion of what it means for a function to be differentiable or nondifferentiable at a point. Give several examples to illustrate corners, cusps, vertical tangents, and discontinuities.

The text denotes a numerical approximation to $f'(a)$ by the symbol NDER $f(a)$ or NDER $(f(x), a)$. Each student should be able to use his or her grapher to calculate numerical derivatives. If a particular grapher does not perform this calculation automatically, NDER $f(a)$ can be calculated as $y_2(a)$, where $y_1 = f(x)$ and $y_2 = \dfrac{y_1(x + 0.001) - y_1(x - 0.001)}{0.002}$. This is the formula used for NDER by most graphers.

A discussion of Exercises 1–4 in connection with the Intermediate Value Theorem for Derivatives can be an effective way to conclude the lesson. Have students explain why the functions whose graphs are shown do not violate this theorem. (See Alternate Assessment, below.)

Notes on Examples

- Example 3 shows a function for which NDER gives wrong results. Emphasize the importance of the existence of $f'(a)$ if NDER is used to approximate $f'(a)$.

Common Errors

Students must know when $f'(a)$ fails to exist. For example, let

$$f(x) = \begin{cases} 2x + 1, & x \le 2 \\ \dfrac{1}{2}x^2 + 4, & x > 2 \end{cases}.$$

Note that f is not continuous at $x = 2$, so $f'(2)$ does not exist.

Graph $y_1 = (2x + 1)(x \le 2) + \left(\dfrac{1}{2}x^2 + 4\right)(x > 2)$ in dot mode.

Calculate NDER$(y_1, x, 2) = 502.00025$

Verify that $\dfrac{f(2 + h) - f(2 - h)}{2h}$ with $h = 0.001$ is $\dfrac{\frac{1}{2}(2.001)^2 + 4 - (2(1.999) + 1)}{0.002} = 502.00025$

NDER is not wrong. NDER is just not an approximation for $f'(a)$ if $f'(a)$ fails to exist. Emphasize that today's technology makes it more important than ever to know when the derivative exists at a point.

Exploration Extensions

Exploration 1. Graph $h(x) = -2.05 + \sqrt{0.0025 + (x - 1)^2}$ and zoom in on the point $(1, -2)$ several times. Is the function differentiable at $x = 1$? What function of the form $y = |x - h| + k$ does the function resemble near $x = 1$? **(Yes; $y = |x - 1| - 2$)** Note that $y = |x - 1| - 2$ never loses its sharp point.

Exploration 2. Repeat steps 1, 2, and 3 using $h = 0.001$. Compare your results to your previous results. **(20.001, off by 0.001; 20, exact; 300.030001, off by 0.030001; 300.000001, off by 0.000001; estimates are more accurate using $h = 0.001$.)**

Notes on Exercises

- Ex. 5–10 visually explore the relationship between differentiability and continuity.

- Ex. 11–16 require students to distinguish between corners, cusps, vertical tangents, and discontinuities.

- Ex. 31 gives an example of a function which is nondifferentiable due to oscillation.

Assignment Guide

Ex. 1–23 odd

PREPARATION FOR ADVANCED PLACEMENT EXAM

Ex. 29, 31

COOPERATIVE LEARNING

Ex. 24–28

ALTERNATE ASSESSMENT

Interview In Exercise 2, the points (0, 2) and (2, 4) are on the graph and 1 is between $f'(0)$ and $f'(2)$, but there is no value of x where $f'(x) = 1$. Have students explain why this does not violate the Intermediate Value Theorem for Derivatives.

3.3 Rules for Differentiation

Objectives

- Students will be able to use the rules of differentiation to calculate derivatives, including second and higher order derivatives.

Key Ideas

Positive Integer Powers, Multiples, Sums, and Differences

Products and Quotients

Negative Integer Powers of x

Second and Higher Order Derivatives

Teaching Notes

One way to begin this lesson is by discussing derivatives of linear functions. Students should easily understand this discussion, and the results are good examples for demonstrating that the power rule is plausible.

By the end of this section, students should be able to differentiate all polynomial and rational functions. Encourage students to confirm differentiation results by graphing $y = \text{NDER} f(x)$ and the calculated $y = f'(x)$ in the same viewing window. The two graphs should be the same. (The *trace* feature should be used to verify that both graphs actually exist within the chosen viewing window!) Alternately, a table can be used to compare several values of NDER $f(x)$ and the calculated $f'(x)$.

Learning the differentiation rules and their correct use is essential for all that follows, including the applications of derivatives and the antidifferentiation process. You might want to suggest the following mnemonic for the remembering the quotient rule:

$$d\left(\frac{\text{hi}}{\text{low}}\right) = \frac{\text{low di hi} - \text{hi di low}}{\text{low}^2}$$

To help students *discover* the derivative of a polynomial function, have them try the following grapher exercise.

> Let y_1 be any fifth degree polynomial function.
> For example, let $y_1(x) = 5x^5 - 3x^4 + 9x^3 - 6x^2 + 11x + 14$.
> Let $y_2 = \text{NDER}(y_1(x))$.
>
> In the statistics editor, list the integers from -5 to 5 in L_1, and generate L_2 by calculating $y_2(L_1)$.
>
> Set the decimal mode to 2 decimal places. Then calculate the quartic regression between L_1 and L_2 and paste the regression equation Y_3.
>
> Ask the students, "By studying the $Y=$ screen, can you guess the rule for finding the derivative of a polynomial function?"

The discussion of second and higher order derivatives is an excellent way to summarize and conclude. Point out the use of the differentiation rules in calculating second and third derivatives of several functions.

Notes on Examples

- In Example 3, stress the importance of using unrounded values of x when finding the corresponding values of y. Many graphers simplify this process by automatically storing the value of x when calculating the zeros of a function.

- When discussing Example 6, mention that it is normally desirable to leave the denominator of the answer in factored form when using the Quotient Rule.

- In Example 7, you may wish to show students an alternate method of finding the derivative, using the quotient rule. Students need to be aware that there are often several correct ways to solve a problem in calculus, and that one way is often much easier than another.

Common Errors

Students make many errors when using the rules for differentiation, both in applying the rules and in simplifying answers. Encourage them to use NDER to confirm answers.

When applying the Quotient Rule, students often interchange the terms in the numerator of the derivative. Students who cannot remember the order of the terms should be able to use a simple function such as $f(x) = x^2/1$ in order to determine the correct order.

Notes on Exercises

- Ex. 15 can be used to show several different methods for differentiating one function.

- Ex. 16 can be rewritten as a quotient before differentiating.

- Ex. 18 requires students to know the derivative of $\sqrt{x}$, which was given in Example 2 of Section 3.1.

- Ex. 22 requires students to use the Quotient Rule or the Power Rule for Integer Powers of x to find a formula for the derivative of $1/f(x)$.

Assignment Guide

Ex. 3–33 multiples of 3

PREPARATION FOR ADVANCED PLACEMENT EXAM

Ex. 28, 30

COOPERATIVE LEARNING

Ex. 35–39

ALTERNATE ASSESSMENT

Self Assessment Have students write a paragraph describing any difficulties they encountered while using the rules for differentiation and any techniques they developed for remembering these rules.

3.4 Velocity and Other Rates of Change

Objectives

- Students will be able to use derivatives to analyze straight line motion and solve other problems involving rates of change.

Key Ideas

Instantaneous Rates of Change

Motion along a Line

Sensitivity to Change

Derivatives in Economics

Teaching Notes

You can open this lesson by recalling Example 2 of Section 2.1, in which the instantaneous speed of a falling rock was determined. Explain the difference between speed and velocity, and present velocity as an example of a rate of change.

The main topic of this section is the motion of a particle along a straight line, with emphasis on free fall motion. Exploration 2 gives a method of simulating particle motion on a grapher using the *trace* feature.

The concepts of velocity, speed, and acceleration are essential to an understanding of this section. Emphasize that velocity is the rate of change of position, and acceleration is the rate of change of velocity.

The acceleration due to gravity can be either a positive or a negative number, depending on how one defines a coordinate system. In the equations given in the Free-fall Constants box on page 125, the positive direction is downward, but in Example 4, the positive direction is upward. Discuss the importance of choosing a convention and remaining consistent within any particular application.

In Exploration 2, encourage students to use the *path* or *animate* feature of the grapher, if available.

The discussion of marginal cost and marginal revenue is an excellent way to conclude the lesson. Students should recognize that many rates of change do not involve time or position.

Notes on Examples

- Example 3 is useful for illustrating why speed is different from velocity.

- In Example 6, have students compare the marginal cost with the actual additional cost of producing one more radiator per day, $c(11) - c(10)$ (assuming that the $c(x)$ function given is valid for $x = 11$). In this example, it turns out that the marginal cost is a somewhat poor approximation of this quantity.

Common Errors

Some students have trouble distinguishing between speed and velocity.

Exploration Extensions

Exploration 1. Explain why $\dfrac{dA}{dr} = 2\pi r$.

Exploration 2. Repeat steps 1–3 for $x_1(t) = \sin t$, $y_1(t) = 7$, in the window $[-1.5, 1.5]$ by $[-1, 8]$ for $0 \le t \le 2\pi$. $\left(\textbf{Particle reverses direction at } t = \dfrac{\pi}{2} \textbf{ and at } t = \dfrac{3\pi}{2}.\right)$

Exploration 3. A baseball is propelled straight up with a velocity of 40 ft/sec from a height of 24 ft above the ground. It reaches a height of $s = 24 + 40t - 16t^2$ ft after t seconds. Give the parametric equations and the appropriate values of tMin and tMax that you would use to simulate the ball's motion. (**One possible answer:** $x(t) = 3(t < 1.25) + 3.1(t \ge 1.25)$, $y_1(t) = 24 + 40t - 16t^2$, $t\textbf{Min} = 0$, $t\textbf{Max} = 3$)

Notes on Exercises

- Ex. 7 can be completed using a technique similar to Exploration 3.
- Ex. 14 previews the concept of antidifferentiation.
- Ex. 23–29 involve visual representations of position, velocity, or acceleration.

Assignment Guide

Ex. 1, 2, 4, 5, 10, 13, 14, 16, 24, 25, 27, 29, 30, 31, 33, 37, 38

PREPARATION FOR ADVANCED PLACEMENT EXAM

Ex. 16, 21, 23–26, 29, 36

COOPERATIVE LEARNING

Ex. 18, 20–22, 27

ALTERNATE ASSESSMENT

Interview Have students graph $y = 0.5x^3 - 3x$ in a $[-4, 4]$ by $[-3, 3]$ window. Ask: If $f'(x) = 0.5x^3 - 3x$, what does the graph tell you about the function of $f(x)$?

3.5 Derivatives of Trigonometric Functions

Objectives

- Students will be able to use the rules for differentiating the six basic trigonometric functions.

Key Ideas

Derivative of the Sine Function

Derivative of the Cosine Function

Simple Harmonic Motion

Jerk

Derivatives of the Other Basic Trigonometric Functions

Teaching Notes

You can begin this lesson by having students complete Exploration 1, which allows students to guess rules for the derivatives of the sine and cosine functions. In connection with this exploration, you may wish to have students set $h = 0.001$ and graph the difference quotient, $\dfrac{\sin(x + h) - \sin x}{h}$. Students should recognize the graph of $y = \cos x$.

The rule for differentiating sin x is proved directly from the definition of derivative, using the two fundamental limits $\lim\limits_{h\to 0}\dfrac{\sin h}{h} = 1$ and $\lim\limits_{h\to 0}\dfrac{(\cos h) - 1}{h} = 0$. The rule for differentiating cos x can be derived in a similar manner (see Exercise 14). You may wish to point out the important role of the angle sum formulas for sin $(a + b)$ and cos $(a + b)$ in these derivations.

The rules for differentiating the other four basic trigonometric functions can be shown easily by using the identities and the rules for differentiating the sine and cosine functions. See Exercises 15 and 16.

Remind students that most graphers require the secant, cosecant, and cotangent functions to be entered as $\dfrac{1}{\cos x}$, $\dfrac{1}{\sin x}$, and $\dfrac{\cos x}{\sin x}$, respectively.

The concepts of velocity and acceleration are extended in this section with a discussion of jerk, the derivative of acceleration.

You can summarize the lesson by presenting a table showing the derivatives of the basic trigonometric functions. Have students discuss various ways to remember these derivatives.

Notes on Examples

- Example 1 shows students how to use the derivative of the sine and cosine functions in combination with previously learned rules of differentiation.

- Example 2 introduces the concept of simple harmonic motion.

- Example 3 is related to the concept of jerk. If students have trouble understanding the connection between the acceleration of gravity and "just sitting around," you can explain that sitting still under the influence of gravity is equivalent to undergoing a constant acceleration of 32 ft/sec^2 (without gravity).

Common Errors

Students sometimes forget or misapply the basic trigonometric identities. You may wish to review the reciprocal, Pythagorean, angle sum, and half-angle identities.

When using a grapher, students sometimes forget to use radian mode or to enter expressions such as cos^2 x as $(\cos x)^2$.

Exploration Extensions

Exploration 1. Based on your results, find a formula for the *second* derivative of sin x. Confirm graphically using $y_1 = \sin x$ and $y_2 = $ NDER (NDER (sin x)). ($-\textbf{sin } \boldsymbol{x}$)

Notes on Exercises

- Ex. 14–16 provide practice in deriving formulas for derivatives of trigonometric functions. Students should recognize that these methods can be used whenever they forget one of the basic derivatives.

- Ex. 25 can be used to show students why we use radians instead of degrees in calculus. This will be further explored in Section 3.6, Example 8.

Assignment Guide

Ex. 2–22 even, 25, 27, 33

PREPARATION FOR ADVANCED PLACEMENT EXAM

Ex. 20, 27, 31

COOPERATIVE LEARNING
Ex. 23–24

ALTERNATE ASSESSMENT
Journal Exercise 28

3.6 Chain Rule

Objectives

- Students will be able to differentiate composite functions using the Chain Rule.
- Students will be able to find slopes of parametrized curves.

Key Ideas

Derivative of a Composite Function
"Outside-Inside" Rule
Repeated Use of the Chain Rule
Slopes of Parametrized Curves
Power Chain Rule

Teaching Notes

Examples 1 and 2 can provide an introduction to the Chain Rule. Since these examples are fairly easy to understand, they help to make the Chain Rule seem plausible. A rigorous treatment of the Chain Rule appears in Appendix A4.

The text takes a traditional approach for teaching the correct usage of the Chain Rule. First, students are taught to differentiate $y = f(g(x))$ by setting $u = g(x)$, calculating the two derivatives $f'(u)$ and $g'(x)$, and then applying the Chain Rule to obtain $y' = f'(u)g'(x) = f'(g(x))g'(x)$. The process is then shortened by dispensing with the u and simply referring to $g(x)$ as the *inside function*. This abbreviated process is called the *outside-inside* rule. Students should get plenty of practice with the Chain Rule so that its use becomes automatic.

When presenting the Leibniz form of the chain rule, $\dfrac{dy}{dx} = \dfrac{dy}{du} \cdot \dfrac{du}{dx}$, emphasize that $\dfrac{dy}{du}$ is evaluated at $u = g(x)$ and $\dfrac{du}{dx}$ is evaluated at x.

You can summarize most of the lesson by discussing Exercise 19.

Notes on Examples

- Examples 1 and 2 are meant to motivate the idea behind the Chain Rule.
- Example 7 shows how to use the Power Chain Rule. You may wish to point out that these calculations can also be performed using the regular Chain Rule.

Common Errors

In applying the outside-inside rule to differentiate $f(g(x))$, a common mistake is to omit the factor $g'(x)$ in the answer.

Notes on Exercises

- Ex. 6 and 14 require more work in simplifying trigonometric expressions than most of the exercises here.
- Ex. 33–38 require evaluating the derivative of a composite function at a given point.
- Ex. 39–40 emphasize that there are often several correct ways to solve a problem.
- Ex. 41–50 involve parametric equations.
- Ex. 14, 15, 16, 20, 27, 28, 33, 35, 45, 56f, 56h, 62, and 63 require students to know the derivative of $\sqrt{x}$, which was given in Example 2 of Section 3.1.

Assignment Guide

Ex. 3–69 multiples of 3

PREPARATION FOR ADVANCED PLACEMENT EXAM

Ex. 50, 57, 61, 64

COOPERATIVE LEARNING

Ex. 61, 69

ALTERNATE ASSESSMENT

Portfolio Have each student select an exercise demonstrating his or her understanding of derivatives of composite functions.

3.7 Implicit Differentiation

Objectives

- Students will be able to find derivatives using implicit differentiation.
- Students will be able to find derivatives using the Power Rule for Rational Powers of x.

Key Ideas

Implicitly Defined Functions

Lenses, Tangents, and Normal Lines

Derivatives of Higher Order

Rational Powers of Differentiable Functions

Teaching Notes

You may wish to begin this lesson with an informal discussion about graphs of equations of the form $F(x, y) = c$. Use equations whose graphs can be displayed on a graphing utility, in either parametric mode or rectangular mode, by graphing the separate branches in the same window.

Implicit differentiation is a powerful and important technique. It is used in applications and in deriving rules for differentiating inverse functions. The four steps for the computational process appear on page 151.

Point out the difference between the two power rules: $\frac{d}{dx}x^n = nx^{n-1}$ and $\frac{d}{dx}u^n = nu^{n-1}\frac{du}{dx}$.

You may wish to also show the power rule in the equivalent form $\frac{d}{dx}y^n = ny^{n-1}y'$.

You can summarize this lesson by discussing Exercise 38.

Notes on Examples

- In Example 2, the slope at a point on a circle is found using implicit differentiation. Challenge students to confirm the answer using analytic geometry.

- The relation in <u>Example</u> 4 can be graphed by solving for y and graphing $y = 0.5(x \pm \sqrt{28 - 3x^2})$ in rectangular mode. Gaps may appear in the graph near the two points where vertical tangents occur.

- Example 6a presents another way to obtain the result given in Example 2 of Section 3.1.

Common Errors

It is easy to make mistakes in taking derivatives which require the Product Rule and/or the Chain Rule. Students may forget to use the Product Rule when differentiating the term xy.

Exploration Extensions

Exploration 1. Consider the set of all points (x, y) that satisfy the equation $4x^2 + 4xy + y^2 = 9$. Use two different methods to find dy/dx. $(y' = -2)$

Notes on Exercises

- Ex. 23–26 require finding second derivatives using implicit differentiation. Example 5 shows a technique for doing this.

- Ex. 43 introduces the concept of orthogonal curves.

- Ex. 50 discusses the normal lines of a parabola.

Assignment Guide

Ex. 3–45 multiples of 3, 46, 50

PREPARATION FOR ADVANCED PLACEMENT EXAM

Ex. 40–42, 48

COOPERATIVE LEARNING

Ex. 40

ALTERNATE ASSESSMENT

Project Have students research the life and work of Descartes. In particular, what was his intent when he created the folium of Descartes (shown in Figure 3.45 of the text)?

3.8   Derivatives of Inverse Trigonometric Functions

Objectives

- Students will be able to calculate derivatives of functions involving the inverse trigonometric functions.

Key Ideas

Derivatives of Inverse Functions

Derivative of the Arcsine

Derivative of the Arctangent

Derivative of the Arcsecant

Derivatives of the Other Three

Teaching Notes

You may wish to begin this lesson by discussing the relationship between the slopes of linear functions and their inverses. This discussion can help to make the relationship shown in Figure 3.50 seem obvious to students.

When discussing Figure 3.50, stress the relationship between the value a in the domain of f and the value $f(a)$ in the domain of f^{-1}.

Exploration 1 will help students to understand how the derivatives for inverse functions are derived. For many students, an understanding of these concepts is much more useful than memorized formulas.

The inverse function-inverse cofunction identities and calculator conversion identities are very important. It is essential for students to know how to enter all inverse trigonometric functions into a calculator.

You can summarize the lesson by presenting a table showing the derivatives of the basic inverse trigonometric functions. Have students discuss various ways to remember these derivatives.

Notes on Examples

- Examples 1–3 are straightforward exercises showing how to take derivatives of functions involving the inverse trigonometric functions.

Common Errors

When using a calculator to evaluate $\cot^{-1}x$, students may attempt to use $\tan^{-1}(1/x)$. Point out that these two functions cannot be the same because the ranges are different and also because $\tan^{-1}(1/x)$ is undefined at $x = 0$.

Exploration Extensions

Exploration 1. Note that $(3, 248)$ is on the graph of f. Find $\dfrac{df^{-1}}{dx}(248)$, and explain how you found your answer. ($\approx \mathbf{2.457 \times 10^{-3}}$)

Notes on Exercises

- Ex. 24–26 require students to derive formulas for the derivatives of inverse trigonometric functions. Students are expected to use the inverse function-inverse cofunction identities for this exercise. If desired, you can challenge students to derive the formulas directly, using implicit differentiation.

- Ex. 34–35 show geometric representations of inverse tangents.

Assignment Guide

Ex. 3–33 multiples of 3

PREPARATION FOR ADVANCED PLACEMENT EXAM

Ex. 21–23

COOPERATIVE LEARNING

Ex. 22–23

ALTERNATE ASSESSMENT

Self Assessment Have students write a paragraph describing any difficulties they encountered while taking derivatives of functions in this section.

3.9 Derivatives of Exponential and Logarithmic Functions

Objectives

- Students will be able to calculate derivatives of exponential and logarithmic functions.

Key Ideas

Derivative of e^x

Derivative of a^x

Derivative of $\ln x$

Derivative of $\log_a x$

Power Rule for Arbitrary Real Powers

Teaching Notes

You may wish to begin the discussion of this section by discussing the graph of $y = e^x$ and having students decide what properties the derivative of this function ought to have.

A brief review of the properties of logarithms is appropriate, since students will need these concepts in order to understand the material in this section. For a visualization of $\dfrac{d(\ln x)}{dx}$, you can set up a table for the difference quotient $\dfrac{\ln (x + h) - \ln x}{h}$ using 0.001 for h, Xmin $= 0$, and $\Delta x = 1$.

A discussion of logarithmic differentiation (Example 7) is a good way to conclude this lesson. Make sure students understand why the derivative of $y = x^x$ cannot be found directly using the Power Rule or the rule for taking derivatives of exponential functions. You may also have students graph $\dfrac{dy}{dx}$ in Example 7 and discuss when it is not appropriate to use algebraic methods to find the derivative.

Notes on Examples

- Example 3 is an interesting twist on the concept of finding a tangent line to a graph. In this case, the point of tangency is unknown. Ask students to find the point of tangency $(e, 1)$.

- Example 4 can be used to show more than one method for solving one problem. Emphasize that a lot of time can often be saved—and the likelihood of error reduced—by simplifying an expression before taking the derivative.

- Example 7 presents logarithmic differentiation, a very important method which can often be used to find derivatives of exponential and some complicated functions.

Common Errors

Students may not understand how the Power Rule for Arbitrary Real Powers differs from previous results. Point out that, until now, the Power Rule has only been proved for rational powers.

Exploration Extensions

Exploration 1. Determine algebraically when the milk reaches a temperature of 71°F. What is the rate of change of the temperature of the milk at this time? (**After about 168.4 minutes; about 0.02° per minute**)

Notes on Exercises

- Ex. 43–46 require students to use logarithmic differentiation.
- Ex. 48 requires students to use two different methods to prove a result.
- Ex. 52 involves two orthogonal families of curves.

Assignment Guide

Ex. 3–42 multiples of 3, 47, 48, 50, 52

PREPARATION FOR ADVANCED PLACEMENT EXAM

Ex. 49, 53

COOPERATIVE LEARNING

Ex. 43–46

ALTERNATE ASSESSMENT

Interview Ask students to explain why the derivative of $y = x^x$ cannot be found directly using the Power Rule or the rule for taking derivatives of exponential functions.

Chapter 3 Review Exercises

PREPARATION FOR ADVANCED PLACEMENT EXAM

Ex. 59–67, 70, 78

CHAPTER
4
Applications of Derivatives

Bibliography

FOR STUDENTS:

Insights into Calculus with the Graphing Calculator. Herbert A. Hollister, Lexington KY: D.C. Heath, 1993.

FOR TEACHERS:

Applications of Calculus. Philip Straffin, ed., MAA Notes Number 29. *Resources for Calculus* Collection. MAA, 1993.

The Laboratory Approach to Teaching Calculus. Carl L. Leinbach, Joan R. Hundhausen, Arnold M. Ostebee, Lester J. Senechal, and Donald B. Small, eds., MAA Notes Number 20. MAA, 1993.

VIDEO:

MAA Calculus in Video Format, Tape 2. MAA.

Chapter Opener

The Chapter Opener introduces students to a cubic function that models the gas mileage of a particular car as a function of velocity.

Solution: The graph suggests that $m(v) = 0.00015v^3 - 0.032v^2 + 1.8v + 1.7$ has a maximum of at $v \approx 39$ mph.

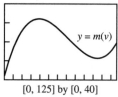

[0, 125] by [0, 40]

$m'(v) = 0.00045v^2 - 0.064v + 1.8 = 0$

$$v = \frac{0.064 \pm \sqrt{(-0.064)^2 - 4(0.00045)(1.8)}}{2(0.00045)}$$

$v \approx 38.6$ or $v \approx 103.6$

A relative maximum value of about 32.1 miles per gallon occurs at $v \approx 38.6$ mph. You should drive at a speed of about 38.6 miles per hour to obtain the best mileage. (The model gives higher values of $m(v)$ for $v > 136.1$, but we assume the model is not accurate for such high speeds.)

4.1 Extreme Values of Functions

Objectives

- Students will be able to determine the local or global extreme values of a function.

Key Ideas

Absolute (Global) Extreme Values
Local (Relative) Extreme Values
Finding Extreme Values

Teaching Notes

One way to begin this lesson is to sketch an arbitrary function such as the one shown in Figure 4.4 and discuss the local and global (absolute) minima and maxima of the function. Students can understand the definitions of these concepts more easily if they have an intuitive introduction to their meaning.

An understanding of minima and maxima is critical to the study of the applications of a derivative. Students need to understand the language of calculus, so emphasize the terminology of this section. Since confirmation of what is seen in a viewing window comes from analysis, it is important to incorporate previously acquired algebraic skills into the study of calculus.

Exploration 1 provides a meaningful conclusion for this lesson.

Notes on Examples

- Example 2 demonstrates how the extrema of a simple polynomial function can vary depending on the domain chosen. You may wish to extend this example by discussing the local and global extrema on additional domains such as $[-4, 2]$, $(-4, 2)$, and $[-4, \infty)$.

- In Example 6, it is instructive to note that, because the natural log function is an increasing function, the maxima of $f(x)$ correspond to the maxima of $\left|\dfrac{x}{1 + x^2}\right|$. On the other hand, the minimum value of $\left|\dfrac{x}{1 + x^2}\right|$ occurs at $x = 0$, where $f(x)$ is undefined.

Common Errors

Some students will assume that a critical point always corresponds to a local extreme value. It is essential that students see some examples where this is not the case. (This concept will explored in detail in Section 4.3.)

When finding the critical points of a function, some students will neglect to find the points where the derivative is undefined.

Exploration Extensions

Exploration 1. Compare the values of x where the extreme values occur with the values found in Example 6. Explain any relationships you see.

Notes on Exercises

- In Ex. 7–30, note that students should find and identify both local and global extreme values.

Assignment Guide

Ex. 3–30 multiples of 3, 37, 39, 42, 45, 48, 49, 52

PREPARATION FOR ADVANCED PLACEMENT EXAM

Ex. 35–36, 45–48, 49

COOPERATIVE LEARNING

Ex. 31–34, 53

ALTERNATE ASSESSMENT

Portfolio Have each student select an exercise that demonstrates his or her understanding of how to find the extreme values of a function.

4.2   Mean Value Theorem

Objectives

- Students will be able to apply the Mean Value Theorem and to find the intervals on which a function is increasing or decreasing.

Key Ideas

Mean Value Theorem

Physical Interpretation

Increasing and Decreasing Functions

Other Consequences

Teaching Notes

To motivate the Mean Value Theorem, you may wish to begin this lesson by discussing an simple application such as those presented in Example 3 and Exercises 39–42.

Spend some time discussing both the hypotheses and the conclusions of the Mean Value Theorem. The significance of the Mean Value Theorem is that it allows us to deduce properties of a function from its derivative.

In Corollary 1, note the use of open and closed intervals in describing where a function is increasing or decreasing. Students need to understand that the statement that f is increasing on $[a, b]$ does not mean that $f'(a) > 0$ or $f'(b) > 0$. They should also understand that if f is increasing on $[a, b]$ and decreasing on $[b, c]$, this does not mean that f is "both increasing and decreasing" at $x = b$.

The concept of antiderivative is a very important one. You may wish to conclude this lesson by having students discuss strategies for finding antiderivatives of simple functions such as those presented in Exercises 25–34.

Notes on Examples

- Example 3 provides a real-world application of the Mean Value Theorem by showing the connection between average rates and instantaneous rates.

- Example 4 stresses the use of closed intervals in describing where a function increases or decreases.

- Examples 6 and 7 are classic *initial value problems* requiring the determination of a particular antiderivative. We do not use the phrase *initial value problem* in this chapter, but students should be comfortable solving this type of problem.

Common Errors

In applying Corollary 1 in order to determine where a function f is increasing, mistakes can be made in solving the inequality $f'(x) > 0$, either by incorrectly factoring $f'(x)$ or by incorrect sign analysis. Graphical confirmation should enable students to detect such mistakes.

Some students have trouble with the use of closed intervals in describing where a function is increasing or decreasing.

Notes on Exercises

- Ex. 1–14 provide practice in finding intervals on which a function is increasing or decreasing.
- Ex. 15–24 are designed to help students to understand the meaning of the Mean Value Theorem.
- Ex. 39–42 are applications of the Mean Value Theorem. In discussing these problems, it is important to note the implicit assumption that the appropriate functions are continuous and differentiable.

Assignment Guide

Ex. 3–33 multiples of 3, 39, 42, 43, 45, 48, 52

PREPARATION FOR ADVANCED PLACEMENT EXAM

Ex. 43

COOPERATIVE LEARNING

Ex. 35–38, 51

ALTERNATE ASSESSMENT

Journal Exercise 46

4.3 Connecting f' and f'' with the Graph of f

Objectives

- Students will be able to use the First and Second Derivative Tests to determine the local extreme values of a function.
- Students will be able to determine the concavity of a function and locate the points of inflection by analyzing the second derivative.
- Students will be able to graph f using information about f'.

Key Ideas

First Derivative Test for Local Extrema

Concavity

Points of Inflection

Second Derivative Test for Local Extrema

Learning about Functions from Derivatives

Teaching Notes

You can motivate Theorem 4, the First Derivative Test, by presenting several graphs and having students discuss the derivatives and how they relate to the extreme values of the function.

This section presents several tests that are fundamental to analyzing a function and sketching its graph. These are the First Derivative Test for Local Extrema (Theorem 4), the Concavity Test, and the Second Derivative Test for Local Extrema (Theorem 5).

Although the use of these tests to sketch graphs of functions has been de-emphasized in recent years due to technology, it is vital that students understand the connection between the first and second derivatives and the graph of a function. The analysis of the first and second derivatives establishes all of the important features suggested by the graph on a graphing calculator and can confirm that the chosen viewing window does not exclude important features of the function's graph.

Students will need to learn to use their own judgment in deciding which test to apply in finding the local extreme values of a function. Sometimes y'' is too complicated or lengthy to find algebraically; the First Derivative Test may be easier than the Second Derivative Test.

Encourage students to write sentences describing their conclusions.

Many of the exercises in this section require students to report answers as decimals. In Section 4.2, we encouraged students to use their judgment in determining how many decimal places to report, but students should be aware that many standardized tests will specify a particular degree of accuracy. In particular, the Advanced Placement test specifies a certain number of decimal places to use in reporting free-response answers. The number of digits specified on the AP test may vary from year to year.

Exploration 2 provides an excellent conclusion for this lesson. Students will need to use most of the concepts in the lesson in order to complete this Exploration. Note that a graphing utility is *not* useful in completing the Explorations in this lesson.

Notes on Examples

• Example 6 is an application of logistic regression. Students should discuss why the ceiling found in part (c) is *not* an extreme value of the function. You may also wish to discuss whether or not the ceiling is realistic.

Common Errors

It is important for students to understand that the condition $f'(c) = 0$ does not guarantee that f has a local extremum at $(c, f(c))$. Likewise, some students identify any points for which $f''(x) = 0$ as points of inflection. Remind them that a change in concavity must exist in order for a function to have a point of inflection.

Exploration Extensions

Exploration 1. Let $g'(x) = 5x^4 - \cos x$. Find three different functions with derivative equal to $g'(x)$. How are the graphs of the three functions related? (**Any three functions of the form** $g(x) = x^5 - \sin x + C$; **vertical translations**)

Exploration 2. Sketch a possible graph of a function g that has all of the same properties as f except that $g'(0) = g''(0) = 0$.

Notes on Exercises

• In Ex. 13–28, encourage students to use both graphical and analytic techniques, as appropriate.

• Ex. 43–48 provide practice in sketching the graph of a function based on its properties.

Assignment Guide

Ex. 1–11 odd, 15–30 multiples of 3, 37, 40, 42, 44, 48

PREPARATION FOR ADVANCED PLACEMENT EXAM

Ex. 3–6, 33–34, 41–42, 50

COOPERATIVE LEARNING

Ex. 31–36

ALTERNATE ASSESSMENT

Interview Ask students to show how to sketch a curve having $f'(x) > 0$ and $f''(x) > 0$ for $x < 2$, and $f'(x) < 0$ and $f''(x) > 0$ for $x > 2$, given (**a**) $f(x)$ is continuous at $x = 2$, (**b**) $f(x)$ has a discontinuity at $x = 2$.

4.4 Modeling and Optimization

Objectives

- Students will be able to solve application problems involving finding minimum or maximum values of functions.

Key Ideas

Examples from Business and Industry

Examples from Mathematics

Examples from Economics

Modeling Discrete Phenomena with Differentiable Functions

Teaching Notes

You may wish to begin this lesson by having students come up with situations in which one might want to find the minimum or maximum values of a function. Be prepared to give several examples in case the students do not come up with any.

Students traditionally have difficulty with optimization problems, particularly with the formulation of the function to be optimized and the determination of the appropriate domain for the problem situation. In this regard, stress the six-step "Strategy for Solving Max-Min Problems" given on page 208.

You can summarize this lesson by going over an interesting application problem such as Exercise 31.

Notes on Examples

- In Example 2, it is important to note that the appropriate domain for the problem is the open interval $(0, \infty)$. It is enlightening for students to discuss what happens as $r \to 0^+$ and as $r \to \infty$.

- Note that an alternate method of solving Example 6 is to find an explicit formula for the average cost and then minimize this function. It is instructive for students to try both methods and verify that the result is the same using either method.

Common Errors

In optimization problems, students may overlook endpoints as possible candidates for optimal values, or find solutions that are outside of the domain of the input variable.

In graphing or optimization problems involving trigonometric functions, alternative solutions to $f'(x) = 0$ or $f''(x) = 0$ are often overlooked. The periodic nature of the trigonometric functions must always be kept in mind in these problems, except in some cases where the physical conditions of the problem restrict the domain.

Exploration Extensions

Exploration 1. Suppose that the disk had a radius of 10 in. instead of 4 in. Find a formula for the volume $V(x)$, and determine where the cone has its maximum volume and what that volume is.

$$\left(V(x) = \frac{\pi}{3} \left(\frac{20\pi - x}{2\pi} \right)^2 \sqrt{100 - \left(\frac{20\pi - x}{2\pi} \right)^2}; \ x = 20\pi - \frac{20\pi\sqrt{6}}{3} \approx 11.530 \text{ in.};$$

$$\textbf{volume} \approx \textbf{403.067 in}^3 \right)$$

Notes on Exercises

- Ex. 7, 11, 16–19, 22, 25–27, 31, and 42 are various applications involving volume. Some of them require students to maximize a volume, and others require students to optimize another quantity when the volume is fixed. Students need to understand the difference between these two types of problems.

- Ex. 32 and 33 are very similar. The *strength* of a beam refers to how much weight the beam will support without breaking, while *stiffness* refers to how well the beam resists deformation when supporting a weight. A very brittle beam would be stiff but not strong, while beam made from a different material might be strong without being very stiff.

- Ex. 55 is extremely challenging.

Assignment Guide

Ex. 1, 5, 9, 12, 17, 19, 20, 26, 31, 35, 36, 38, 40, 41, 43, 45, 46, 49, 50

PREPARATION FOR ADVANCED PLACEMENT EXAM

Ex. 41, 45–50

COOPERATIVE LEARNING

Ex. 18–19, 43, 54–55

ALTERNATE ASSESSMENT

Project Have students research the subject of "tin pest" (Exercise 47). What factors influence the value of k?

4.5   Linearization and Newton's Method

Objectives

- Students will be able to find linearizations and use Newton's method to approximate the zeros of a function.

- Students will be able to estimate the change in a function using differentials.

Key Ideas

Linear Approximation

Newton's Method

Differentials

Estimating Change with Differentials

Absolute, Relative, and Percentage Change

Sensitivity to Change

Teaching Notes

Exploration 1 motivates the idea of a linearization and is a good way to begin this lesson. Linearizations can provide useful estimates when dealing with complicated functions, especially if a calculator is not available.

Newton's method is a fast, efficient way to approximate roots of differentiable functions. Exploration 2 gives an outline on how to use Newton's method on a grapher.

The discussion of differential estimates of change is the final topic in this section and is a good way to conclude the lesson. It is important to note the connection between linearization and estimates of change; the differential estimate of the change in f when x changes by dx is based on a linearization of f.

Notes on Examples

- Example 1 is very important in the development of linearization. Stress the discussion at the end of the example.

- Example 2 is short, but very important. Example 3 shows the usefulness of Example 2.

- An interesting variation of Example 11 is to state the problem in reverse: If the radius is measured with an error $dr \leq 0.5r$, how accurately could we calculate the surface area?

Common Errors

When using Newton's method to find the zeros of a function, some students may stop after finding one zero or may not choose appropriate values for the initial guess x_1.

Exploration Extensions

Exploration 1. Repeat steps 1–4 using the function $g(x) = \tan^{-1} x$ and the line $y = \frac{1}{2}x - \frac{1}{2} + \frac{\pi}{4}$ (In step 2, zoom in on the point $\left(1, \frac{\pi}{4}\right)$.)

Exploration 2. Use Newton's method to find the zeros of several *linear* functions. Explain what happens. **(For nonhorizontal lines, Newton's method will immediately give the exact root, because the linearization is the same as the function.)**

Notes on Exercises

- In Ex. 8, have students write each expression in the form $(1 + u)^k$ and find an approximation for the function when u is near 0. The resulting approximations are reasonably accurate when $x \approx 0$.

- Ex. 50–51 are interesting because they give examples of functions for which Newton's method does not work.

Assignment Guide

Ex. 3, 5–9, 11, 14, 15, 18, 19, 22, 25, 27, 30, 33, 36, 39, 44, 50, 51

PREPARATION FOR ADVANCED PLACEMENT EXAM

Ex. 37, 46

COOPERATIVE LEARNING

Ex. 48

ALTERNATE ASSESSMENT

Self Assessment Have students write a paragraph describing any difficulties they encountered while using Newton's method.

4.6 Related Rates

Objectives

- Students will be able to solve related rate problems.

Key Ideas

Related Rate Equations

Solution Strategy

Simulating Related Motion

Teaching Notes

A good way to open this lesson is to review the topics of the Chain Rule, as applied to parametric curves, and implicit differentiation. These topics are difficult for most students, but a mastery of these topics is crucial to success in solving related rate problems where there is not a direct functional relationship between two quantities.

The six-step Related Rate Problem Strategy on page 233 affords students a step-by-step process to follow in order to reach the desired result. Students should also be aware of appropriate ways to support graphically, as in Exploration 1. Investigate all the features of a grapher that will help support the very difficult topic of related rates.

Exploration 1 concludes the lesson by showing how parametric mode on a calculator can be used to simulate the motion of a moving object when that motion can be expressed as a function of time.

Notes on Examples

- Examples 2–4 are designed to demonstrate the six-step Related Rate Problem Strategy.

Common Errors

The most common student error in solving related rate problems is premature evaluation or substitution, which makes it impossible to take the appropriate derivatives. Emphasize that evaluation is the final step in the six-step Related Rate Problem Strategy.

Exploration Extensions

Exploration 1. How fast is the top of the ladder moving as it begins its motion at $t = 0$? **(0 ft/sec)**

Notes on Exercises

- Ex. 12, 15–20, 24, and 32 are applications involving volumes.
- Ex. 13, 21, 31, 33, 34, 35 and 36 investigate rates of change involving angles.
- Ex. 29–30 require students to use similar triangles.

Assignment Guide

Ex. 3–39 multiples of 3

PREPARATION FOR ADVANCED PLACEMENT EXAM

Ex. 23, 34, 39, 40

COOPERATIVE LEARNING

Ex. 25

ALTERNATE ASSESSMENT

Portfolio Have each student select an exercise that demonstrates his or her understanding of related rates.

Chapter 4 Review Exercises

PREPARATION FOR ADVANCED PLACEMENT EXAM

Ex. 23, 32, 35–39, 53, 56, 58, 67

CHAPTER
5
The Definite Integral

Bibliography

FOR STUDENTS:

Preparing for the AP Calculus Examinations. Shirley O. Hockett, Barron's Educational Series, Hauppague, NY, 1998.

FOR TEACHERS:

Calculus Labs and Student Projects (revised field test version). Gregory D. Foley and David K. Ruch, Sam Houston State University, 1995.

Problems for Student Investigation. Michael B. Jackson and John R. Ramsay, eds., MAA Notes Number 30. *Resources for Calculus* Collection. MAA, 1993.

VIDEO:

The Mechanical Universe #7: Integration. David Goodstein et. al., California Institute of Technology, 1985.

Chapter Opener

The Chapter Opener teaches students how to find the future value of an annuity, that is, a series of payments. The formula assumes that payments are received continuously and interest is compounded continuously. Students are required to compare the values of two different payment methods for a sweepstakes prize.

Solution: Since it would not be fair to compare the value of one prize after 15 years with the value of the other prize after 30 years, we shall assume that the 15-year earnings are invested for an additional 15 years and we will compare the values of both prizes 30 years from the date payments begin. We will assume that interest is earned at the rate of 5%, compounded continuously.

First, we integrate to find an explicit formula for the value A.

$$A = e^{rT}\int_0^T mPe^{-rt}\,dt = mPe^{rT}\left[\frac{e^{-rt}}{-r}\right]_0^T = mPe^{rT}\left[-\frac{e^{-rT}}{r} + \frac{1}{r}\right] = \frac{mP}{r}(e^{rT} - 1)$$

Prize paid over 30 years:

The value after 30 years will be

$$A = \frac{mP}{r}(e^{rT} - 1) = \frac{(1)(167{,}000)}{0.05}(e^{(0.05)(30)} - 1) \approx \$11{,}628{,}841.$$

Prize paid over 15 years:
The value after 15 years will be

$$A = \frac{mP}{r}(e^{rT} - 1) = \frac{(1)(334,000)}{0.05}(e^{(0.05)(15)} - 1) \approx \$7,461,560.$$

We may use the continuously compounded interest formula, $A = Pe^{rT}$, to determine the value after this money is invested for an additional 15 years. This value is $7,461,560e^{(0.05)(15)} \approx \$15,796,123$.

The value of the prize is much greater if it is paid over 15 years instead of 30 years. At 5% interest, the 30-year future value of the 15-year prize is more than \$4 million greater than that of the 30-year prize. The results are even more dramatic at higher interest rates.

5.1 Estimating with Finite Sums

Objectives

- Students will be able to approximate the area under the graph of a nonnegative continuous function by using rectangle approximation methods.

- Students will be able to interpret the area under a graph as a net accumulation of a rate of change.

Key Ideas

Distance Traveled

Rectangular Approximation Method (RAM)

Volume of a Sphere

Cardiac Output

Teaching Notes

The Quick Review exercises provide an excellent introduction to this lesson. Have students discuss how these problems are related to the area concept.

Several methods of using rectangles to estimate the area under the graph of a nonnegative continuous function are introduced in this section. It is important that students graph the curve over the desired interval in order to visualize the area being sought. The built-in *shade* feature of many graphers can be helpful here.

You may wish to introduce sigma notation in order to allow for a simple and effective way to express the sums used in finding RAM approximations. This notation will be used in the definition of the definite integral.

Exploration 1 is important because it enhances the understanding of how estimates obtained using various RAM methods are related to an actual area under a curve. Students will learn that LRAM underestimates the area under the graph of an increasing function but overestimates the area under a decreasing function, while RRAM does the opposite.

For small values of n, students should be able to calculate $LRAM_n$, $RRAM_n$, and $MRAM_n$ by hand. For large values of n, students should use a RAM program. You may also wish to help students discover ways to use the list menu on a grapher in calculating various RAM estimates.

As n increases, students will see the approximating sums converge to a limit, which, after all, is the whole idea of integral calculus. An understanding of the RAM method can lead to a much greater appreciation of the Fundamental Theorem.

Example 4 provides a meaningful conclusion to this lesson.

Notes on Examples

- Example 4 is a very interesting application of areas under a curve, but students may not find it obvious that the cardiac output is indeed the number of milligrams of dye divided by the area under the dye concentration curve. See the Teaching Notes for Section 5.3 for an alternate way to demonstrate that this is indeed correct.

Common Errors

Some students may assume that the MRAM estimate will always be the average of the LRAM and RRAM estimates. Give an example (any quadratic function will do) to show that this is not the case. (See also Exercise 28.)

Exploration Extensions

Exploration 1. For each of the following functions, use the *x*-interval [0, 5] and an arbitrary value of *n*. Without doing any calculations, order the LRAM, RRAM, and MRAM approximations from greatest to smallest.

$$f(x) = 3x - 5 \qquad\qquad g(x) = 3\cos\frac{x}{4} \qquad\qquad h(x) = e^x$$

(For *f*(x): RRAM, MRAM, LRAM; for *g*(x): LRAM, MRAM, RRAM; for *h*(x): RRAM, MRAM, LRAM)

Notes on Exercises

- In Ex. 5–9, students can choose which RAM method to use.
- Ex. 14–21 provide practice in finding volumes.

Assignment Guide

Ex. 1–4, 6, 9, 12, 14, 15, 18, 20, 21, 24, 26

PREPARATION FOR ADVANCED PLACEMENT EXAM

Ex. 24

COOPERATIVE LEARNING

Ex. 27

ALTERNATE ASSESSMENT

Journal Exercise 26

5.2 Definite Integrals

Objectives

- Students will be able to express the area under a curve as a definite integral and as a limit of Riemann sums.

- Students will be able to compute the area under a curve using a numerical integration procedure.

Key Ideas

Riemann Sums

Terminology and Notation of Integration

Definite Integral and Area

Constant Functions

Integrals on a Calculator

Discontinuous Integrable Functions

Teaching Notes

A review of sigma notation is essential to the understanding of this lesson. You may wish to use the Quick Review exercises for this purpose.

The formal definition of the definite integral as a limiting value of Riemann sums is presented in this section. To understand how the definition works it is easiest to first assume that the function is nonnegative. In that case, the value of the definite integral is the exact area under the curve, and a Riemann sum is a rectangular approximation of that area. Students should understand that in the Riemann sum, $f(c_k)$ and Δx_k represent the height and width of the kth rectangle, so the Riemann sum represents the sum of the areas of n rectangles. As the norm of the partition approaches 0, these approximating Riemann sums approach the exact value of the area. Emphasize that LRAM, MRAM, and RRAM are *examples* of Riemann sums.

Students should then discuss the case when the function takes on negative values at some or all of the points in the interval of integration. The main idea to establish here is that the definite integral represents the *signed* or net area of the region between the graph of the function and the x-axis.

Students may think the proof of Theorem 2 is unnecessarily tedious, since $c(b - a)$ is clearly the area of the rectangles according to the simple geometry formula, $A = bh$. In some sense, what this proof shows is that the area, defined as an integral, is in fact the same as our usual notion of area. Note that, while integrals are commonly thought of as areas, there are many different kinds of quantities that can be represented as integrals.

Be sure that students understand Exploration 1, which provides a conceptual understanding of the integral.

Many graphers have a built-in numerical integrator. Make sure that each student can translate from a definite integral to the notation utilized by his or her grapher and vice versa. Although the NINT notation is very convenient, it is important to note that the Advanced Placement test requires students to use integral notation, not calculator notation, for credit on free response questions.

A discussion of mathematical induction (Appendix A2) is an interesting way to supplement and conclude your presentation of this lesson. Mathematical induction can be used to verify the formula used in Exercise 48.

Notes on Examples

• Example 2 shows how to use the well-known formula for the area of a circle to evaluate an integral that would be difficult to evaluate using other methods.

• In Example 3, it is important to discuss how the units of the answer are obtained. Students should understand that the dt inside the integral includes the units of time.

Common Errors

In writing definite integrals, students will often omit the dx.

Some students will assume that values reported by NINT are always very nearly exact. NINT is likely to fail when a function is nearly zero except in a very small portion of an interval, as in

$$\int_0^{4000} e^{-x} \, dx \text{ or } \int_0^{1000} e^{-x^2} \, dx.$$

Exploration Extensions

Exploration 1. Determine the values of $\int_0^{2\pi} (3 + \sin x)\, dx$ and $\int_0^{\pi/2} \sin 2x\, dx$. Give a convincing argument for each value, based on the graph of the function. **(6π; 1)**

Exploration 2. Use areas to show that $\int_{-4}^6 \text{int}\, |2x|\, dx = 47$.

Notes on Exercises

- In Ex. 7–38 and 44, NINT may be used to check answers. However, this method will not necessarily work for Ex. 43, 45, or 46, since the calculator will report an error if it attempts to evaluate the formula at a point where it is undefined.

Assignment Guide

Ex. 3–27 multiples of 3, 39, 40, 41, 43, 46

PREPARATION FOR ADVANCED PLACEMENT EXAM

Ex. 43–46

COOPERATIVE LEARNING

Ex. 29–38

ALTERNATE ASSESSMENT

Interview Ask students to explain their solutions to Exercise 27.

5.3 Definite Integrals and Antiderivatives

Objectives

- Students will be able to apply rules for definite integrals and find the average value of a function over a closed interval.

Key Ideas

Properties of Definite Integrals

Average Value of a Function

Mean Value Theorem for Definite Integrals

Connecting Differential and Integral Calculus

Teaching Notes

A review of Example 5 in Section 5.2 can be used to open the lesson with a discussion of the Additivity rule for definite integrals. This rule, along with the other algebra rules of the definite integral are given without detailed proofs. Students should discuss their intuitive understanding of these rules.

Note that the Max-Min Inequality in Table 5.3 can be derived as a consequence of the

Domination rule: Let $g(x) = \min f$. Then $f(x) \geq g(x)$ on $[a, b]$,

so $\int_a^b f(x)\, dx \geq \int_a^b g(x)\, dx = \min f \cdot (b - a)$. Similarly, $\int_a^b f(x)\, dx \leq \max f \cdot (b - a)$

An interesting way to apply the concept of the average value of a function is to verify the formula used in Example 4 of Section 5.1, as follows:

(Amount of blood pumped)(average concentration) = total amount of dye

$$(\text{cardiac output} \cdot \text{time})\left(\frac{\text{area under curve}}{\text{time}}\right) = \text{total amount of dye}$$

$$\text{cardiac output} = \frac{\text{total amount of dye}}{\text{area under curve}}$$

The lesson concludes with a discussion which foreshadows the Fundamental Theorem of Calculus. Exploration 2 is a critically important visual proof of the Fundamental Theorem. This Exploration will help students achieve one of the goals of the course—to understand the relationship between derivatives and integrals. The historical perspective is intended to give students a sense of discovery as they work through Exploration 2.

The function $F(x) = \int_a^x f(t)\, dt$ is sometimes called the *accumulation function* of f.

Notes on Examples

- Example 1 allows students to investigate the definite integral rules without the use of particular functions. This type of problem reinforces the idea that the capabilities of machines are not always necessary or sufficient in finding answers.

Common Errors

Students often make algebraic mistakes when finding antiderivatives. Students should get in the habit of differentiating their answer to verify that they found the correct antiderivative.
In finding the area of a region between a curve and the x-axis, some students neglect to pay attention to the sign of the function. Functions that have both positive and negative values warrant special consideration. The region should be divided so that intervals for which the curve is above the x-axis and below the x-axis are considered separately. For any portion of the region below the x-axis, the value of the integral will be negative and is negated to represent the area. A good way to check results for this kind of problem is to find $\text{NINT}(|f(x)|, x, a, b)$. This procedure is stated explicitly in Section 5.4, page 284.

Exploration Extensions

Exploration 1. Find the value of x for which the function $y = 2\sqrt{r^2 - x^2}$ assumes the value found in step 4. $\left(x = r\sqrt{1 - \dfrac{\pi^2}{16}}\right)$

Exploration 2. Suppose you chose a different value, also less than x, for a. Would the value of $F'(x)$ change? Explain. **(No)**

Notes on Exercises

- Ex. 1–6 require an understanding of the algebraic properties of the definite integral. Point out that NINT is of no use in solving these problems.

- Ex. 7–24 provide practice in evaluating integrals or calculating areas. Results can be verified using numerical integrals of $f(x)$ or $|f(x)|$.

Assignment Guide

Ex. 1, 3, 4, 6, 7, 10, 11, 13, 16, 17, 20, 21, 24, 25, 28, 29, 32, 36, 38, 40, 43, 44

PREPARATION FOR ADVANCED PLACEMENT EXAM

Ex. 2, 4, 29, 33–35

COOPERATIVE LEARNING

Exploration 2; Ex. 33–34

ALTERNATE ASSESSMENT

Self Assessment Have students write a paragraph describing any difficulties they encountered while evaluating definite integrals.

5.4   Fundamental Theorem of Calculus

Objectives

- Students will be able to apply the Fundamental Theorem of Calculus.
- Students will understand the relationship between the derivative and the definite integral as expressed in both parts of the Fundamental Theorem of Calculus.

Key Ideas

Fundamental Theorem, Part 1

Graphing the Function $\int_a^x f(t)\, dt$

Fundamental Theorem, Part 2

Area Connection

More Applications

Teaching Notes

One way to begin this lesson is let $f(x) = c$ and $F(x) = cx$, and observe that $F(x) = \int_0^x c\, dt = \int_0^x f(x)\, dt$ and $F'(x) = f(x)$. A simple example like this can help students to become comfortable with a function definition in the form $F(x) = \int_a^x f(t)\, dt$ and can help to make the Fundamental Theorem of Calculus easier to understand.

Defining a function in the form $F(x) = \int_a^x f(t)\, dt$ plays a critical role in the fundamental theorems. When $f(x)$ is a positive function, $F(x)$ can be interpreted as the area under the graph of f over the interval $[a, x]$. Observe in this case that $F(x) > 0$ when $x > a$, $F(x) < 0$ when $x < a$, and $F(a) = 0$. Changing the value of a will create a new function which differs from $F(x)$ by a constant. In fact, if $G(x) = \int_b^x f(t)\, dt$, then $G(x) = F(x) - F(b)$. This equation should become obvious to students when it is rewritten in the form $\int_b^x f(t)\, dt = \int_a^x f(t)\, dt - \int_a^b f(t)\, dt$.

Exploration 2 demonstrates that the Fundamental Theorem of Calculus, Part 1, can be supported graphically by graphing NDER(NINT($f(x)$, x, a, x)) for particular functions $f(x)$. All such graphs will be the same regardless of the value of a. Since the graphing of this function is quite slow in function plotting mode, it may be a good idea to adjust the x-resolution or to use parametric mode with a somewhat large value of Tstep, using $x = t$ and $y = $ NDER(NINT($f(x)$, x, a, t), t).

A discussion of economic applications provides a meaningful conclusion to this lesson.

Notes on Examples

- In Example 4, it is important to note the choice $a = 3$ for the lower limit of integration. A student who writes $f(x) = \int_a^x \tan t \, dt$ and then attempts to determine the value of a would probably become frustrated. In discussing Example 4, you may wish to use the notation $F(x)$ instead of $f(x)$, as this may help to clarify the connection with the Fundamental Theorem. With this notation, Example 4 leads directly to the equation $F(x) - F(3) = \int_3^x \tan t \, dt$, which leads directly to the Fundamental Theorem, Part 2. Finally, note that the nature of the tangent function means that there are some important domain issues involved in Example 4. These issues are the subject of Exploration 1.

Common Errors

Some students are misled by the fact that the expression NINT($f(x)$, x, a, x) is understood by most graphers. It is important for students to realize that the variable x should not represent two different quantities within one mathematical expression, so the expression $\int_a^x f(x) \, dx$ is to be avoided. Note that graphing utilities also understand the notations NINT($f(t)$, t, a, x) or NINT($f(x)$, x, a, t).

Exploration Extensions

Exploration 1. Suppose $G(x) = \int_3^x \csc x \, dx$. What is the domain of $G(x)$? (**The domain is $(0, \pi)$.**)

Exploration 2. Graph NDER(NINT(x^2, x, x, 0)). How is the graph of $y = \dfrac{d}{dx} \int_x^0 f(t) \, dt$ related to the graph of $\dfrac{d}{dx} \int_0^x f(t) \, dt$? (**Each graph is the reflection of the other over the x-axis.**)

Notes on Exercises

- Ex. 1–14 provide practice in calculating integrals analytically using the Fundamental Theorem, Part 2.

- In Ex. 25–28, students need to examine the shaded region in order to establish a way to find the area. Ex. 25 and 26 require two integrals, and Ex. 27 and 28 require subtraction. The values can be found analytically.

- Ex. 37–42 can be done in either of two ways: by using the Fundamental Theorem, Part 1 in combination with the Chain Rule (see Example 2), or by evaluating the definite integral and then differentiating. Encourage students to try both methods and verify that the results are the same.

Assignment Guide

Ex. 3–51 multiples of 3, 52, 54, 59

PREPARATION FOR ADVANCED PLACEMENT EXAM

Ex. 53–55, 56, 60, 64

COOPERATIVE LEARNING

Ex. 53–55

ALTERNATE ASSESSMENT

Portfolio Have each student select an exercise demonstrating his or her understanding of the relationship between differential and integral calculus.

5.5 Trapezoidal Rule

Objectives

- Students will be able to approximate the definite integral by using the Trapezoidal Rule and by using Simpson's Rule, and estimate the error in using the Trapezoidal and Simpson's Rules.

Key Ideas

Trapezoidal Approximations

Other Algorithms

Error Analysis

Teaching Notes

You can begin this lesson by having students discuss the relative accuracy of the LRAM, MRAM, and RRAM methods, and see if students can think of ways to improve the accuracy without increasing the number of intervals used.

Many definite integrals cannot be computed algebraically by any means. The Trapezoidal Rule and Simpson's Rule are powerful tools for finding those integrals numerically.

In the Trapezoidal Rule, the region between the graph of f and the x-axis is partitioned into n equal subintervals as in the RAM methods, but trapezoids are used in place of rectangles. The top of each trapezoid is the line segment connecting two consecutive partition points on the curve. The approximation of the integral is the sum of the areas of the n trapezoids. Since the chord joining two consecutive points will in general fit a curve better than a horizontal line, the Trapezoidal Rule generally gives better results than a RAM method.

In Simpson's Rule, the interval of integration is divided into an *even* number n of equal subintervals. Over each consecutive *pair* of subintervals, the curve is approximated by the *parabola* determined by the three consecutive partition points. The approximation of the definite integral is the sum of the integrals of the $n/2$ parabolic arcs. Simpson's Rule generally gives very accurate results for relatively small values of n.

As with the RAM methods, students can use grapher programs to compute the Trapezoidal Rule and Simpson's Rule approximations for the definite integral of a function. Students should note how many more subintervals are required for RAM methods to get answers that are as accurate as those given by the Trapezoidal Rule and by Simpson's Rule.

A discussion of the error formulas for the Trapezoidal Rule and Simpson's Rule provide a meaningful conclusion to this lesson. The error formulas show that the amount of possible error quickly decreases as the number of partitions increases. Computing the possible error of each will help establish the accuracy of the two methods.

Notes on Examples

- Example 2 demonstrates that rules such as the Trapezoidal Rule can be used to analyze numerical data, even if no related function is known.

- In Example 2, you can highlight the effectiveness of Simpson's Rule by having students compare the result with the results for the Trapezoidal Rule MRAM ($T_4 = 35.3125$; $MRAM_4 \approx 30.3516$.)

Common Errors

Some students will assume that the Trapezoidal Rule is equivalent to MRAM. The simple function $y = x^2$ can be used to illustrate how the two rules differ. For this function, the Trapezoidal Rule will always give an overestimate of the integral, and MRAM will always give an underestimate.

Exploration Extensions

Exploration 1. Use the result of step 4 to calculate the area under the graph of $y = -2x^2 + 3x + 15$ over the interval $-2 \leq x \leq 2.$ $\left(\mathbf{49\frac{1}{3}} \right)$

Notes on Exercises

- In Ex. 1–6, Trapezoidal Rule approximations are compared to exact values of definite integrals.

- Ex. 8–9 are real-world problems that cannot be solved using a definite integral because the function is not known. This illustrates the need for numerical techniques such as the Trapezoidal Rule and Simpson's Rule.

- Ex. 23–24 establish relationships between the Trapezoidal Rule, Simpson's Rule, and the RAM methods.

Assignment Guide

Ex. 1, 4, 7, 8, 10, 11, 13, 16, 17, 18, 23

PREPARATION FOR ADVANCED PLACEMENT EXAM

Ex. 19

COOPERATIVE LEARNING

Ex. 19–20

ALTERNATE ASSESSMENT

Project Have students use a map and the Trapezoidal Rule to estimate the area of a lake, state, or county in your area. Students should sketch and measure equally spaced, parallel lines on the map (see the figure accompanying Exercise 8). After calculations are completed, have students compare their results with the area given in an almanac or atlas.

Chapter 5 Review Exercises

PREPARATION FOR ADVANCED PLACEMENT EXAM

Ex. 46, 51, 54

C H A P T E R

6

Differential Equations
and Mathematical Modeling

Bibliography

FOR STUDENTS:

Barron's How to Prepare for Advanced Placement Examinations: Mathematics. Shirley O. Hockett, Barron's Education Services, 1998.

Real-World Math with the CBL™ System. Chris Brueningsen, Bill Bower, Linda Antione, and Elisa Brueningsen, Texas Instruments.

FOR TEACHERS:

Readings for Calculus. Underwood Dudley, ed., MAA Notes Number 31, *Resources for Calculus* Collection, MAA, 1993.

AP Calculus with the TI-83, George Best and Sally Fischbeck, Venture Publishing, Andover, MA, 1997.

Chapter Opener

The Chapter Opener introduces students to a method for determining underwater light intensity. Note that the value of k will be smallest if the water is very clear.

Solution: We need to find the depth x for which $I_x = 0.01I_o$.

$$k = \frac{1.7}{\text{Secchi depth}} = \frac{1.7}{55}$$

$$0.01I_0 = I_0 e^{-kx}$$

$$0.01 = e^{-1.7x/55}$$

$$\ln 0.01 = -\frac{1.7x}{55}$$

$$x = \frac{-55 \ln 0.01}{1.7} \approx 148.991$$

The depth is about 149 meters.

6.1   Antiderivatives and Slope Fields

Objectives

- Students will be able to construct antiderivatives using the Fundamental Theorem of Calculus.
- Students will be able to find antiderivatives of polynomials, e^{kx}, and selected trigonometric functions of kx, as well as linear combinations of these functions.
- Students will be able to solve initial value problems of the form $\frac{dy}{dx} = f(x)$, $y_0 = f(x_0)$.
- Students will be able to construct slope fields using technology and interpret slope fields as visualizations of differential equations.

Key Ideas

Solving Initial Value Problems

Antiderivatives and Indefinite Integrals

Properties of Indefinite Integrals

Applications

Teaching Notes

Begin this lesson with a discussion of differential equations and slope fields. It is extremely important for students to understand that the solution to a differential equation given an initial condition is a *function*.

In Exploration 1, students construct part of a slope field by hand. Students should complete this activity so that they will understand what a calculator is doing when it graphs a slope field.

Point out that the expression for dy/dx used to determine a slope field may involve only x, only y, or both x and y.

The integral formulas listed in Table 6.2 serve as a beginning for the long process of learning the techniques for computing antiderivatives. Whereas the Product Rule, Quotient Rule, and Chain Rule make formal differentiation a purely mechanical process, there are no such general rules for *reversing* the differentiation process. Thus antidifferentiation is a much more difficult and problematic operation. (A larger table of integrals appears in Appendix A7.)

Conclude the lesson by discussing applications such as Examples 7 and 8.

Notes on Examples

- Example 3 shows several different possible antiderivatives of $2x$. Stress the importance of adding an arbitrary constant when evaluating indefinite integrals.
- Example 5 shows that an indefinite integral can be interpreted as a definite integral plus an arbitrary vertical shift.
- In Example 6, it is important for students to discuss how the constants C_1, C_2, and C_3 can be combined into a single arbitrary constant.
- Example 7 (Draining a Tank) can also be solved using separation of variables, which is discussed in Section 6.2.

Common Errors

Algebraic mistakes are very common in evaluating antiderivatives. Students should get in the habit of checking answers by differentiating.

Exploration Extensions

Exploration 1. Sketch a slope field for $\dfrac{dy}{dx} = \dfrac{2}{x + 1}$ in the window. Then use the slope field to sketch a possible solution curve passing through (2, 4).

Notes on Exercises

- Ex. 39–42 are initial value problems involving particle motion.
- Ex. 45–48 introduce antiderivative formulas involving inverse trigonometric functions.
- Exercise 57 is a challenging exercise that is similar to Example 7.

Assignment Guide

Ex. 3–51, multiples of 3, 52, 61

PREPARATION FOR ADVANCED PLACEMENT EXAM

Ex. 49, 53–55, 57, 62

COOPERATIVE LEARNING

Ex. 43, 44, 63–66

ALTERNATE ASSESSMENT

Journal Exercise 26

6.2   Integration by Substitution

Objectives

- Students will be able to compute indefinite and definite integrals by the method of substitution.
- Students will be able to solve a differential equation of the form $\dfrac{dy}{dx} = f(x)$, in which the variables are separable.

Key Ideas

Power Rule in Integral Form
Trigonometric Integrands
Substitution in Indefinite Integrals
Substitution in Definite Integrals
Separable Differential Equations

Teaching Notes

A review of the Chain Rule is an effective way to begin this lesson, since u-substitution is a method for "reversing" the process of using the Chain Rule.

The method of substitution is the most important of all algebraic methods for finding antiderivatives and evaluating definite integrals. It takes a certain amount of skill and experience to recognize a correct substitution to be used and, indeed, to recognize those forms in which a substitution will work. Discuss Examples 1 through 7 carefully, stressing the three basic steps for finding an antiderivative by substitution, which are found on page 318. When verifying calculations by differentiation, point out the connection between u-substitution and the Chain Rule.

The formula for substitution in definite integrals, shown on page 319, is of fundamental importance. The instructor may want to include additional examples using this formula besides Example 8. To emphasize the effect of the variable change on the limits of integration, you may want to write the formula as $\int_{x=a}^{x=b} f(g(x)) \cdot g'(x) \, dx = \int_{u=g(a)}^{u=g(b)} f(u) \, du$. Pay particular attention to Exploration 2, which discusses the two basic strategies for calculating a definite integral.

When discussing separation of variables to solve differential equations, stress the importance of writing the constant of integration at the time the integrals are evaluated. Further transformations of the solution must take the constant of integration into account. Usually, this does *not* have the same effect as adding an arbitrary constant to the final answer.

Separation of variables is a useful technique which lends itself to many applications. You may wish to conclude this lesson by showing how Section 6.1, Example 7 or Exercise 57, can be solved using separation of variables. Additional applications will be presented in Sections 6.4 and 6.5.

Notes on Examples

- Examples 3–5 and 7 show how to use substitution when the integrand is a trigonometric expression.

- Example 9 shows how to solve a differential equation using separation of variables.

Common Errors

Student errors in using the substitution method are legion. One of the most common is to insert the wrong constant multiplier. To prevent this type of mistake, emphasize the mechanical nature of the process, once the correct substitution is identified. For example, if $u = 2x$, then $du = 2 \, dx$ so we may solve for dx to obtain $dx = \frac{1}{2} \, du$. Thus $\int \cos 2x \, dx$ becomes $\int \cos u \cdot \frac{1}{2} \, du$.

Many different types of mistakes occur when substituting into definite integrals. Before starting a calculation, students should decide which of the two methods discussed in Exploration 2 is to be used and should use that method throughout. You may wish to encourage students to write the variable name with the limits of integration (e.g., $\int_{u=3}^{u=5} u^2 \, du$ instead of $\int_{3}^{5} u^2 \, du$) in order to avoid mistakes caused by using the limits of x with the expression in u.

When solving differential equations using separation of variables, students may not recognize alternate versions of a solution, particularly if the solution has been rewritten to isolate y.

Exploration Extensions

Exploration 1. Use the technique in part 4 to graph five different antiderivatives for $(2 + 1.5 \sin x)^{3/2}$.

Exploration 2. Use two different methods, as in parts 1 and 2, to find $\int_{0}^{1/2} x \cos (\pi x^2) \, dx$. $\left(\frac{\sqrt{2}}{4\pi} \right)$

Notes on Exercises

- Ex. 31–38 can be solved by either of the two methods discussed in Exploration 2. You may wish to have students use both methods and verify that the results are the same using either method.

- Ex. 39–44 require students to solve differential equations using separation of variables.

- Ex. 47–48 require students to use the two methods discussed in Exploration 2.

Assignment Guide

Ex. 1–17 odd, 18–42 multiples of 3, 43, 44, 49

PREPARATION FOR ADVANCED PLACEMENT EXAM

Ex. 44, 45, 49

COOPERATIVE LEARNING

Ex. 46

ALTERNATE ASSESSMENT

Interview Ask students to explain their solutions to Exercise 18.

6.3 Integration by Parts

Objectives

- Students will be able to use integration by parts to evaluate indefinite and definite integrals.
- Students will be able to use tabular integration or the method of solving for the unknown integral in order to evaluate integrals that require repeated use of integration by parts.

Key Ideas

Product Rule in Integral Form

Repeated Use

Solving for the Unknown Integral

Tabular Integration

Teaching Notes

Integration by parts is a very powerful technique. We suggest beginning this lesson by using the Product Rule for derivatives to derive the formula for integration by parts.

The LIPET method shown on page 324 is not a foolproof method for choosing u, but it is often helpful. The main idea is that u should be a quantity that will become simpler when differentiated, while dv needs to be something that we can integrate.

After establishing the basic technique, demonstrate that the process can be repeated if the new integrand is still not an elementary form. If the original integrand reappears, apply the algebraic method of Example 5.

Be sure to mention that integration by parts can sometimes be useful even when the integrand is not a product, as in $\int \ln x \, dx$ or $\int \cos^{-1} x \, dx$.

Tabular integration is an efficient shortcut. Students appreciate the simplicity of this technique, and some students may prefer to use it even in simple situations where integration by parts is used only once. Note, however, that tabular integration cannot be used for problems like Example 5, nor can it be easily used for problems like Exercise 20.

A discussion of *why* tabular integration works can be a very effective way to conclude the lesson, because the connection between tabular integration and integration by parts is not very obvious. The connection is easily seen in the simple case where $u(x)$ is a linear function of x (so that u' is constant and $u'' = 0$). In this case, tabular integration with $f(x) = u(x)$ and $g(x) = v'(x)$ gives $\int u \, dv = uv - u' \int v \, dx = uv - \int vu' \, dx = uv - \int v \, du$. Note that the middle equality is justified by the Constant Multiple Rule because we assumed u is linear; a more detailed analysis is required to show that tabular integration works in other cases.

Notes on Examples

- Example 5 is a classic example of the algebraic technique of solving for the unknown integral and is worthwhile to demonstrate.

- Examples 6 and 7 illustrate the power of tabular integration.

Common Errors

Some students will make a wrong choice for u and dv, and then give up when their choice does not work. Encourage them to keep trying different strategies until they find one that works.

It is important to keep track of signs. Errors commonly occur when the expression for du or $\int v \, du$ involves a minus sign. Sign errors are also common in tabular integration.

Another common mistake is to antidifferentiate incorrectly to find v, or to antidifferentiate incorrectly in the tabular integration format.

Exploration Extensions

Exploration 1. Use integration by parts to find $\int x \ln x \, dx$. If f has domain $(0, \infty)$ and $f''(x) = \ln x$, what is f? Give all possibilities. $\left(\int x \ln x \, dx = \dfrac{x^2}{2} \ln x - \dfrac{x^2}{4} + C; f(x) = \dfrac{x^2}{2} \ln x - \dfrac{3x^2}{4} + Cx + D \right)$

Notes on Exercises

- Ex. 2, 7, 10–12, 15, 16, 19, 24, 26, and 29 require tabular integration or repeated application of integration by parts.

- Ex. 13, 14, 17, 18, 25, and 30 require solving for the unknown integral.

Assignment Guide

Ex. 3–33 multiples of 3

PREPARATION FOR ADVANCED PLACEMENT EXAM

Ex. 23–25

COOPERATIVE LEARNING

Ex. 25, 26

ALTERNATE ASSESSMENT

Self Assessment Have students write a paragraph describing any difficulties they encountered while integrating by parts.

6.4   Exponential Growth and Decay

Objectives

- Students will be able to solve problems involving exponential growth and decay in a variety of applications.

Key Ideas

Law of Exponential Change

Continuously Compounded Interest

Radioactivity

Newton's Law of Cooling

Resistance Proportional to Velocity

Teaching Notes

The Quick Review exercises provide a suitable way to begin this lesson. By reviewing the algebraic rules for logarithms and exponents, students will be prepared to discuss the material at hand.

The problems in this section model exponential growth and decay. Although the formulas for various applications have different forms, almost all of them are based on the fact that the solution to $y' = ry$ is $y = y_0 e^{rt}$. Even Newton's Law of Cooling can be written in this form by letting $y = T - T_S$.

In the discussion of resistance proportional to velocity preceding Exploration 1, we are assuming that the object continues to have the same shape and size as m changes, since changes of shape or size would affect the value of k. It is worth noting that our assumption (resistance proportional to velocity) is valid for what physicists call a "slow projectile." A real-life object would also be subjected to other forces (such as friction) which are not proportional to velocity.

One way to summarize the lesson is to make a table showing how each of the applications in this section is related to the basic equation $y = y_0 e^{rt}$, as shown. This table can easily be extended to include the applications in Exercises 25–29.

Application	Equation	y	r
Continuously compounded interest	$A(t) = A_0 e^{rt}$	$A(t)$	r
Radioactive decay	$y = y_0 e^{-kt}$	y	$-k$
Newton's Law of Cooling	$T - T_s = (T - T_s)e^{-kt}$	$T - T_s$	$-k$
Resistance proportional to velocity	$v = v_0 e^{-(k/m)t}$	v	$-k/m$

Notes on Examples

- Notice that in Example 3, the original amount of the sample is irrelevant. The value y_0 cancels in the equation to determine t. (Point out that this will also happen in problems that ask how long it will take for a population or a savings account to double.)

- You can challenge your students by asking them to show that the answer to Example 7 can be determined without knowing Ashley's weight. If we let $d =$ coasting distance, then $k = \dfrac{v_0 m}{d}$ and the distance function is $s(t) = \dfrac{v_0 m}{k}(1 - e^{-(k/m)t}) = d(1 - e^{-(v_0/d)t})$

Common Errors

Students frequently use the wrong units of measure or make errors in converting to the correct units. Always establish the correct units of measure from the given data at the beginning of a problem.

Exploration Extensions

Exploration 1. Find an expression for the acceleration $a(t)$ and explain why "Slowing Down More Slowly" is an appropriate title for this Exploration. $\left(a(t) = -\dfrac{50}{m}e^{-(0.5/m)t}\right)$

Notes on Exercises

- Ex. 25–29 require students to apply the concepts of exponential growth and decay in unfamiliar contexts.

- Ex. 38 is especially challenging because it involves a different kind of function from the rest of the section and requires significant algebraic manipulation. The air resistance here is assumed to be proportional to the *square* of the velocity. Physicists use this approximation for "fast projectiles."

Assignment Guide

Ex. 3–33, multiples of 3

PREPARATION FOR ADVANCED PLACEMENT EXAM

Ex. 12, 17, 25, 27, 29

COOPERATIVE LEARNING

Ex. 32–34

ALTERNATE ASSESSMENT

Portfolio Have each student select an exercise demonstrating his or her understanding of exponential decay.

6.5 Population Growth

Objectives

• Students will be able to solve problems involving exponential or logistic population growth.

Key Ideas

Exponential Model

Logistic Growth Model

Logistic Regression

Teaching Notes

The discussion of exponential population growth provides a suitable opening for this lesson. Students should follow this discussion easily, since it mirrors the material in Section 6.4.

The presentation of this lesson should include a review of the partial fraction decomposition method for the simple case of rational functions in which the denominator is a product of two linear factors. The partial fraction method will be discussed in detail in Section 8.4. (If you wish to postpone discussion of the method of undetermined coefficients, you can instead present the "trick" shown below in the note for Example 2.)

This section emphasizes the use of differential equations to model physical situations. This material is very important for students who plan to take the Advanced Placement test, since recent changes in the Advanced Placement Calculus Curriculum call for increased emphasis on this topic.

You can conclude the lesson by having students discuss ways to determine when it is appropriate to use logistic regression.

Notes on Examples

• In Example 2, you can use a simple "trick" to obtain the partial fraction decomposition as follows:

$$
\begin{aligned}
\frac{1}{P(100 - P)} &= \frac{1}{100} \cdot \frac{100}{P(100 - P)} \\
&= \frac{1}{100} \cdot \frac{(100 - P) + P}{P(100 - P)} \\
&= \frac{1}{100}\left(\frac{100 - P}{P(100 - P)} + \frac{P}{P(100 - P)} \right) \\
&= \frac{1}{100}\left(\frac{1}{P} + \frac{1}{100 - P} \right)
\end{aligned}
$$

- In Examples 3 and 4, note that Figures 6.14 and 6.16 appear slightly different from actual grapher displays, in which some of the points would appear as filled-in dots, Also, a grapher may give a slightly different result for *x* than the one shown in Figure 6.15. Indeed, the value given by a particular grapher may vary each time the calculation is made, due to the limitations on the accuracy of the grapher.

Common Errors

Students often fail to understand that the relative growth rate (in percent per year) is different from the actual percent change over one year. It may help to compare these quantities to a continuously compounded savings account. The relative growth rate is like the annual interest rate, while the actual percent change corresponds to the annual yield.

It is easy to make computational errors when taking derivatives of logistic functions. NDER can be used to check results numerically.

Notes on Exercises

- In Ex. 13–14, you may wish to tell students to begin by rewriting the equation in the form
$$P(t) = \frac{M}{1 + Ae^{-kt}}.$$
- In Ex. 15, note that we are assuming the *relative growth rate* is constant. This is not the same as assuming that the rate of 1 person every 14 seconds remains constant.

Assignment Guide

Ex. 1–29 odd

PREPARATION FOR ADVANCED PLACEMENT EXAM

Ex. 9–12, 16, 18, 20–21

COOPERATIVE LEARNING

Ex. 19, 31, 32

ALTERNATE ASSESSMENT

Project Have students research the population statistics for your state and determine whether the population can be accurately modeled by one of the growth models that have been studied.

6.6 Numerical Methods

Objectives

- Students will be able to use Euler's method and the improved Euler's method to find approximate solutions to differential equations with initial values.

Key Ideas

Euler's Method
Numerical Solutions
Graphical Solutions
Improved Euler's Method

Teaching Notes

The Quick Review exercises provide an appropriate introduction to this lesson. The concept of a linearization is essential in understanding Euler's method.

You may wish to briefly explain *why* the Improved Euler's method is really an improvement over Euler's basic method. The key is that the expression $\dfrac{f(x_{n-1}, y_{n-1}) + f(x_n, z_n)}{2}$ is a better estimate than $f(x_{n-1}, y_{n-1})$ for the average slope of the solution curve between x_{n-1} and x_n. A graph like the ones used to illustrate Euler's Method can help students to visualize this.

Most of the Exercises in this section require students to use the grapher programs EULERT, EULERG, IMPEULT, and IMPEULG. A discussion of grapher techniques for solving these problems is a worthwhile conclusion to this lesson.

Notes on Examples

• Example 1 shows how to use Euler's method to compute approximations "by hand," without using EULERT.

Common Errors

It is easy for students to make "typographical" errors when entering the programs into a calculator. If your students all use the same calculator, you may wish to electronically provide the programs used in this section. Also, some students will call up the wrong program to solve a particular problem.

Notes on Exercises

• Ex. 9–14 and 17–22 depend on results obtained from previous exercises.

• Ex. 9–30 require students to have the appropriate grapher programs available.

Assignment Guide

Ex. 2, 3, 6, 7, 9, 12, 15, 17, 19, 22, 24, 25, 28

PREPARATION FOR ADVANCED PLACEMENT EXAM

Ex. 17, 18

COOPERATIVE LEARNING

Ex. 13, 14

ALTERNATE ASSESSMENT

Self Assessment Have students write a paragraph describing any difficulties they encountered while obtaining numerical or graphical solutions to differential equations.

Chapter 6 Review Exercises

Note on Exercise

• 43b Students may get an overflow error message. If so, advise them to quit and look at the graph.

PREPARATION FOR ADVANCED PLACEMENT EXAM

Ex. 33, 34, 39, 52, 54

CHAPTER
7
Applications of Definite Integrals

Bibliography

FOR STUDENTS:

CBL Explorations in Calculus for the TI-82. Meridian Creative Group, 1985.

CBL Explorations in Calculus for the TI-85. Meridian Creative Group, 1985.

How to Prepare for the AP Calculus Advanced Placement Examination, Shirley O. Hockett, Barron's Educational Series, Inc., Hauppague, NY, 1998. Chapters 7 and 8.

Multiple-Choice and Free-Response Questions in Preparation for the AP Calculus (AB) Exam, 7th Edition, David Lederman, D and S Marketing Systems, 1997.

FOR TEACHERS:

Calculus: Readings from the Mathematics Teacher. NCTM, 1977.

Solutions to AP Calculus Problems, Part II, Latimer, Kennelly, Gasque, and Allen, Department of Mathematics, Francis Marion College, Florence, SC 29501.

VIDEO:

MAA Calculus Films in Video Format, Tape 1. MAA.

Chapter Opener

The Chapter Opener requires students to determine the amount of clay needed to create a vase.

Solution: Outside radius of vase: $y_1 = 5.0 + 2 \sin \frac{x}{4}$

Inside radius of vase: $y_2 = 4.0 + 2 \sin \frac{x}{4}$

Cross sectional area is

$$\pi y_1{}^2 - \pi y_2{}^2 = \pi\left[\left(5.0 + 2 \sin \frac{x}{4}\right)^2 - \left(4.0 + 2 \sin \frac{x}{4}\right)^2\right]$$

$$= \pi\left(25 + 20 \sin \frac{x}{4} + 4 \sin^2 \frac{x}{4} - 16 - 16 \sin \frac{x}{4} - 4 \sin^2 \frac{x}{4}\right)$$

$$= \pi\left(9 + 4 \sin \frac{x}{4}\right)$$

$$\text{Volume} = \int_0^{8\pi} \pi\left(9 + 4 \sin \frac{x}{4}\right) dx = \pi\left(9x - 16 \cos \frac{x}{4}\right)\Big]_0^{8\pi}$$

$$= \pi(72\pi - 16 \cos 2\pi - 0 + 16 \cos 0)$$

$$= \pi(72\pi - 16 + 16) = 72\pi^2$$

The amount of clay needed is $72\pi^2 \approx 711$ cubic inches.

7.1 Integral as Net Change

Objectives

- Students will be able to solve problems in which a rate is integrated to find the net change over time in a variety of applications.

Key Ideas

Linear Motion Revisited

General Strategy

Consumption over Time

Net Change from Data

Work

Teaching Notes

We suggest beginning this lesson with a review of the concepts of position, velocity, and acceleration. Stress that the techniques used in studying particle motion can be generalized to other kinds of rates.

Students need to understand that the integral of a rate gives the net change. The key objective of this chapter is not only that students will be able to solve the specific problem types discussed in the text, but also that students will be able to apply their problem solving skills to unfamiliar situations.

Students often wonder why it is so important to determine positions from rates. There are numerous examples where this is done in real life. Here are several such examples:

A car odometer can be interpreted as a device that calculates position from rate data. Furthermore, if the odometer breaks, one can record rate information by hand in order to determine the distance driven.

In astronomy, Doppler effects can be used to determine how fast a star is moving toward or away from us. In this way, the velocity is often determined more accurately than the distance can be determined.

Since global warming has been a hot topic in recent years, scientists are using rate data regarding temperature changes in order to predict the planet's future and to determine what needs to be done to protect our habitat. (This example illustrates not only the critical importance of analyzing rates, but also the *uncertainty* involved in real-life applications where data is involved.)

Most Star Trek episodes include a scene where rates are used to determine where some kind of space ship or other object will be at a particular time, and how to connect with it or avoid it.

And this is the same kind of calculation that anyone makes, automatically, when catching a ball or playing a video game.

Some other rate applications that are covered in this chapter or the previous one include population growth, Newton's Law of Cooling, work and energy, fluid force, and probability functions.

A discussion in which students come up with other examples where rates are analyzed is an effective way to conclude the lesson. Student suggestions can often be made into interesting problem situations which can be discussed at length.

Notes on Examples

- Example 2 uses a Riemann sum to show how position can be calculated when the velocity function and initial position are known.

- Examples 5–7 show how the analysis of rates can be applied to problems that do not involve position and velocity.

Common Errors

Many students neglect to pay adequate attention to the units given in an exercise. In particular, students should realize that the newton and the pound are both units of *force*, whereas the kilogram is a unit of *mass*. (See the chart on page 411.)

Exploration Extensions

Exploration 1. Are the results obtained in parts 2 and 3 a coincidence? (**No**) Discuss.

Notes on Exercises

- Ex. 1–20 deal with position and velocity.

- Ex. 26–28 explore how to find a function using rate data.

- Ex. 29–30 relate to the concept of work.

- Ex. 33–35 relate to finding the center of mass of a two-dimensional object with a given density.

Assignment Guide

Ex. 1–11 odd, 12–17, 20–22, 24–27, 30, 31

PREPARATION FOR ADVANCED PLACEMENT EXAM

Ex. 12–16, 17, 19, 21–23

COOPERATIVE LEARNING

Ex. 26, 27

ALTERNATE ASSESSMENT

Journal Exercise 25

7.2 Areas in the Plane

Objectives

- Students will be able to use integration to calculate areas of regions in a plane.

Key Ideas

Area Between Curves

Area Enclosed by Intersecting Curves

Boundaries with Changing Functions

Integrating with Respect to y

Saving Time with Geometry Formulas

Teaching Notes

One way to begin this lesson is to perform the Riemann sum analysis as given in the text using concrete functions such as $f(x) = 2x + 3$ and $g(x) = x^2$.

The first step in finding the area of a region between two curves is to graph the region. By graphing the two curves in sequential mode, students will be able to see which formula gives the upper curve. The SHADE function can also help in this regard. On many graphers, SHADE(y_1, y_2) will shade the region above $y = y_1(x)$ and below $y_2(x)$.

Determining the limits of integration may involve finding the points where $y = f(x)$ and $y = g(x)$ intersect. This will mean solving $f(x) = g(x)$ to find the x-coordinates of the intersection points. Students sometimes have trouble with the algebra here. Being able to visually estimate these points on the grapher can be a big help.

As in all of the applications in this chapter, the formula for the area is established by first approximating with a Riemann sum, and then letting the partition norm approach 0 to obtain the exact area. Using a Riemann sum approximation is, in fact, a good way to remember the correct integration formula.

Examples 4, 5, and 7 provide an effective way to conclude the lesson by showing the same problem solved using three different methods.

Notes on Examples

- Example 5 shows how to find the area of a region by integrating with respect to y instead of x.

Common Errors

In situations such as Exercises 9 and 10, some students will attempt to use a single integral without paying attention to which function forms the upper boundary of the region.

Exploration Extensions

Exploration 1. Repeat parts 1–5 for the region enclosed by the graphs of $y = k \sin kx$ and $y = -k \sin kx$. ($A_k = 4$ for all k; $\lim\limits_{k \to \infty} A_k = 4$; $\lim\limits_{k \to \infty} P_k = \infty$)

Notes on Exercises

- Ex. 3, 4, 7, 8, 18–21, and 31 can be solved easily by integrating with respect to y.
- Ex. 44 requires students to derive the formula for the area of an ellipse.
- Ex. 45 requires students to prove Cavalieri's theorem. See page 384 for more information about Bonaventura Cavalieri.

Assignment Guide

Ex. 3–36 multiples of 3, 40, 42, 43, 46

PREPARATION FOR ADVANCED PLACEMENT EXAM

Ex. 36–38, 43, 46

COOPERATIVE LEARNING

Ex. 37–40, 44

ALTERNATE ASSESSMENT

Interview Have students explain two different methods for solving Exercise 6.

7.3 Volumes

Objectives

- Students will be able to use integration (by slices or shells) to calculate volumes of solids.
- Students will be able to use integration to calculate surface areas of solids of revolution.

Key Ideas

Volume as an Integral

Square Cross Sections

Circular Cross Sections

Cylindrical Shells

Other Cross Sections

Teaching Notes

Begin by discussing the general case where a solid region can be divided into slices having arbitrary cross sections. Students should then recognize that disks and washers are just special cases of this situation.

Visualizing the result of rotating a plane region about an axis is difficult for many students. It is much easier to visualize what happens if a single rectangle with sides drawn perpendicular to that axis is rotated about the axis. For the disk method, if a rectangle of height $R(x)$ and width Δx, with base lying on the x-axis, is rotated about the x-axis, the result will be a *disk* of volume $\Delta V = \pi[R(x)]^2 \Delta x$. The volume of a solid of revolution about the x-axis is approximated by summing the volumes of such disks. By taking the limit of Riemann sums, we see that the exact volume is given by $V = \int_a^b \pi R^2(x)\, dx$, where $R^2(x)$ represents $[R(x)]^2$.

The same idea is used for the washer method. In this case, if we rotate a single rectangle whose base lies *above* the x-axis about the x-axis, the result is a *washer* whose volume is $\Delta V = \pi[R^2 - r^2]\Delta x$, where R is the outer radius and r is the inner radius. Thus, the exact volume is given by $V = \int_a^b \pi[R^2(x) - r^2(x)]\, dx$.

The washer method can be applied to calculating the volume of a solid of revolution about the y-axis or some other axis.

A grapher can display a cross section of a solid of revolution in the xy-plane by graphing the bordering curves and their reflections across the axis of revolution.

Exploration 1 presents the cylindrical shell method. Note that the region is rotated about the line $x = -1$, not the y-axis.

In Exploration 2, students discover how to find the (lateral) surface area of a solid of revolution. A discussion of surface areas can be a very effective conclusion to this lesson.

Notes on Examples

- For Example 3, we entered $y_1 = (2 + x \cos x)(-2 \le x)(x \le 2)$ and used connected mode to obtain the graph in Figure 7.19. We did this so that the grapher would simulate drawing the vertical line segments at $x = \pm 2$. The reason it appears to draw the vertical line segments is that the value of $y_1 = (2 + x \cos x)(-2 \le x)(x \le 2)$ is 0 for $x < -2$ and for $x > 2$. The grapher connects the first and last points on the actual graph of $y = 2 + \cos x$, $-2 \le x \le 2$, to the x-axis.

- For Example 4, we entered $y_1 = (\cos x)/[(0 \le x)(x \le \pi/4)]$ and $y_2 = (\sin x)/[(0 \le x)(x \le \pi/4)]$ and used connected mode to obtain the graphs in Figure 7.21. Dividing by $(0 \le x)(x \le \pi/4)$ forces the domain of y_1 and y_2 to be $0 \le x \le \pi/4$. Both y_1 and y_2 have no value for $x < 0$ and for $x > \pi/4$. If we use this method in Figure 7.19, the vertical line segments will disappear. Try it! If we use the method of Figure 7.19 in Figure 7.21, the grapher will appear to draw a vertical line segment from the point $(1, \ 1/\sqrt{2})$ to the *x*-axis. Try it!

- Example 5 can also be done using washers. You may wish to demonstrate that either method produces the same result.

- Example 6 can be solved analytically by using the identity $\sin^2 x = \dfrac{1 - \cos 2x}{2}$.

Common Errors

In the washer method, the volume element is sometimes mistakenly written as $\pi(R - r)^2 \Delta x$ instead of $\pi(R^2 - r^2)\Delta x$.

In problems involving solids of revolution, students often make errors in determining the plane region to be rotated.

Exploration Extensions

Exploration 1. The triangle enclosed by the function $f(x) = 6 - 3x$ and the *x*- and *y*-axes is revolved about the *y*-axis to generate a solid. Use cylindrical shells to find the volume of this solid. Verify your answer by using the formula $V = \dfrac{1}{3}\pi r^2 h$ for the volume of a cone. **(8π)**

Exploration 2. Write an integral for the surface area of the solid obtained by revolving the graph of $y = -\ln(\cos x)$, $0 \le x \le \pi/3$, about the *x*-axis. Then use NINT to estimate the surface area. $\left(\displaystyle\int_0^{\pi/3} -2\pi \sec x \ln(\cos x)\,dx \approx 2.0754 \right)$

Notes on Exercises

- Ex. 35–38 are intended to emphasize the different ways to set up an integral, depending on the axis of rotation. Once the integrals are set up, their values can be found algebraically or by using NINT.

- Ex. 43a and 44a involve volumes that are much easier to find using cylindrical shells than with washers.

- Ex. 56–64 involve surface areas of solids of revolution.

Assignment Guide

Ex. 1–17 odd, 22, 25, 28, 29, 33, 39, 42, 44, 49, 53, 57, 60, 63

PREPARATION FOR ADVANCED PLACEMENT EXAM

Ex. 7, 12, 49–50

COOPERATIVE LEARNING

Ex. 35–38

ALTERNATE ASSESSMENT

Portfolio Have each student select an exercise demonstrating his or her understanding of finding volumes by circular cross sections.

Lengths of Curves

Objectives

• Students will be able to use integration to calculate lengths of curves in a plane.

Key Ideas

A Sine Wave
Length of a Smooth Curve
Vertical Tangents, Corners, and Cusps

Teaching Notes

We suggest beginning the lesson with the Group Exploration on page 395, in which students estimate the length of the sine curve shown in Figure 7.31.

The formula for arc length is one of the fundamental applications of integration. If you have the time, a careful discussion of the derivation of this formula will be very rewarding. If your students completed Exploration 2 in the previous section, you will want to point out the similarities here. The length of a curve is approximated by the length of a polygonal path which closely fits the curve. Using the Mean Value Theorem, the length of the polygonal path can be interpreted as a Riemann sum and this leads to the definition of arc length as a definite integral.

Applying the formula requires a large amount of algebraic manipulation since dy/dx must be calculated, and then the expression $\sqrt{1 + (dy/dx)^2}$ has to be formed and simplified before integrating. Point out to students that this integral often needs to be evaluated numerically. (The functions in Example 2 and in many of the exercises have been carefully chosen so that the integrals can be evaluated algebraically.)

To facilitate numerical calculation of curve lengths, you may suggest that students use $y_2 = \sqrt{1 + (\text{NDER } y_1)^2}$. This way, each function whose graph is being analyzed can be entered as y_1 and the length can be computed as $\text{NINT}(y_2, x, a, b)$

The formula requires dy/dx to exist and to be continuous on the interval for which the arc length is sought. If this condition fails at a point, it may be possible to find arc length by defining the curve as a function of y and integrating the expression $\sqrt{1 + (dy/dx)^2}$ over the appropriate range of y-values. (It may also be possible to find the arc length using an improper integral. Improper integrals are covered in Section 8.3.)

You may wish to conclude the lesson with an example involving a cusp, such as the length of the curve $y = \sqrt{|x|}$ for $-1 \le x \le 1$. Since dy/dx approaches $\pm\infty$ as x approaches 0, the length of each piece of the curve should be found by integrating with respect to y.

Notes on Examples

• In Example 3, it is easy for students to overlook the real reason that we are integrating with respect to y instead of x. To emphasize the point, display a graph of $y = \sqrt{1 + \left(\dfrac{1}{3x^{2/3}}\right)^2}$, which has a vertical asymptote at $x = 0$.

Common Errors

Algebraic errors will inevitably occur when simplifying the expression $1 + (dy/dx)^2$. Encourage students to check solutions numerically and/or estimate curve lengths visually by graphing in a square window.

Notes on Exercises

- Ex. 25 is very challenging, in part because the curves have both vertical and horizontal tangents. One approach to finding the length of lane 1 is to first evaluate the length for $-22.3606 \le x \le 22.3606$ and then add in the lengths of the two small pieces at the ends, which can be easily approximated by assuming that each is a vertical line segment.

- Ex. 26 should be solved by solving for x and then integrating the appropriate expression with respect to y.

- Ex. 28–30 involve curves that are *nonsmooth* in the sense that $y'(0)$ is undefined.

Assignment Guide

Ex. 3–30 multiples of 3

PREPARATION FOR ADVANCED PLACEMENT EXAM

Ex. 19, 21, 25, 27, 29

COOPERATIVE LEARNING

Ex. 19–20

ALTERNATE ASSESSMENT

Self Assessment Have students write a paragraph describing any difficulties they encountered while finding lengths of curves.

7.5   Applications from Science and Statistics

Objectives

- Students will be able to adapt their knowledge of integral calculus to model problems involving rates of change in a variety of applications, possibly in unfamiliar contexts.

Key Ideas

Work Revisited

Fluid Force and Fluid Pressure

Normal Probabilities

Teaching Notes

One way to begin this lesson is with a review of Example 7 in Section 7.1. The concept of work is central to the current lesson.

Students who plan to take the Advanced Placement exam need to be aware that the recently revised guidelines require students to be able to adapt their knowledge to solve application problems in unfamiliar contexts. Rather than memorizing formulas related to work, for example, students should concentrate on a thorough understanding of the modeling process and the methods used to solve problems.

The fluid pressure formula $p = wh$ has been simplified in the sense that it neglects the effect of air pressure, which would add approximately 2116 pounds per square foot.

A discussion of normal probability density functions provides a fitting conclusion to the lesson.

Notes on Examples

• In Example 3a, note that the result can also be calculated by multiplying the volume by the weight density.

• In Example 3b, note that we are not considering force as a vector. If force is considered as a vector here, the forces in opposite directions will cancel, resulting in a net force of 0 lb against the bottom foot of the tank wall.

Common Errors

Students often make errors in setting up problems or in using units.

Notes on Exercises

• Ex. 1–12 and 17–24 involve the concept of work.

• Ex. 13–16 and 25–26 involve fluid pressure.

• Ex. 27–30 involve probability functions.

• Ex. 33–40 involve work and kinetic energy.

Assignment Guide

Ex. 3–12 multiples of 3, 17, 21, 24, 25–31, 33, 35, 39

PREPARATION FOR ADVANCED PLACEMENT EXAM

Ex. 25

COOPERATIVE LEARNING

Ex. 13–16

ALTERNATE ASSESSMENT

Project Have students research normal probability functions. Each student should give several examples of applications where it is appropriate to use normal probability functions, as well as several examples of probability applications where the normal probability function does not apply.

Chapter 7 Review Exercises

PREPARATION FOR ADVANCED PLACEMENT EXAM

Ex. 2, 3, 5, 15, 17, 19, 24, 30, 31, 39

CHAPTER

8

L'Hôpital's Rule, Improper Integrals, and Partial Fractions

Bibliography

FOR STUDENTS:

Mathematica. Stephan Wolfram, Addison-Wesley (51502), 1991.

FOR TEACHERS:

Solutions: AP Calculus Free Response Questions 1983–1997, Part II AB and BC. Judith Broadwin, George Lenchner, and Martin Rudolph, Mathematical Olympiads for Elementary and Middle Schools, updated annually.

Chapter Opener

The Chapter Opener requires students to determine the approximate amount of work needed to send the Pathfinder to Mars.

$$
\text{Solution: Work} = \int_{4000}^{\infty} F \, dr = \int_{4000}^{\infty} \frac{16{,}000{,}000w}{r^2} \, dr
$$

$$
= 16{,}000{,}000w \int_{4000}^{\infty} r^{-2} \, dr
$$

$$
= 16{,}000{,}000w \lim_{b \to \infty} \int_{4000}^{b} r^{-2} \, dr
$$

$$
= 16{,}000{,}000w \lim_{b \to \infty} \left[-r^{-1} \right]_{4000}^{b}
$$

$$
= 16{,}000{,}000w \lim_{b \to \infty} \left[-\frac{1}{b} + \frac{1}{4000} \right]
$$

$$
= \frac{16{,}000{,}000w}{4000} = 4000w
$$

Since the force was given in pounds and the distance was given in miles, the units for this calculation are mile-pounds. The weight of the Pathfinder is about 2000 pounds, so the work done is $4000(2000) = 8{,}000{,}000$ mile-pounds. Multiplying by 5280 ft/mile, the work done is about 4.22×10^{10} foot-pounds.

8.1 L'Hôpital's Rule

Objectives

- Students will be able to find limits of indeterminate forms using l'Hôpital's Rule.

Key Ideas

Indeterminate Form 0/0

Indeterminate Forms ∞/∞, $\infty \cdot 0$, $\infty - \infty$

Indeterminate Forms 1^{∞}, 0^0, ∞^0

Teaching Notes

You may want to begin this lesson by reviewing those parts of Chapter 2 where limits of the form 0/0 or ∞/∞ were solved by simplifying or rewriting the fraction $f(x)/g(x)$. L'Hôpital's Rule will now provide a more general method for calculating limits of these forms.

A concrete example can help to illustrate the graphical argument in the proof of Theorem 1. For example, let $y_1 = x^2 - 4$ and let $y_2 = 0.25x^3 - 5x + 8$. Have students zoom in on the point $(2, 0)$ to see that $\lim_{x \to 2} \dfrac{y_1(x)}{y_2(x)} = \lim_{x \to 2} \dfrac{y_1'(x)}{y_2'(x)} = -2$. Also observe that the graphs of $y_3 = y_1/y_2$ and $y_4 = \text{NDER}(y_1)/\text{NDER}(y_2)$ intersect only at $x = 2$. This fact can be used to emphasize that l'Hôpital's Rule works only at a point $x = a$ where $f(a) = g(a) = 0$.

Once students are comfortable with the first form of the rule (Theorem 1), introduce the more general version (Theorem 2), which allows repeated applications. It is important to observe that the theorem still applies if a is replaced by ∞ or $-\infty$. This is what we mean when we say that the a can be finite or infinite. Also emphasize that the fraction f/g must *always* be verified to have one of the indeterminate forms 0/0 or ∞/∞ before applying l'Hôpital's Rule.

The forms $0 \cdot \infty$ and $\infty - \infty$ can usually be rewritten algebraically as 0/0 or ∞/∞. The forms 0^0, 1^{∞}, and ∞^0 are usually converted to 0/0 or ∞/∞ using logarithms. The limits are then found by applying l'Hôpital's Rule and the result shown in the box above Example 8.

Graphical support can be helpful in these problems because the graph of $y = f(x)/g(x)$ will often suggest the correct limit as x approaches a or ∞. However, in cases where f and g approach 0 or ∞ too quickly, the grapher may lack sufficient precision to give an accurate graph near the limit point.

Example 10 can be used to summarize many of the main points of the lesson.

Notes on Examples

- Example 7 shows how to convert the form $\infty - \infty$ to the form 0/0 by writing an expression as a single fraction. The function in this Example also exhibits interesting behavior near $x = 0$. You can use this function to illustrate the danger of using a grapher to estimate limits without confirming algebraically.

Common Errors

Some students tend to misapply the rule by replacing $\lim f/g$ with $\lim (f/g)'$ rather than with $\lim f'/g'$. Exploration 1 highlights this potential pitfall.

Another common error is to attempt to apply l'Hôpital's Rule to a form which is not indeterminate.

Exploration Extensions

Exploration 1. Let $f(x) = \dfrac{\cot x}{4x^2 - \pi^2}$. Use l'Hôpital's Rule to find $\lim_{x \to \pi/2} f(x)$. Then complete parts 2 and 3, using appropriate functions for y_1 and y_2. $\left(\lim_{x \to \pi/2} f(x) = -\dfrac{1}{4\pi} \right)$

Notes on Exercises

- Ex. 47–48 require students to use l'Hôpital's Rule to solve problems involving removable discontinuities.

- Ex. 51 involves the volume of a solid of revolution.

Assignment Guide

Ex. 3–51 multiples of 3

PREPARATION FOR ADVANCED PLACEMENT EXAM

Ex. 47, 48, 51

COOPERATIVE LEARNING

Ex. 43, 44

ALTERNATE ASSESSMENT

Journal Exercise 50

8.2 Relative Rates of Growth

Objectives

- Students will be able to use little-oh and big-oh notation in determining, investigating, and comparing the rates of growth of functions.

Key Ideas

Comparing Rates of Growth

Order and Oh-Notation

Sequential versus Binary Search

Teaching Notes

The discussion of exponential and logarithmic functions beginning on page 425 is an interesting way to begin this lesson.

Students may want to use a mnemonic to help remember which functions grow faster than others. One such mnemonic is N^N FEPL, pronounced "enfepple," for N^N, factorial (for integers), exponential, polynomial, logarithmic.

The definitions of relative rates of growth as $x \to \infty$, given on page 426, are the key ideas of this section. Note that end behavior models form a special case of functions that grow at the same rate, in the sense that if g is a right end behavior model for a positive function f, then f and g grow at the same rate. L'Hôpital's Rule is frequently used to determine whether two functions grow at the same rate.

The transitivity of the relation "grows at the same rate" is discussed after Example 3. This relation is an *equivalence relation* because it is also *symmetric* (if f grows at the same rate as g, then g grows at the same rate as f) and *reflexive* (f grows at the same rate as itself). A discussion of equivalence relations is beyond the scope of this course, but students should have no trouble understanding intuitively that two functions grow at the same rate if each of them grows at the same rate as a third function.

The idea of f and g growing at the same rate is central to the limit comparison test for the convergence of an improper integral, which we will discuss in Section 8.3 . Later on, the test will reappear in Section 9.5 for the convergence of an infinite series.

Related to these ideas are the definitions of $f = o(g)$ and $f = O(g)$, which are a standard part of the literature in real analysis.

Graphical support for the examples and exercises can be accomplished by graphing $y = f(x)/g(x)$. In some instances it may be a challenge to find the appropriate viewing window for doing this. When f and g have too rapid a growth rate, it may be impossible to graphically support $f/g \to L$ in a direct manner because of the range limitations on the calculator. One way around this is to graphically support the equivalent (for positive-valued functions) limit statement $\ln f - \ln g \to \ln L$.

You can summarize the lesson by asking students to discuss how the concepts of little-oh, big-oh, and relative rates of growth are related. $f = o(g)$ means that g grows faster than f, while $f = O(g)$ means that either g grows faster than f or the functions f and g grow at the same rate as $x \to \infty$.

Notes on Examples

- Example 4 uses the transitivity of the relation "grows at the same rate" in order to establish that two functions grow at the same rate.

- Example 7 involves the same function as Quick Review Exercise 9.

Common Errors

Students often mistakenly believe that two functions grow at the same rate if and only if one of the functions is an end behavior model for the other. Stress that two functions f and g which are positive for x sufficiently large grow at the same rate if $\lim\limits_{x \to \infty} \dfrac{f(x)}{g(x)}$ is *any* finite, positive constant.

Exploration Extensions

Exploration 1. Show that x^a grows faster than x^b if and only if $a > b$.

Notes on Exercises

- Ex. 35–38 and 41–46 give students an opportunity to apply their reasoning ability in writing proofs or exploring new concepts.

- Ex. 39–40 involve the efficiency of computer algorithms.

Assignment Guide

Ex. 3–36 multiples of 3, 37, 38, 40, 42, 43

PREPARATION FOR ADVANCED PLACEMENT EXAM

Ex. 37, 38

COOPERATIVE LEARNING

Ex. 35–37, 38

ALTERNATE ASSESSMENT

Interview Have students explain their solutions to Exercise 18.

8.3 Improper Integrals

Objectives

- Students will be able to use limits to evaluate improper integrals.

- Students will be able to use the direct comparison test and the limit comparison test to determine the convergence or divergence of improper integrals.

Key Ideas

Infinite Limits of Integration

The Integral $\int_{1}^{\infty} \dfrac{dx}{x^p}$

Integrands with Infinite Discontinuities

Tests for Convergence and Divergence

Applications

Teaching Notes

One way to begin this lesson is by writing several improper integrals such as $\int_{0}^{1} \dfrac{dx}{x^2}$ on the board and have students discuss how one might go about determining their values.

Reinforce the idea that the integral *converges* when the limit exists. Demonstrate an example of convergence as well as divergence. Emphasize the fact that an unbounded region may have either a finite or infinite area. Students should be familiar with the results for $\int_{1}^{\infty} \dfrac{1}{x^p}\,dx$ and $\int_{0}^{1} \dfrac{1}{x^p}\,dx$ (see Example 3 and Exploration 1).

The direct comparison test and the limit comparison test are very useful techniques for determining convergence, but they cannot be used to evaluate integrals. It is important to note that the direct comparison test can be adapted to work in situations involving vertical asymptotes, as follows:

> Let D represent the interval $(a, b]$, the interval $[a, b)$, or the set $[a, c) \cup (c, b]$.
> Let f and g be continuous on D with $0 \leq f(x) \leq g(x)$ for all x in D. Then:
> 1. $\displaystyle\int_{a}^{b} f(x)\,dx$ converges if $\displaystyle\int_{a}^{b} g(x)\,dx$ converges.
> 2. $\displaystyle\int_{a}^{b} g(x)\,dx$ diverges if $\displaystyle\int_{a}^{b} f(x)\,dx$ diverges.

Encourage students to support results numerically or graphically.

The applications in Examples 10 and 11 provide an interesting conclusion to this lesson.

Notes on Examples

- In Example 2, observe that the function $y = \dfrac{1}{1 + x^2}$ is even, so an alternate method of solving this problem is to evaluate $2 \displaystyle\int_{0}^{\infty} \dfrac{dx}{1 + x^2}$. (See Exercise 52.)

Common Errors

Students often overlook infinite discontinuities which occur at *interior points* of the interval of integration. They should use proper limit notation when improper integrals are evaluated.

Exploration Extensions

Exploration 1. Evaluate, $\displaystyle\int_{0}^{1} \dfrac{dx}{x^p}$, where $0 < p < 1$. $\left(\dfrac{1}{1 - p} \right)$.

Notes on Exercises

- In Ex. 3, 8, 17, 18, 22, and 25 it is necessary to split the interval of integration into two pieces.

- In Ex. 28 and 31, students need to realize that the direct comparison test can be applied to situations involving vertical asymptotes.

- Ex. 49 describes a solid with finite volume and infinite surface area.

Assignment Guide

Ex. 3–48 multiples of 3, 49, 51, 52, 55, 56

PREPARATION FOR ADVANCED PLACEMENT EXAM

Ex. 49, 52–53

COOPERATIVE LEARNING

Ex. 50–52, 54, 56–58

ALTERNATE ASSESSMENT

Portfolio Have each student select an exercise that demonstrates his or her understanding of the limit comparison test.

8.4   Partial Fractions and Integral Tables

Objectives

- Students will be able to evaluate integrals using partial fractions, integral tables, or trigonometric substitutions.

Key Ideas

Partial Fractions
General Description of the Method
Integral Tables
Trigonometric Substitutions

Teaching Notes

You may wish to begin the lesson by developing the method of partial fractions using examples that are not integrals, such as Exercises 1–6. Stress the special rules when irreducible quadratic factors or repeated factors occur. Then use the process to evaluate several integrals. Remind students to use division if the degree of the numerator is greater than or equal to the degree of the denominator.

The key to the trigonometric substitution process is to choose the correct replacement. Emphasize the three different replacements and their connections to the Pythagorean identities. Encourage the use of right triangles when replacing trigonometric functions in antiderivatives.

One effective way to conclude this lesson is to discuss how to recognize situations when trigonometric substitution can be used and how to determine which substitution to use.

Notes on Examples

- Example 4 involves an improper fraction, so polynomial division is used before partial fraction decomposition.
- Example 7 illustrates the use of both trigonometric substitution and integral tables.

Common Errors

In applying partial fractions, students often forget to use polynomial division when the degree of the numerator is greater than or equal to the degree of the denominator.

In applying trigonometric substitution, students often forget to complete their calculation of indefinite integrals. The variables in the antiderivative must be replaced so that the final result is given in terms of the original variable.

Notes on Exercises

- Ex. 27–30 are initial value problems that can be solved by using the method of separation of variables in combination with partial fractions.

- Ex. 49–53 introduce another kind of trigonometric substitution.

Assignment Guide

Ex. 3–42 multiples of 3, 43–48

PREPARATION FOR ADVANCED PLACEMENT EXAM

Ex. 29, 30, 47

COOPERATIVE LEARNING

Ex. 31, 32

ALTERNATE ASSESSMENT

Self Assessment Have students write a paragraph describing any difficulties they encountered while using partial fractions and the integral tables.

Chapter 8 Review Exercises

PREPARATION FOR ADVANCED PLACEMENT EXAM

Ex. 67–69

CHAPTER
9
Infinite Series

Bibliography

FOR STUDENTS:

Multiple-Choice and Free-Response Questions in Preparation for the AP Calculus (BC) Exam, 6th Edition, David Lederman, D and S Marketing Systems, Brooklyn, NY, 1997.

FOR TEACHERS:

1992, 1993, and 1994 TICAP Participant Submitted Examples and Sample Multiple-Choice and Essay Graphing Calculator Questions. Campus Copy Shop, 384 College Avenue, #1 Rubin Square, Clemson, SC 29631, 1-864-654-3863.

VIDEO:

Series and e. Michael Peet, producer, Open University World Wide, distributed by Films for the Humanities and Sciences (#6351), 1988.

Chapter Opener

The Chapter Opener introduces students to a way to estimate the value of π numerically.

Solution: The number of terms added in 24 hours is

$$24 \text{ hours} \cdot \frac{60 \text{ minutes}}{1 \text{ hour}} \cdot \frac{60 \text{ seconds}}{1 \text{ minute}} \cdot \frac{1{,}000{,}000 \text{ terms}}{1 \text{ second}} = 8.64 \times 10^{10} \text{ terms.}$$

The error is $R_n \leq \dfrac{1}{8.64 \times 10^{10}} \approx 1.16 \times 10^{-11} = 0.0000000000116$. The error is probably in the 11th decimal place, so the computer's calculation of $\dfrac{\pi^2}{6}$ would be accurate to 10 decimal places.

9.1 Power Series

Objectives

- Students will be able to apply the properties of geometric series.
- Students will be able to differentiate, integrate, or substitute into a known power series in order to find additional power series representations.

Key Ideas

Geometric Series

Representing Functions by Series

Differentiation and Integration

Identifying a Series

Teaching Notes

You may wish to begin this lesson with a review of the basic concept of sequence, terms of a sequence, and convergence or divergence of a sequence. The Quick Review exercises on p. 466 could be assigned before you start the lesson. An understanding of sequences is crucial if students are to be successful in working with series.

One way to lead into the topic of series is to generate a sequence on a calculator to illustrate that the series $1 - \dfrac{1}{2} + \dfrac{1}{3} - \cdots$ approaches $\ln 2$.

In this lesson, we begin the study of infinite series with an intuitive approach. We feel that this approach is appropriate because this is difficult material for most students, and they need to have an intuitive grasp of the material before they can comprehend the theorems. The important theorems are presented rigorously later in this chapter.

Students need to understand that a convergent infinite series is one whose sequence of partial sums converges. The sum of an infinite series is the limit of its sequence of partial sums. Geometric series and telescoping series (see Section 9.4) are good examples to illustrate this definition because their partial sums have simple formulas.

Note that some of the series used in this section begin with an $n = 0$ term, while others begin with an $n = 1$ term. One reason that this occurs is that, when finding the derivative of a power series, the derivative of the original $n = 0$ term is 0. You may wish to call this to the attention of your students when it occurs.

Since the partial sums of most series will not have simple closed formulas, the use of a program like PARTSUMT to generate a table of values of partial sums can be a valuable visual aid. For a convergent series it can be used to estimate the sum. Alternately, PARTSUMG can be used to see the partial sums visually.

The formula for the sum of a geometric series leads naturally to the simple power series $1 + x + x^2 + x^3 + \cdots + x^n + \cdots = \dfrac{1}{1 - x}$. A power series defines a function f whose domain is the interval of convergence of the series and whose value at any x is the sum of the series at x. Theorems 1 and 2 imply that the interval of convergence is unaffected by integration or differentiation, *except* that separate calculations are needed to determine if convergence occurs at the endpoints, if any.

The partial sum $\displaystyle\sum_{k=0}^{n} c_k(x - a)^k$ of a power series is a polynomial of degree $\leq n$ and is denoted $P_n(x)$. By definition, $P_n(x) \to f(x)$ at each x in the interval of convergence. The graphs of the polynomials $P_n(x)$ can be generated on a grapher either using a built-in feature of the grapher or using the program GRAPHSUM. If a formula for $f(x)$ is known, then graphing $y_1 = P_n(x)$ and $y_2 = f(x)$ in the same window can demonstrate how well the approximation works. The maximum error of the approximation over an interval can be estimated graphically by generating the graph of $|y_1 - y_2|$, as we shall see in Section 9.3.

Exploration 3 allows students to discover the power series for e^x and is a good way to conclude and summarize this lesson.

Notes on Examples

- Example 2 illustrates the connection between repeating decimals and geometric series. Students will further explore this connection in Exercises 28–35.

- Examples 4 and 5 illustrate differentiation and integration of power series.

Common Errors

Students frequently forget about intervals of convergence and assume that any power series converges for all values of x.

Exploration Extensions

Exploration 1. Find a power series that represents $\dfrac{1}{5-x} = \dfrac{1}{1-(x-4)}$ and give its interval of convergence. $(1 + (x-4) + (x-4)^2 + \cdots + (x-4)^n + \cdots; (3,5))$

Exploration 2. Use your power series from step 2 in order to write an infinite series that equals $\dfrac{\pi}{6} = \tan^{-1}\dfrac{1}{\sqrt{3}}$ and an infinite series that equals $\dfrac{\pi}{3} = \tan^{-1}\sqrt{3}$, if possible.
$\left(\dfrac{\pi}{6} = \dfrac{1}{\sqrt{3}} - \dfrac{1}{3\cdot 3\sqrt{3}} + \dfrac{1}{5\cdot 9\sqrt{3}} - \dfrac{1}{7\cdot 27\sqrt{3}} + \cdots + \dfrac{(-1)^n}{(2n+1)\cdot 3^n\sqrt{3}} + \cdots;$ **Series for** $\dfrac{\pi}{3}$ **cannot be obtained directly but** *can* **be obtained by doubling the sequence for** $\dfrac{\pi}{6}.\right)$

Exploration 3. Find a power series for e^{2x}. $\left(1 + 2x + \dfrac{4x^2}{2!} + \dfrac{8x^3}{3!} + \cdots + \dfrac{(2x)^n}{n!} + \cdots\right)$

Notes on Exercises

- Ex. 30–35 can be done either by the typical method of writing expressions for x and $10 \cdot x$ and then subtracting, or by representing x as a geometric series (or a constant plus a geometric series) and using the $\dfrac{a}{1-r}$ formula.
- Ex. 50–53 are based on the idea of integration and differentiation of series.
- Ex. 54–57 are based on the formal definitions of convergence and the limit of a sequence.

Assignment Guide

Ex. 1–10, 13–23 odd, 26–28, 32, 34, 36–38, 42, 45, 48, 51, 52, 54, 55

PREPARATION FOR ADVANCED PLACEMENT EXAM

Ex. 20, 25, 38, 47, 49–52

COOPERATIVE LEARNING

Ex. 53

ALTERNATE ASSESSMENT

Journal Exercise 26

9.2 Taylor Series

Objectives

- Students will be able to use derivatives to find the Maclaurin series or Taylor series generated by a differentiable function.

Key Ideas

Constructing a Series

Series for sin x and cos x

Beauty Bare

Maclaurin and Taylor Series

Combining Taylor Series

Table of Maclaurin Series

Teaching Notes

We recommend beginning this lesson with Exploration 1, which is designed to help motivate the definition of a Taylor polynomial centered at $x = 0$.

It is plausible that if we were constructing an nth degree polynomial which best approximates a function f on a small interval about $x = a$, we would want the polynomial to have the same function value and the same first n derivatives at $x = a$ that f does. These $n + 1$ conditions uniquely determine the $n + 1$ coefficients of the nth order Taylor polynomial $P_n(x)$.

Observe that $P_1(x)$ and $P_2(x)$ are the standard linear approximation (linearization) and quadratic approximation, respectively, of $f(x)$, as discussed in Section 4.5. Graphing $y_1 = P_n(x)$ and $y_2 = f(x)$ for small values of n in the same window using functions like e^x, sin x, and ln $(1+x)$ should convince students that these polynomials do a remarkable job of estimating $f(x)$ when x is sufficiently close to a. We will use Taylor's Theorem to prove these results in Section 9.3.

Many power series representations can be derived by algebraically manipulating, differentiating, and integrating known Taylor series representations. This is a nice shortcut to establishing Taylor series representations.

The table of Maclaurin series provides a useful conclusion to this lesson. Students should be able to derive these series, but they are used so often that students should memorize or at least be familiar with all of them.

Notes on Examples

- Example 1 is important. Make sure that students understand the notation used and the method for determining the coefficients.

- In Example 2, note that the even coefficients are zero, so the "nth partial sum" of nonzero terms is *not* the Taylor series of order n for sin x. For example, the third partial sum $x - x^3/3! + x^5/5!$ is the Taylor polynomial of order 5 (or 6). The ninth partial sum graphed in Figure 9.4 is $P_{17}(x)$ or $P_{18}(x)$.

- Example 3 shows how we can substitute $2x$ for x in a known power series representation in order to obtain a power series (namely, the Maclaurin series) for cos $2x$.

Common Errors

Algebraic errors frequently occur when calculating Taylor polynomial coefficients. Another common error is to attempt to differentiate $f^{(n)}(0)$ instead of $f^{(n)}(x)$, obtaining 0 for all remaining coefficients. Graphing support can be used to detect errors.

Exploration Extensions

Exploration 1. Suppose you know that $P^{(8)}(0) = 3$ for some polynomial $P(x)$. What can you say about the coefficients of P? (**The coefficient of x^8 is $3 \cdot 8! = 120,960$.**)

Exploration 2. Construct the twelfth order Taylor polynomial at $x = 0$ for cos x^2.
$$\left(1 - \frac{x^4}{2} + \frac{x^8}{24} - \frac{x^{12}}{720}\right)$$

Exploration 3. Write a sequence of calculator commands, similar to the commands given in part 2, that can be used to find the Taylor polynomial approximations for cos 8. **(One possible answer:** $0\rightarrow N:1\rightarrow T$ ENTER $N+1\rightarrow N:T + (-1)$ ^N*8^(2N)/(2N)!$\rightarrow T$ ENTER ENTER $\cdots$ **)**

Notes on Exercises

- Ex. 16–19 require students to use the definition of a Taylor series (or Maclaurin series).
- Ex. 19–22 involve derivatives or integrals of Taylor series (or Maclaurin series).
- In Ex. 33, note that m need not be an integer. When m is not a positive integer, the binomial series is an infinite series.

Assignment Guide

Ex. 1–31 odd

PREPARATION FOR ADVANCED PLACEMENT EXAM

Ex. 16–22, 29–31

COOPERATIVE LEARNING

Exploration 2; Ex. 32

ALTERNATE ASSESSMENT

Project Have students research the lives of mathematicians James Gregory, Colin Maclaurin, Nicolaus Mercator, and/or Brook Taylor. (See page 473)

9.3 Taylor's Theorem

Objectives

- Students will be able to approximate a function with a Taylor polynomial.
- Students will be able to analyze the truncation error of a series using graphical methods or the Remainder Estimation Theorem.
- Students will be able to use Euler's formula to relate the functions $\sin x$, $\cos x$, and e^x.

Key Ideas

About Taylor Polynomials
The Remainder
Remainder Estimation Theorem
Euler's Formula

Teaching Notes

One way to begin this lesson is by again noting that for functions such as e^x, $\sin x$, and $\ln(1 + x)$, the Taylor polynomials do a remarkable job of estimating $f(x)$ when x is sufficiently close to a.

Taylor's Theorem will confirm, under suitable conditions, that the Taylor series of f at $x = a$ is an exact representation of f on an interval about a. For a given x, to show that the Taylor series represents f at x it is necessary to show that the remainder $R_n(x) = f(x) - P_n(x)$ approaches 0, as n approaches ∞. The formula for $R_n(x)$ given by Taylor's Theorem serves this purpose for a number of important cases.

The formula for $R_n(x)$ involves some unknown value c that is between a and x. However, if we can bound the values of $f^{(n+1)}$ on the interval between a and x, then it is possible to find a bound for the absolute error $|R_n(x)|$ when approximating $f(x)$ with $P_n(x)$. Taylor's Theorem provides an analytical method for doing this.

Note that the Remainder Estimation Theorem depends on choosing a particular value of x. This is a somewhat subtle point which can easily confuse students. The Remainder Estimation Theorem does *not* give a *single* bound on the error that applies for the *entire* interval of convergence. It is possible for a Taylor series to converge to f on I even if each and every P_n has an error that approaches ∞ at the endpoints of the interval. A concrete example such as the following can help to clarify this point.

True statement: For each value of x, there is an N such that $\left| e^x - \sum_{k=0}^{n} \frac{x^k}{k!} \right| \leq 0.001$ for all $n \geq N$.

False statement: There is an N such that for all $n \geq N$, $\left| e^x - \sum_{k=0}^{n} \frac{x^k}{k!} \right| \leq 0.001$ for all x.

Note that n can be either fixed or variable in the Remainder Estimation Theorem. Example 5 shows how the theorem is used with n fixed, and Example 4 shows how it can be used when n varies. If n is fixed, the "r" serves no purpose and we can just set $r = 1$. Exercise 57c in the Review Exercises can be used to demonstrate how r can be useful.

Exploration 1 is intended to help students understand Taylor's Theorem by using it to prove that the series for $\cos x$ converges for all real x.

Exploration 2 deals with a Maclaurin series involving complex numbers and is an interesting way to conclude this lesson.

Notes on Examples

- Example 1 illustrates the importance of stating a problem in a meaningful way before attempting to solve it.

- An alternate method for solving Example 2 is to use $\left| 1 + x^2 + x^4 + x^6 - \frac{1}{1 - x^2} \right|$.

- Examples 3 and 4 are fundamental as they demonstrate how Taylor's Theorem establishes that $\sin x$ and e^x are represented by their Maclaurin series for all x.

Common Errors

Students often fail to grasp why the error of an approximation, as given by $|f(x) - P_n(x)|$, can be less than (instead of equal to) the possible error given by the Remainder Estimation Theorem.

Students often assume that the possible error given by the Remainder Estimation Theorem is in fact the actual error. Emphasize that the Remainder Estimation Theorem gives a *maximum possible* error which may or may not be the same as the actual error.

Exploration Extensions

Exploration 1. Modify the steps of the proof in Example 3 to prove that $\sum_{k=0}^{\infty} \frac{x^k}{k!}$ converges to e^x for all real x.

Exploration 2. Use two different methods to find an expression in the form $a + ib$ for e^{2ix}. Use your results to generate the well-known identities for $\cos 2x$ and $\sin 2x$.
$(e^{2ix} = e^{i(2x)} = \cos 2x + i \sin 2x$ and $e^{2ix} = (e^{ix})^2 = (\cos x + i \sin x)^2$
$= \cos^2 x - \sin^2 x + i \cdot 2 \cos x \sin x$, so the identities are $\cos 2x = \cos^2 x - \sin^2 x$ and $\sin 2x = 2 \cos x \sin x$.)

Notes on Exercises

- Ex. 1–10 can be completed either by calculating coefficients using derivatives, or by performing operations on the known Maclaurin series given in Section 9.2. Students may find it instructive to try *both* methods and verify that the results are the same. When using derivatives, students may find it helpful to organize their calculations in a table with columns $n, f^{(n)}(x), f^{(n)}(0),$ and $f^{(n)}(0)/n!$.

- Ex. 11, 12, 13, 14, 24, 25, and 26 can be done either by using the Remainder Estimation Theorem or by using graphing techniques with functions of the form $f(x) - P_n(x)$. You may wish to have students try both methods and verify that the graphical results do not contradict the Remainder Estimation Theorem.

Assignment Guide

Ex. 3–21 multiples of 3, 24–25

PREPARATION FOR ADVANCED PLACEMENT EXAM

Ex. 12, 15, 21, 24–27

COOPERATIVE LEARNING

Ex. 30

ALTERNATE ASSESSMENT

Interview For Exercise 25 or 26, have students explain both a graphical solution and a solution using the Remainder Estimation Theorem. Students should be able to explain why the results are different, and why this difference does not contradict the Remainder Estimation Theorem.

9.4 Radius of Convergence

Objectives

- Students will be able to use the *n*th-Term Test, the Direct Comparison Test, and the Ratio Test to determine the convergence or divergence of a series of numbers or the radius of convergence of a power series.

Key Ideas

Convergence

*n*th-Term Test

Comparing Nonnegative Series

Ratio Test

Endpoint Convergence

Teaching Notes

One way to begin this lesson is by discussing Theorem 5, the Convergence Theorem for Power Series.

The conclusion of the *n*th-Term Test is quite obvious to most students, but it is easy to forget to apply this simple test. When confronted with a new series, one of the first questions to ask is, "Do the terms approach 0 as $n \to \infty$?"

Point out the analogy between the Direct Comparison Test for convergent series and the related test for integrals in Section 8.3. Conceptually, the Direct Comparison Test is easy to understand. However, students often have difficulty using this test since it requires selecting the right series for comparison and then establishing the correct inequality.

The Ratio Test is too crude to determine convergence when a_n is a rational function of n, but it is frequently useful when exponential functions or factorials occur as factors in the numerator or denominator of the nth term a_n. In particular, it can often be used to find the radius of convergence of a power series. Students should get plenty of practice using this test so that they can make the appropriate cancellations involving factorials and exponents almost automatically.

Continue to use graphical and numerical support. In those examples where convergence is fairly rapid, the grapher program PARTSUMT can be used to estimate the sum of a series which the theory indicates is convergent.

The importance of Theorem 8 (Absolute Convergence Implies Convergence) lies in its generality. Now a tool exists to show convergence of any series provided its absolute convergence can be shown, and any of the other tests can be used as appropriate to show that $\Sigma |a_n|$ converges.

The alternating p-series $\sum_{n=1}^{\infty} \frac{(-1)^{n-1}}{n^p}$ with $0 < p \le 1$ is a simple example of a series which converges conditionally. Note that in order to show that a series converges conditionally, one needs to show *both* that Σa_n converges *and* $\Sigma |a_n|$ diverges.

Example 6, regarding telescoping series, provides an interesting conclusion to this lesson.

Notes on Examples

- Example 3 shows how to use the Direct Comparison Test.
- Example 4 shows how to use absolute convergence to show the convergence of a series that has both positive and negative terms.
- Example 5 shows how to use the Ratio Test.

Common Errors

A common error students make is to confuse the nth-Term Test with its converse and falsely infer that a series converges if $a_n \to 0$. Another "error" students make is to overlook the nth-Term Test as an easy way to prove divergence.

When using the Ratio Test, students often make errors when simplifying the fraction $\frac{a_{n+1}}{a_n}$, especially when factorials are involved. Numerical support is useful for detecting errors.

Students often neglect to check the endpoints when determining the interval of convergence.

Exploration Extensions

Exploration 1. The terms of $\sum_{n=1}^{\infty} 1/n$ approach 0 as $n \to \infty$, but the series diverges. Explain why this does *not* contradict the nth-Term Test.

Exploration 2. Find the sum of the series at the right-hand endpoint. (Hint: Use the table of Maclaurin series on page 477.) **(ln 2)**

Notes on Exercises

- Ex. 1–16 require students to determine the convergence or divergence of series of numbers.
- Ex. 19–40 require students to find the radius of convergence or the interval of convergence of power series.
- Ex. 51 involves a telescoping series whose sum is not the "obvious" answer.

Assignment Guide

Ex. 3–39 multiples of 3, 45, 48, 51

PREPARATION FOR ADVANCED PLACEMENT EXAM

Ex. 38, 40, 50, 52

COOPERATIVE LEARNING

Ex. 42, 43, 44, 51, 52

ALTERNATE ASSESSMENT

Portfolio Have each student select an exercise that demonstrates his or her understanding of absolute convergence.

9.5 Testing Convergence at Endpoints

Objectives

* Students will be able to use the Integral Test and the Alternating Series Test to determine the convergence or divergence of a series of numbers.

* Students will be able to determine the convergence or divergence of p-series, including the harmonic series.

* Students will be able to determine the absolute convergence, conditional convergence, or divergence of a power series at the endpoints of its interval of convergence.

Key Ideas

Integral Test

Harmonic Series and p-series

Comparison Tests

Alternating Series

Absolute and Conditional Convergence

Intervals of Convergence

A Word of Caution

Teaching Notes

Begin this lesson with an introduction to the Integral Test. Discuss the connection between the Integral Test and Exploration 1 of Section 9.4.

When employing the Integral Test, make sure that students verify all the conditions that $f(x)$ must satisfy on some $[N, \infty)$. Remind them that the easiest way to show that f is decreasing is to show that $f'(x) < 0$. Once the Integral Test is introduced, have students complete Exploration 1 in order to establish the convergence of the p-series when $p > 1$ and divergence when $p < 1$.

When discussing the Limit Comparison Test, review the related ideas in Section 8.3. In many instances, this test is easier to use than the Direct Comparison Test. It is necessary only to find an appropriate end behavior model for the nth term a_n and calculate a limit. The Limit Comparison Test is a good test to use when a_n is a rational function of n.

The Alternating Series Test (Theorem 12) provides sufficient conditions for the convergence of an alternating series. Just as important, its sequel, the Alternating Series Estimation Theorem (Theorem 13), provides a bound on the error when estimating the sum of an alternating series with its nth partial sum s_n.

For a converging alternating series, the oscillating convergence of its sequence of partial sums should be compared with the monotone convergence obtained when all terms of a series are positive. The grapher programs PARTSUMG and PARTSUMT can be used to illustrate these two fundamental convergence patterns.

The *n*th-Root Test is introduced within the Exercises for this section. Like the Ratio Test, it is too crude to determine convergence when a_n is a rational function of *n*, but it is frequently useful when *n*th powers occur as factors in the numerator or denominator of the *n*th term a_n. In particular, it can often be used to find the radius of convergence of a power series. Students who are tempted to use the *n*th-Root Test when a_n includes a factorial factor should know that $(n!)^{1/n} \to \infty$.

One way to conclude this lesson is to have students discuss ways to select the appropriate test for a given series. Making this selection is a major task for students.

Notes on Examples

- Example 5 demonstrates how the terms of a conditionally convergent series can be rearranged to form a series converging to any preassigned sum.

- Example 6 shows how to use the Ratio Test to determine intervals of convergence.

Common Errors

Some students will attempt to find the sum of a series using the Integral Test. Point out that, while the Integral Test can often be used to determine the convergence or divergence of a series, it cannot be used to find the sum.

Exploration Extensions

Exploration 1. Use the *p*-Series Test to determine the convergence or divergence of

(a) $\sum\limits_{n=1}^{\infty} n^{-1/3}$, (b) $\sum\limits_{n=1}^{\infty} n^2$, (c) $\sum\limits_{n=1}^{\infty} \dfrac{1}{n\sqrt[3]{n}}$, and (d) $\sum\limits_{n=1}^{\infty} \dfrac{1}{\sqrt[5]{n^4}}$. **(Diverges; diverges; converges; diverges)**

Exploration 2. Graph the functions $y_1 = e^{-1/x^2}$, $y_2 = $ NDER y_1, and $y_3 = $ NDER y_2 in the window $[-2, 2]$ by $[-1, 4]$. Comment on what you see.

Notes on Exercises

- Ex. 1–16 require students to determine the convergence or divergence of series of numbers.

- Ex. 17–25 require students to determine the convergence, absolute convergence, or divergence of series of numbers.

- Ex. 27–42 require students to find the interval of convergence of power series.

- Ex. 57–58 introduce the *n*th-Root Test.

Assignment Guide

Ex. 3–54 multiples of 3

PREPARATION FOR ADVANCED PLACEMENT EXAM

Ex. 46, 48–52

COOPERATIVE LEARNING

Ex. 56

ALTERNATE ASSESSMENT

Self Assessment Have students write a paragraph describing any difficulties they encountered while finding intervals of convergence.

Chapter 9 Review Exercises

PREPARATION FOR ADVANCED PLACEMENT EXAM

Ex. 56–61, 63

CHAPTER

10

Parametric, Vector, and Polar Functions

Bibliography

FOR TEACHERS:

"Getting Student Projects Going." Mary Ann Connors, UME Trends (Innovative Teaching Exchange Column), November 1995.

VIDEO:

Curves from Parameters. Pip Surgery, Open University World Wide, distributed by Films for the Humanities and Sciences (#6362), 1986.

Chapter Opener

The Chapter Opener requires students to use vectors in order to help navigate an airplane.

Solution: Let $\mathbf{u} = \langle -600, 0 \rangle$ be the desired velocity of the airplane, let $\mathbf{v} = \langle 100 \cos 45°, 100 \sin 45° \rangle = \langle 50\sqrt{2}, 50\sqrt{2} \rangle$ be the velocity of the wind, and let $\mathbf{w}$ be the vector representing airspeed and direction.

Then $\mathbf{u} = \mathbf{v} + \mathbf{w}$, so $\mathbf{w} = \mathbf{u} - \mathbf{v} = \langle -600 - 50\sqrt{2}, -50\sqrt{2} \rangle$.

$$|\mathbf{w}| = \sqrt{(-600 - 50\sqrt{2})^2 + (-50\sqrt{2})^2} \approx 674.43$$

$$\theta = 180° + \tan^{-1} \frac{-50\sqrt{2}}{-600 - 50\sqrt{2}} \approx 180° + 6.018° = 186.018°.$$

The pilot should direct the plane about 6° south of west at an airspeed of about 674 miles per hour.

10.1 Parametric Functions

Objectives

- Students will be able to find derivatives and second derivatives of parametrically defined functions.

- Students will be able to calculate lengths of parametrically defined curves and calculate surface areas.

Key Ideas

Derivatives

Parametric Formula for $\dfrac{d^2y}{dx^2}$

Length of a Smooth Curve

Cycloids

Surface Area

Teaching Notes

You may wish to begin this lesson with the Quick Review exercises, which provide a review of parametric equations.

A parametrized curve is defined to be *smooth* if the functions for x and y have continuous derivatives which are not simultaneously zero. Thus, the property of smoothness can depend not only on the shape of the curve, but also on how the curve is generated by t. For example, the circle generated by $x = \cos t$, $y = \sin |t|$, $-2\pi \le t \le 2\pi$, is *not* smooth.

When discussing the parametric formula for $\dfrac{d^2y}{dx^2}$, emphasize that differentiating with respect to x is not the same as differentiating with respect to t. In particular, the y' in the formula refers to $\dfrac{dy}{dx}$, not $\dfrac{dy}{dt}$.

Huygens's Clock is introduced on page 516. Students may have learned the formula $f = \dfrac{1}{2\pi}\sqrt{\dfrac{g}{L}}$ for the period of a simple pendulum of length L. This formula suggests that the frequency of a standard pendulum does not depend on the amplitude of the swing, but actually the formula holds only for small swings of the pendulum. To make a pendulum whose frequency is truly independent of the swing amplitude, it is necessary to use Huygens' method .

Example 6, showing how to find the surface area of a surface generated by a smooth parametrized curve, forms an interesting conclusion to this lesson.

Notes on Examples

- Example 2 illustrates the process of finding $\dfrac{d^2y}{dx^2}$ for a parametrized curve.
- Example 3 illustrates the process of finding the length of a parametrized curve.

Common Errors

In finding $\dfrac{d^2y}{dx^2}$ for a parametrically defined curve, some students may assume that the second derivative is given by $\dfrac{d^2y/dt^2}{d^2x/dt^2}$, instead of using the correct method.

Exploration Extensions

Exploration 1. Write parametric equations for a cycloid in which the minimum value of y is attained at $x = 0$, $x = 2$, $x = 4$, and so on. $\left(x = \dfrac{1}{\pi}(t - \sin t), y = \dfrac{1}{\pi}(1 - \cos t)\right)$

Notes on Exercises

- Ex. 11–16 and 23–27 involve lengths of curves.
- Ex. 17–22 and 28–30 require students to calculate surface areas.
- Ex. 35–38 give a preview of Section 10.4.

Assignment Guide

Ex. 1–33 multiples of 3

PREPARATION FOR ADVANCED PLACEMENT EXAM

Ex. 16, 27, 31

COOPERATIVE LEARNING

Ex. 33, 35–38

ALTERNATE ASSESSMENT

Interview Have students explain why the formula for the length of a smooth parametrized curve works.

10.2 Vectors in Plane

Objectives

- Students will be able to represent vectors in the form $\langle a, b \rangle$ and perform algebraic computations involving vectors.

Key Ideas

Component Form

Zero Vector

Vector Operations

Angle Between Vectors

Applications

Teaching Notes

Discuss first how vectors can be represented as directed line segments, and how they can be added and rescaled geometrically. Then show that any vector **v** can be uniquely written in the algebraic form $\mathbf{v} = \langle a, b \rangle$. This is the representation used in calculations and reflects that a vector in the plane corresponds to an ordered pair of numbers.

Using the algebraic representation, the key definitions of vector equality, addition, subtraction, magnitude, and scalar multiplication are all very simple. Spend some time with the geometric interpretation of each one of these. Especially important are the geometric interpretations of $\mathbf{u} + \mathbf{v}$, $\mathbf{u} - \mathbf{v}$, $k\mathbf{u}$, and $-\mathbf{u}$.

The dot product of two vectors can be defined by the formula $\mathbf{u} \cdot \mathbf{v} = |\mathbf{u}|\,|\mathbf{v}| \cos \theta$ or by $\mathbf{u} \cdot \mathbf{v} = u_1 v_1 + u_2 v_2$. The law of cosines can be used to demonstrate that these formulas are equivalent, as shown on page 524.

Example 7 concludes the lesson by showing how vectors can be applied to a real-life situation.

Notes on Examples

- Example 6 recasts the familiar problem of finding a tangent line and normal line to a curve in terms of vectors. The concept of the *slope* of a vector is useful for this type of problem. All you need to do is find the slope of the tangent and normal lines and then construct unit vectors having those slopes.

Common Errors

The fact that different directed line segments can represent the same vector is a source of confusion to students. For example, a student looking at Figure 10.11 might wonder, "How could two different directed line segments both be **v**? The answer, of course, is that both $\overrightarrow{AD}$ and $\overrightarrow{BC}$ *represent* **v**.

Notes on Exercises

- Ex. 19–22 involve unit vectors.
- Ex. 32 requires students to verify the fundamental fact that nonzero vectors **u** and **v** are orthogonal if and only if $\mathbf{u} \cdot \mathbf{v} = 0$. It is also worth noting that the angle between **u** and **v** is acute if $\mathbf{u} \cdot \mathbf{v} > 0$, and obtuse if $\mathbf{u} \cdot \mathbf{v} < 0$.
- Ex. 43–45 are velocity problems similar to Example 7.

Assignment Guide

Ex. 3–24 multiples of 3, 35, 39, 40, 43, 44, 47, 50

PREPARATION FOR ADVANCED PLACEMENT EXAM

Ex. 24

COOPERATIVE LEARNING

Ex. 29–34

ALTERNATE ASSESSMENT

Journal Exercise 42

10.3 Vector-Valued Functions

Objectives

- Students will be able to differentiate and integrate vector-valued functions.
- Students will be able to analyze the motion of a particle in space given its position, velocity, or acceleration as a vector function of time.

Key Ideas

Standard Unit Vectors

Planar Curves

Limits and Continuity

Derivatives and Motion

Differentiation Rules

Integrals

Teaching Notes

One way to begin this lesson is to introduce the standard unit vectors **i** and **j**, and then introduce the concept of a vector-valued function.

A vector-valued function $r(t) = f(t)\mathbf{i} + g(t)\mathbf{j}$ can be regarded as the position vector at time t of a moving particle. It can also be used to define the curve parametrized by the component functions $x = f(t)$, $y = g(t)$. Note that the definition of a smooth vector function is consistent with the definition of a smooth curve established in Section 10.1.

Students often take some time to get used to the idea of differentiating a vector, but the concept is really quite simple. Differentiation of $\mathbf{r}(t)$ is accomplished by differentiating each component of $\mathbf{r}$. If $\mathbf{r}(t)$ is a position vector of a particle, then $\mathbf{r}'(t)$ and $\mathbf{r}''(t)$ are the velocity and acceleration vectors of the particle at time t, and $|\mathbf{r}'(t)|$ is the speed. In discussing the differentiation rules for vector-valued functions, pay particular attention to the Dot Product Rule and the Chain Rule.

Integration, of course, is accomplished by integrating each component of the function. For an indefinite integral, an arbitrary constant vector is added; if an initial condition is known, we merely apply the initial condition to each component.

A discussion of Ex. 31 can be used to summarize the lesson.

Notes on Examples

- Example 4 shows how questions about the continuity of a vector-valued function reduce to questions about the continuity of its components.

- In Example 5, observe that the particle is always 3 units away from the origin. Have students discuss how this fact relates to the fact that $\mathbf{v} \cdot \mathbf{a} = 0$.

- Example 9 shows how to solve an initial value problem involving vectors. Just as is done in rectilinear motion problems, integrate velocity to find the position function, then use the initial condition to find the constant of integration.

Common Errors

Students sometimes fail to recognize that the arbitrary constant added to the indefinite integral of a vector function is itself a vector.

Notes on Exercises

- Ex. 5–8 are intended to reinforce the basic definitions involving particle motion. Students need to get used to thinking of position, velocity, and acceleration as vector quantities.

- Ex. 11–18 are vector integration problems.

- Ex. 19–24, 27, and 29–35 are additional problems involving particle motion.

Assignment Guide

Ex. 3–24 multiples of 3, 25, 27, 31, 35, 38

PREPARATION FOR ADVANCED PLACEMENT EXAM

Ex. 13, 16, 18, 21, 24, 29, 31, 33, 34

COOPERATIVE LEARNING

Ex. 29–32

ALTERNATE ASSESSMENT

Project Have students research the topic of centripetal acceleration in a physics book. How is this concept related to the result of Example 5?

10.4 Modeling Projectile Motion

Objectives

- Students will be able to solve problems involving ideal projectile motion and projectile motion with air resistance.

Key Ideas

Ideal Projectile Motion

Height, Flight Time, Range

Ideal Trajectories Are Parabolic

Firing from (x_0, y_0)

Projectile Motion with Wind Gusts

Projectile Motion with Air Resistance

Teaching Notes

You may wish to begin this lesson by reviewing the concept of free-fall motion covered in Section 3.4. In discussing ideal projectile motion, we are in essence simply adding a horizontal linear component to the vertical free-fall motion we have already studied.

In ideal projectile motion, the projectile moves in the vertical plane determined by the direction of its initial velocity vector. By identifying that plane as the xy-plane with the positive y-axis pointing directly upwards, the equation of motion will have the form $\mathbf{r}(t) = x(t)\mathbf{i} + y(t)\mathbf{j}$. The value of $\mathbf{r}(t)$ is found by integrating the equation $\mathbf{r}''(t) = -g\mathbf{j}$ twice and then finding the constants of integration from the initial position vector $\mathbf{r}_0$ and the initial velocity vector $\mathbf{v}_0$. If $\mathbf{r}_0 = 0$, $\mathbf{r}$ is given by Equations (5). The equations for the maximum height, flight time, and range can be easily derived to get Equations (6), (7), and (8).

More generally, if $\mathbf{r}_0 = x_0\mathbf{i} + y_0\mathbf{j}$, $\mathbf{r}$ is given by Equations (9), which are obtained by simply adding x_0 and y_0 to the expressions for x and y in Equations (5). From these equations it is evident that the trajectory in ideal projectile motion is a parabola.

In the model with air resistance, it is assumed that the drag force at any time caused by air resistance is $-k\mathbf{v}$, where k is a positive constant. Physicists use this approximation for "slow projectiles." (See Exercise 38 in Section 6.4 for another approximation used for "fast projectiles.") The differential equation is $\mathbf{r}''(t) = -g\mathbf{j} - k\mathbf{v}$, or $\mathbf{r}''(t) = -g\mathbf{j} - k\frac{d\mathbf{r}}{dt}$. We show how to solve this differential equation on pages 546–548 Note that we assume $\mathbf{r}_0 = 0$.

Conclude the lesson with Exploration 2 by allowing students to use graphs to analyze the motion of a projectile with a linear drag force.

Notes on Examples

- Example 2 investigates ideal projectile motion. You can challenge your students by asking them to solve this problem *without* using Equations (6), (7), and (8).
- In Example 3, note that the positive x-axis points to the left.
- In Example 4, we assume that there is no air resistance *except* for the effect of an instantaneous force, which we refer to as a gust of wind. You can challenge your students by asking them to solve parts (b) and (c) analytically.

Common Errors

Students may fail to recognize that Equations (6), (7), and (8) apply only to situations where the initial position is the origin. In other situations, a more detailed analysis is necessary.

In problems that give angles in degrees, students may forget to convert to radians or use the degree mode of the calculator.

Exploration Extensions

Exploration 1. Assume there is no gust of wind. To the nearest degree, at what angle is the ball hit if it hits the fence 10 ft above the ground? There are two possible answers. **(18° or 73°)**
Exploration 2. What is the speed of the ball immediately before it hits the ground?
(About 131.9 ft/sec)

Notes on Exercises

- Ex. 1–27 and 31 involve ideal projectile motion.

- Ex. 28–30 and 32 involve projectile motion with linear drag.

Assignment Guide

Ex. 3–21 multiples of 3, 26–28

PREPARATION FOR ADVANCED PLACEMENT EXAM

Ex. 13, 18, 19

COOPERATIVE LEARNING

Ex. 23–25

ALTERNATE ASSESSMENT

Portfolio Have each student select an exercise that demonstrates his or her understanding of projectile motion.

10.5 Polar Coordinates and Polar Graphs

Objectives

- Students will be able to graph polar equations and determine the symmetry of polar graphs.

- Students will be able to convert Cartesian equations into polar form and vice versa.

Key Ideas

Polar Coordinates

Polar Graphing

Relating Polar and Cartesian Coordinates

Teaching Notes

One way to begin this lesson is to show how the polar plane relates to the Cartesian plane. Show students how to plot a given polar point, identify a given point in the plane by its polar coordinates, graph simple polar equations such as $r = a$ or $\theta = \theta_0$, and graph simple inequalities. Polar graph paper can be made available to the class to show what a polar grid looks like and to be used for sketching polar graphs. Mention that one of the distinctions between polar and Cartesian coordinates is that a point in the Cartesian plane is identified by a *unique* pair of Cartesian coordinates, whereas a point in the polar plane is represented by infinitely many coordinate pairs.

By superimposing a rectangular coordinate system onto a polar coordinate system, it is possible to pass from one system to the other whenever it is convenient for a given problem. Students should be able to convert between rectangular and polar coordinates, and convert between the polar and rectangular equations of a given curve. Converting a rectangular equation to its equivalent polar equation is perfectly straightforward, but going the other way can be somewhat more involved.

Note that the graph of a polar equation $r = f(\theta)$ can be created in a Cartesian viewing window by graphing $x = f(t) \cos t$ and $y = f(t) \sin t$ in parametric mode. We are, in effect, substituting t for θ. (See Exercise 65.)

The tests for symmetry about the x-axis, y-axis, or origin are stated in terms of polar coordinates. These tests are relevant since many of the curves being considered satisfy one or all three of these symmetries. (Recall that any two of these symmetries implies the third.)

In graphing a curve of the form $r = f(\theta)$, the θ-interval used is an important matter. The interval may need to be larger than $0 \le \theta \le 2\pi$, depending on the period of f. For more general equations $F(r, \theta) = 0$, there may be restrictions on θ.

For graphs generated on a grapher, the *trace* key can be used to review how the curve was sequentially generated and can show if the curve retraces itself over the interval of θ-values used. Remind students to use a square viewing window so that the curve is not distorted.

Exploration 2 concludes the lesson with an introduction to rose curves.

Notes on Examples

- Example 5 shows how to convert an equation from Cartesian coordinates to polar form. Note that an alternate method of solving this problem is to begin by substituting $r \cos \theta$ for x and $r \sin \theta$ for y, and then simplify the result.

- In Example 6, note that converting the polar equations to their Cartesian equivalents may take a little luck, but with almost no effort the *graphs* of the polar equations would clearly suggest that the solution curves are a circle and a straight line, respectively.

Common Errors

Students often have difficulty with the fact that the polar coordinates of a point are not uniquely determined. For example, they might conclude that the point $(1, 0)$ is not on the graph of $r = \sin 0.5\theta$ because the coordinates do not satisfy the equation. This point is in the curve because it can also be identified by the coordinates $(-1, 3\pi)$.

When graphing a polar curve, some students may choose a θ-interval that is too small to display the entire curve.

Exploration Extensions

Exploration 1. Graph $r = \sin 0.5\theta$ and repeat parts 2–4 for this polar equation.
(Interval: $0 \le \theta \le 4\pi$)

Exploration 2. How do the graphs of $r = 2 \sin n\theta$ differ from the ones you found in parts 1 and 4? $\left(\textbf{Rotated clockwise } \dfrac{1}{n} \cdot \textbf{90}°\right)$

Notes on Exercises

- In Ex. 7–18, the directions are to graph the equation or inequality. You may wish to have students provide an analysis which includes the symmetries the curve satisfies, the polar range needed to produce all of the points on the graph, and a table showing specific points (r, θ) on the curve.

- Ex. 19–48 require students to convert equations from polar to Cartesian form or vice versa.

Assignment Guide

Ex. 1–5 odd, 6–57 multiples of 3, 65

PREPARATION FOR ADVANCED PLACEMENT EXAM

Ex. 67

COOPERATIVE LEARNING

Ex. 59–62

ALTERNATE ASSESSMENT

Self Assessment Have students write a paragraph describing any difficulties they encountered while converting equations from polar coordinates to Cartesian coordinates.

10.6 Calculus of Polar Curves

Objectives

- Students will be able to calculate slopes, lengths, areas of regions in the plane, and surface areas determined by polar curves.

Key Ideas

Slope

Area in the Plane

Length of a Curve

Area of a Surface of Revolution

Teaching Notes

You may wish to begin this lesson by again emphasizing the connection between polar equations and parametric equations. This connection is exploited in finding a formula for the slope of a polar curve.

The general formula for the slope of a polar curve is given by Equation (1). Calculating the slope at the origin is a special case; the curve may pass through the origin more than once at different angles.

When calculating the area of a region in the polar plane, it is important to graph the region to determine the correct limits of integration and to observe any symmetry that may simplify the integration. This is particularly true when the region is bounded by two curves (Equation (2)).

The formulas for the arc length of a polar curve and the surface area generated by rotating a polar curve about the x- or y-axis are special cases of the corresponding formula given in Section 10.1.

Example 7 concludes the lesson by showing how to find the surface area of the solid generated by revolving a lemniscate.

Notes on Examples

- In Examples 4 and 5, challenge your students to find the values of the integrals without using NINT.

Common Errors

The equation for the area between polar curves on page 563 is sometimes mistakenly written $\int_{\alpha}^{\beta} \frac{1}{2}(r_2 - r_1)^2 \, d\theta.$

Notes on Exercises

- Ex. 13–30 require students to find areas of regions.
- Ex. 31–38, 43, 45, 47, and 48 involve lengths of curves.
- Ex. 39–42 and 46 involve surface areas.
- Ex. 49–50 require students to find centroids of regions. The centroid of a flat object is the same as its center of mass, provided that the density of the object (in weight per unit area) is constant.

Assignment Guide

Ex. 1–7 odd, 15–45 multiples of 3

PREPARATION FOR ADVANCED PLACEMENT EXAM

Ex. 44, 47, 48

COOPERATIVE LEARNING

Ex. 9–12

ALTERNATE ASSESSMENT

Journal Exercise 30

Chapter 10 Review Exercises

PREPARATION FOR ADVANCED PLACEMENT EXAM

Ex. 13, 46, 53, 58, 61, 63

Cumulative Review Exercises

Given below is the section students can review if they have difficulty with an exercise.

1. 2.1	**41.** 4.2	**81.** 10.6
2. 2.1	**42.** 4.1, 4.2, 4.3	**82.** 7.3
3. 2.1	**43.** 4.3	**83.** 10.1
4. 2.2	**44.** 4.4	**84.** 10.6
5. 8.1	**45.** 4.5	**85.** 7.3
6. 8.1	**46.** 4.5	**86.** 7.3
7. 8.1	**47.** 4.6	**87.** 7.1
8. 8.1	**48.** 4.6	**88.** 7.5
9. 2.3, 3.2	**49.** 5.1	**89.** 7.5
10. 2.3	**50.** 5.2, 7.2	**90.** 8.2
11. 2.2	**51.** 5.2, 7.2	**91.** 8.3
12. 2.2	**52.** 5.4	**92.** 8.3
13. 2.4	**53.** 5.4	**93.** 8.3
14. 3.3	**54.** 6.2	**94.** 8.3
15. 3.6	**55.** 6.1	**95.** 8.3
16. 3.5	**56.** 10.6	**96.** 8.3
17. 3.9	**57.** 6.2	**97.** 9.1
18. 3.9	**58.** 8.4	**98.** 9.1, 9.2
19. 3.8	**59.** 6.2	**99.** 9.2
20. 3.9	**60.** 6.3	**100.** 9.2
21. 3.6	**61.** 6.2, 8.4	**101.** 9.5
22. 3.8	**62.** 5.5	**102.** 9.2, 9.3
23. 3.7	**63.** 4.2, 6.1	**103.** 9.4, 9.5
24. 3.7	**64.** 4.2, 6.1	**104.** 9.4, 9.5
25. 3.6	**65.** 6.3	**105.** 9.4, 9.5
26. 3.9	**66.** 6.3	**106.** 9.4, 9.5
27. 5.4	**67.** 6.4	**107.** 9.5
28. 5.4	**68.** 6.4	**108.** 9.5
29. 3.7	**69.** 6.5	**109.** 10.3
30. 3.6	**70.** 6.2	**110.** 10.2
31. 3.4	**71.** 6.6	**111.** 10.3
32. 3.1	**72.** 5.2	**112.** 10.3
33. 3.5	**73.** 7.2	**113.** 10.4
34. 3.7	**74.** 7.2	**114.** 10.5
35. 3.6	**75.** 10.6	**115.** 10.5
36. 10.6	**76.** 7.3	**116.** 10.6
37. 3.1	**77.** 7.3	
38. 3.2, 4.1	**78.** 5.3	
39. 4.2	**79.** 7.4	
40. 4.3	**80.** 10.1	

Answers to Student Edition Exercises

Chapter 1
Prerequisites for Calculus

1.1 Lines
(pp. 1–9)

Quick Review 1.1

1. -2
2. -1
3. -1
4. $\dfrac{5}{4}$
5. (a) Yes   (b) No
6. (a) Yes   (b) No
7. $\sqrt{2}$
8. $\dfrac{5}{3}$
9. $y = \dfrac{4}{3}x - \dfrac{7}{3}$
10. $y = \dfrac{2}{5}x - \dfrac{3}{5}$

Section 1.1 Exercises

1. $\Delta x = -2, \Delta y = -3$
2. $\Delta x = 2, \Delta y = -4$
3. $\Delta x = -5, \Delta y = 0$
4. $\Delta x = 0, \Delta y = -6$
5. (a) and (c)

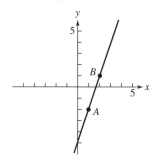

(b) 3

6. (a) and (c)

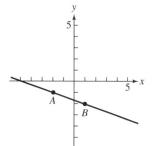

(b) $-\dfrac{1}{3}$

7. (a) and (c)

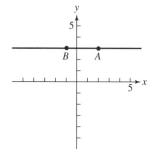

(b) 0

8. (a) and (c)

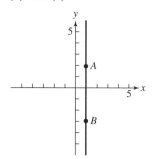

(b) Has no slope (undefined)

9. (a) $x = 2$ (b) $y = 3$
10. (a) $x = -1$ (b) $y = \dfrac{4}{3}$
11. (a) $x = 0$ (b) $y = -\sqrt{2}$

12. (a) $x = -\pi$ **(b)** $y = 0$
13. $y = 1(x - 1) + 1$ **14.** $y = -1(x + 1) + 1$
15. $y = 2(x - 0) + 3$ **16.** $y = -2(x + 4) + 0$
17. $3x - 2y = 0$ **18.** $y - 1$
19. $x = -2$ **20.** $3x + 4y = -2$
21. $y = 3x - 2$ **22.** $y = -x + 2$
23. $y = -\dfrac{1}{2}x - 3$ **24.** $y = \dfrac{1}{3}x - 1$
25. $y = \dfrac{5}{2}x$ **26.** $y = \dfrac{2}{5}x$
27. (a) $-\dfrac{3}{4}$ **(b)** 3
(c)

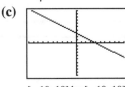

[−10, 10] by [−10, 10]

28. (a) -1 **(b)** 2
(c)

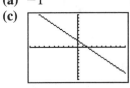

[−10, 10] by [−10, 10]

29. (a) $-\dfrac{4}{3}$ **(b)** 4
(c)

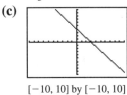

[−10, 10] by [−10, 10]

30. (a) 2   **(b)** 4
(c)

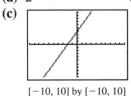

[−10, 10] by [−10, 10]

31. (a) $y = -x$ **(b)** $y = x$
32. (a) $y = -2x - 2$ **(b)** $y = \dfrac{1}{2}x + 3$
33. (a) $x = -2$ **(b)** $y = 4$
34. (a) $y = \dfrac{1}{2}$ **(b)** $x = -1$
35. $m = \dfrac{7}{2}, b = -\dfrac{3}{2}$ **36.** $m = -\dfrac{3}{2}, b = 2$
37. $y = -1$ **38.** $x = -6$
39. (a) $y = 0.680x + 9.013$
    (b) The slope is 0.68. It represents the
       approximate average weight gain in pounds
       per month.
(c)

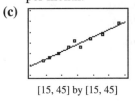

[15, 45] by [15, 45]

39. continued
    (d) 29 pounds
40. (a) $y = 1,060.4233x - 2,077,548.669$
    (b) The slope is 1,060.4233. It represents the
       approximate increase in earnings in dollars per
       year.
    (c)

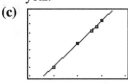

[1975, 1995] by [20,000, 35,000]

    (d) Approximately \$43,298
41. $y = 1(x - 3) + 4$
    $y = x - 3 + 4$
    $y = x + 1$, which is the same equation.
42. (a) When $y = 0$, $x = c$; when $x = 0$, $y = d$.
    (b) The x-intercept is $2c$ and the y-intercept is $2d$.
43. (a) $k = 2$ **(b)** $k = -2$
44. (a) -3.75 degrees/inch **(b)** -16.1 degrees/inch
    (c) -7.1 degrees/inch
    (d) Best: fiberglass; poorest: gypsum wallboard
       The best insulator will have the largest
       temperature change per inch, because that will
       allow larger temperature differences on
       opposite sides of thinner layers.
45. 5.97 atmospheres ($k = 0.0994$)
46. (a) $d(t) = 45t$
    (b)

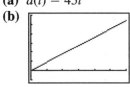

[0, 6] by [−50, 300]

    (c) Slope is 45, which is the speed in miles per
       hour.
    (d) Suppose the car has been traveling 45 mph for
       several hours when it is first observed at point
       P at time $t = 0$.
    (e) The car starts at time $t = 0$ at a point 30 miles
       past P.
47. (a) $y = 5632x - 11,080,280$
    (b) The rate at which the median price is
       increasing in dollars per year
    (c) $y = 2732x - 5,362,360$
    (d) In the Northeast
48. (a) Yes, -40 degrees
    (b)

[−90, 90] by [−60, 60]

It's related because all three lines pass through
the point $(-40, -40)$ where the Fahrenheit
and Celsius temperatures are the same.

49. The coordinates of the three missing vertices are $(5, 2)$, $(-1, 4)$ and $(-1, -2)$.

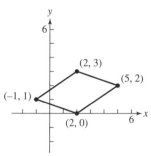

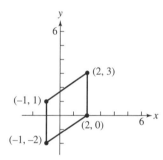

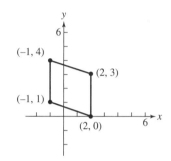

50. Suppose that the vertices of the original quadrilateral are (a, b), (c, d), (e, f), and (g, h). When the midpoints are connected, the pairs of opposite sides of the resulting figure have slopes $\frac{f - b}{e - a}$ or $\frac{h - d}{g - c}$, and opposite sides are parallel.

51. $y = -\frac{3}{4}(x - 3) + 4$ or $y = -\frac{3}{4}x + \frac{25}{4}$

52. (a) $y = \frac{B}{A}(x - a) + b$

(b) The coordinates are
$$\left(\frac{B^2a + AC - ABb}{A^2 + B^2}, \frac{A^2b + BC - ABa}{A^2 + B^2} \right).$$

(c) Distance $= \dfrac{|Aa + Bb - C|}{\sqrt{A^2 + B^2}}$

1.2 **Functions and Graphs**
(pp. 9–19)

Quick Review 1.2

1. $[-2, \infty)$ **2.** $(-\infty, 0) \cup (2, \infty)$
3. $[-1, 7]$ **4.** $(-\infty, -3] \cup [7, \infty)$
5. $(-4, 4)$ **6.** $[-3, 3]$

---

7. Translate the graph of f 2 units left and 3 units downward.
8. Translate the graph of f 5 units right and 2 units upward.
9. (a) $x = -3, 3$ **(b)** No real solution
10. (a) $x = -\frac{1}{5}$ **(b)** No solution
11. (a) $x = 9$ **(b)** $x = -6$
12. (a) $x = -7$ **(b)** $x = 28$

Section 1.2 Exercises

1. $A = \dfrac{\pi d^2}{4}$ **2.** $h = \dfrac{\sqrt{3}}{2}s$

3. $S = 6e^2$ **4.** $V = \dfrac{4}{3}\pi r^3$

5. (a) All reals   **(b)** $(-\infty, 4]$
(c)

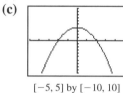

$[-5, 5]$ by $[-10, 10]$

(d) Symmetric about y-axis
6. (a) All reals   **(b)** $[-9, \infty)$
(c)

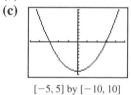

$[-5, 5]$ by $[-10, 10]$

(d) Symmetric about y-axis
7. (a) $[1, \infty)$ **(b)** $[2, \infty)$
(c)

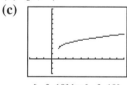

$[-3, 10]$ by $[-3, 10]$

(d) None
8. (a) $(-\infty, 0]$ **(b)** $(-\infty, 0]$
(c)

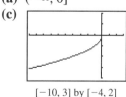

$[-10, 3]$ by $[-4, 2]$

(d) None
9. (a) $(-\infty, 3]$ **(b)** $[0, \infty)$
(c)

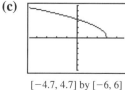

$[-4.7, 4.7]$ by $[-6, 6]$

(d) None
10. (a) $(-\infty, 2) \cup (2, \infty)$ **(b)** $(-\infty, 0) \cup (0, \infty)$

10. continued

(c)

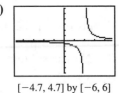

[−4.7, 4.7] by [−6, 6]

(d) None

11. (a) All reals   **(b)** All reals

(c)

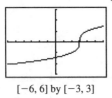

[−6, 6] by [−3, 3]

(d) None

12. (a) All reals   **(b)** (−∞, 1]

(c)

[−6, 6] by [−3, 3]

(d) Symmetric about *y*-axis

13. (a) (−∞, 0]   **(b)** [0, ∞)

(c)

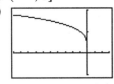

[−10, 3] by [−1, 2]

(d) None

14. (a) (−∞, 0) ∪ (0, ∞)   **(b)** (−∞, 1) ∪ (1, ∞)

(c)

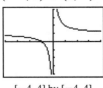

[−4, 4] by [−4, 4]

(d) None

15. (a) [−2, 2]   **(b)** [0, 2]

(c)

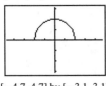

[−4.7, 4.7] by [−3.1, 3.1]

(d) Symmetric about *y*-axis

16. (a) All reals   **(b)** [0, ∞)

(c)

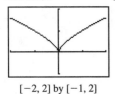

[−2, 2] by [−1, 2]

(d) Symmetric about *y*-axis

17. (a) (−∞, 0) ∪ (0, ∞)   **(b)** (1, ∞)

(c)

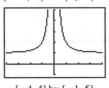

[−4, 4] by [−1, 5]

(d) Symmetric about *y*-axis

18. (a) [0, ∞)   **(b)** [0, ∞)

(c)

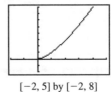

[−2, 5] by [−2, 8]

(d) None

19. Even   **20.** Neither
21. Neither   **22.** Even
23. Even   **24.** Odd
25. Odd   **26.** Neither
27. Neither   **28.** Even

29. (a)

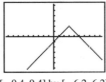

[−9.4, 9.4] by [−6.2, 6.2]

(b) All reals   **(c)** (−∞, 2]

30. (a)

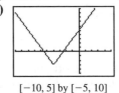

[−10, 5] by [−5, 10]

(b) All reals   **(c)** [−3, ∞)

31. (a)

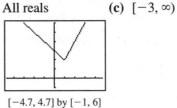

[−4.7, 4.7] by [−1, 6]

(b) All reals   **(c)** [2, ∞)

32. (a)

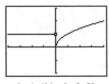

[−4, 4] by [−2, 3]

(b) All reals   **(c)** [0, ∞)

33. (a)

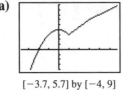

[−3.7, 5.7] by [−4, 9]

(b) All reals   **(c)** All reals

34. (a)

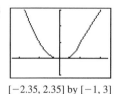

[−2.35, 2.35] by [−1, 3]

(b) All reals   **(c)** [0, ∞)

35. Because if the vertical line test holds, then for each *x*-coordinate, there is at most one *y*-coordinate giving a point on the curve. This *y*-coordinate would correspond to the value assigned to the *x*-coordinate. Since there's only one *y*-coordinate, the assignment would be unique.

36. If the curve is not $y = 0$, there must be a point (x, y) on the curve where $y \neq 0$. That would mean that (x, y) and $(x, -y)$ are two different points on the curve and it is not the graph of a function since it fails the vertical line test.

37. No   **38.** Yes
39. Yes   **40.** No

41. $f(x) = \begin{cases} x, & 0 \le x \le 1 \\ 2 - x, & 1 < x \le 2 \end{cases}$

42. $f(x) = \begin{cases} 2, & 0 \le x < 1 \\ 0, & 1 \le x < 2 \\ 2, & 2 \le x < 3 \\ 0, & 3 \le x \le 4 \end{cases}$

43. $f(x) = \begin{cases} 2 - x, & 0 < x \le 2 \\ \dfrac{5}{3} - \dfrac{x}{3}, & 2 < x \le 5 \end{cases}$

44. $f(x) = \begin{cases} -3x - 3, & -1 < x \le 0 \\ -2x + 3, & 0 < x \le 2 \end{cases}$

45. $f(x) = \begin{cases} -x, & -1 \le x < 0 \\ 1, & 0 < x \le 1 \\ \dfrac{3}{2} - \dfrac{x}{2}, & 1 < x < 3 \end{cases}$

46. $f(x) = \begin{cases} \dfrac{x}{2}, & -2 \le x \le 0 \\ -2x + 2, & 0 < x \le 1 \\ -1, & 1 < x \le 3 \end{cases}$

47. $f(x) = \begin{cases} 0, & 0 \le x \le \dfrac{T}{2} \\ \dfrac{2}{T}x - 1, & \dfrac{T}{2} < x \le T \end{cases}$

48. $f(x) = \begin{cases} A, & 0 \le x < \dfrac{T}{2} \\ -A, & \dfrac{T}{2} \le x < T \\ A, & T \le x < \dfrac{3T}{2} \\ -A, & \dfrac{3T}{2} \le x \le 2T \end{cases}$

49. (a) $x^2 + 2$ **(b)** $x^2 + 10x + 22$
    (c) 2   **(d)** 22
    (e) −2   **(f)** $x + 10$

50. (a) x **(b)** x
    (c) 0   **(d)** 0
    (e) −4   **(f)** $x + 2$

51. (a) For $f \circ g$:

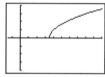

[−10, 70] by [−10, 3]

Domain: [0, ∞); Range: [−7, ∞)
For $g \circ f$:

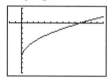

[−3, 20] by [−4, 4]

Domain: [7, ∞); Range: [0, ∞)

(b) $(f \circ g)(x) = \sqrt{x} - 7$; $(g \circ f)(x) = \sqrt{x - 7}$

52. (a) For $f \circ g$:

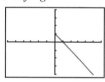

[−6, 6] by [−4, 4]

Domain: [0, ∞); Range: (−∞, 1]
For $g \circ f$:

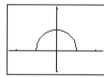

[−2.35, 2.35] by [−1, 2.1]

Domain: [−1, 1]; Range: [0, 1]

(b) $(f \circ g)(x) = 1 - (\sqrt{x})^2 = 1 - x, x \ge 0$
$(g \circ f)(x) = \sqrt{1 - x^2}$

53. (a) For $f \circ g$:

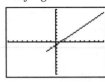

[−10, 10] by [−10, 10]

Domain: $[-2, \infty)$; Range: $[-3, \infty)$

For $g \circ f$:

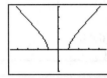

[−4.7, 4.7] by [−2, 4]

Domain: $(-\infty, -1] \cup [1, \infty)$; Range: $[0, \infty)$

(b) $(f \circ g)(x) = (\sqrt{x + 2})^2 - 3$

$\qquad\qquad = x - 1, x \ge -2$

$(g \circ f)(x) = \sqrt{x^2 - 1}$

54. (a) For $f \circ g$:

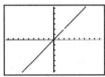

[−9.4, 9.4] by [−6.2, 6.2]

Domain: $(-\infty, 2) \cup (2, \infty)$;
Range: $(-\infty, 2) \cup (2, \infty)$

For $g \circ f$:

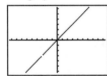

[−9.4, 9.4] by [−6.2, 6.2]

Domain: $(-\infty, -3) \cup (-3, \infty)$
Range: $(-\infty, -3) \cup (-3, \infty)$

(b) $(f \circ g)(x) = x, x \ne 2$

$\quad (g \circ f)(x) = x, x \ne -3$

55. Domain: $(-\infty, -2) \cup (2, \infty)$; Range: $(0, \infty)$

56. Domain: $(-3, 3)$; Range: $\left[\dfrac{2}{\sqrt{3}}, \infty\right)$

57. Domain: $(-\infty, -3) \cup (-3, 3) \cup (3, \infty)$

Range: $(-\infty, 0) \cup \left[\dfrac{2}{\sqrt[3]{9}}, \infty\right)$

58. Domain: $(-\infty, -1) \cup (-1, 1) \cup (1, \infty)$
Range: $(-\infty, -1] \cup (0, \infty)$

59. (a)

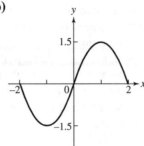

(b)

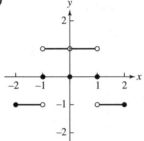

60. (a)

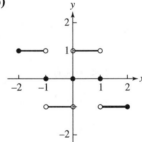

(b)

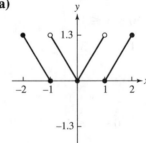

61. (a)

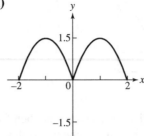

61. continued

(b)

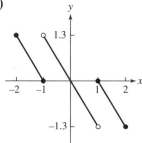

62. (a)

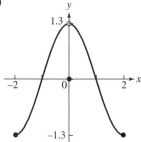

(b)

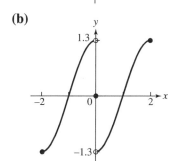

63. (a) $g(x) = x^2$　　**(b)** $g(x) = \dfrac{1}{x-1}$

(c) $f(x) = \dfrac{1}{x}$　　**(d)** $f(x) = x^2$

(Note that the domain of the composite is $[0, \infty)$).

64. (a) $y = 27.1094x^{2.651044}$

(b)

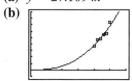

$[0, 30]$ by $[-20{,}000, 180{,}000]$

(c) Approximately $223,374

(d) Approximately $200,064

65. (a) Because the circumference of the original circle was 8π and a piece of length x was removed.

(b) $r = \dfrac{8\pi - x}{2\pi} = 4 - \dfrac{x}{2\pi}$

(c) $h = \sqrt{16 - r^2} = \dfrac{\sqrt{16\pi x - x^2}}{2\pi}$

(d) $V = \frac{1}{3}\pi r^2 h = \dfrac{(8\pi - x)^2 \sqrt{16\pi x - x^2}}{24\pi^2}$

66. (a) $C(x) = 180\sqrt{800^2 + x^2} + 100(10{,}560 - x)$

(b) $C(0) = \$1{,}200{,}000$
$C(500) \approx \$1{,}175{,}812$
$C(1000) \approx \$1{,}186{,}512$
$C(1500) = \$1{,}212{,}000$
$C(2000) \approx \$1{,}243{,}732$
$C(2500) \approx \$1{,}278{,}479$
$C(3000) \approx \$1{,}314{,}870$
Values beyond this are all larger. It would appear that the least expensive location is less than 2000 feet from point P.

67. (a)

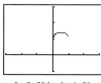

$[-3, 3]$ by $[-1, 3]$

(b) Domain of y_1: $[0, \infty)$
Domain of y_2: $(-\infty, 1]$
Domain of y_3: $[0, 1]$

(c) The results for $y_1 - y_2$, $y_2 - y_1$, and $y_1 \cdot y_2$ are the same as for $y_1 + y_2$ above.

Domain of $\dfrac{y_1}{y_2}$: $[0, 1)$

Domain of $\dfrac{y_2}{y_1}$: $(0, 1]$

(d) The domain of a sum, difference, or product of two functions is the intersection of their domains.
The domain of a quotient of two functions is the intersection of their domains with any zeros of the denominator removed.

68. (a) Yes. Since
$$(f \cdot g)(-x) = f(-x) \cdot g(-x)$$
$$= f(x) \cdot g(x)$$
$$= (f \cdot g)(x),$$
the function $(f \cdot g)$ will also be even.

(b) The product will be even, since
$$(f \cdot g)(-x) = f(-x) \cdot g(-x)$$
$$= (-f(x)) \cdot (-g(x))$$
$$= f(x) \cdot g(x)$$
$$= (f \cdot g)(x).$$

1.3 Exponential Functions (pp. 20–26)

Quick Review 1.3

1. 2.924　　　　　　**2.** 4.729
3. 0.192　　　　　　**4.** 2.5713
5. 1.8882　　　　　　**6.** ± 1.0383
7. $630.58　　　　　**8.** $1201.16

9. $x^{-18}y^{-5} = \dfrac{1}{x^{18}y^5}$　　**10.** $a^2 b^{-1} c^{-6} = \dfrac{a^2}{bc^6}$

Section 1.3 Exercises

1. (a)   **2.** (d)
3. (e)   **4.** (c)
5. (b)   **6.** (f)

7.

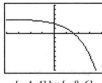

[−4, 4] by [−8, 6]

Domain: All reals
Range: $(-\infty, 3)$
x-intercept: ≈ 1.585
y-intercept: 2

8.

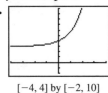

[−4, 4] by [−2, 10]

Domain: All reals
Range: $(3, \infty)$
x-intercept: None
y-intercept: 4

9.

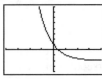

[−4, 4] by [−4, 8]

Domain: All reals
Range: $(-2, \infty)$
x-intercept: ≈ 0.405
y-intercept: 1

10.

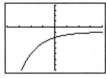

[−4, 4] by [−8, 4]

Domain: All reals
Range: $(-\infty, -1)$
x-intercept: None
y-intercept: -2

11. 3^{4x} **12.** 2^{12x}
13. 2^{-6x} **14.** 3^{-3x}
15. $x \approx 2.3219$ **16.** $x \approx 1.3863$
17. $x \approx -0.6309$ **18.** $x \approx -1.5850$

19.

x	y	Δy
1	−1	
2	1	2
3	3	2
4	5	2

20.

x	y	Δy
1	1	
2	−2	−3
3	−5	−3
4	−8	−3

21.

x	y	Δy
1	1	
2	4	3
3	9	5
4	16	7

22.

x	y	Δy
1	8.155	
2	22.167	2.718
3	60.257	2.718
4	163.794	2.718

23. After 19 years
24. (a)   1915: 12,315
        1940: 24,265
    (b)   1967 [76.651 years after 1890]
25. (a) $A(t) = 6.6\left(\dfrac{1}{2}\right)^{t/14}$

    (b)   About 38.1145 days later
26. ≈ 10.129 years   **27.** ≈ 11.433 years
28. ≈ 11.119 years   **29.** ≈ 11.090 years
30. ≈ 19.650 years   **31.** ≈ 19.108 years
32. ≈ 19.106 years   **33.** $2^{48} \approx 2.815 \times 10^{14}$
34. (a) ≈ 10.319 years   (b) ≈ 41.275 years
35. Since $\Delta x = 1$, the corresponding value of Δy is
equal to the slope of the line. If the changes in x
are constant for a linear function, then the
corresponding changes in y are constant as well.
36. (a)   100   (b)   6394
    (c)   After about 1 hour, which is the doubling time
37. (a)   Regression equation:
       $P(x) = 6.033(1.030)^x$, where $x = 0$
       represents 1900

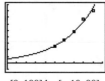

[0, 100] by [−10, 90]

    (b)   Approximately 6.03 million, which is not very
       close to the actual population
    (c)   The annual rate of growth is approximately
       3%.
38. (a)   Regression equation:
       $P(x) = 4.831(1.019)^x$

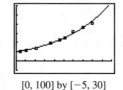

[0, 100] by [−5, 30]

    (b)   26.3 million

38. continued

   (c) The annual rate of growth is approximately 1.9%.

39. 7609.7 million

40. (a)

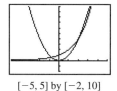

$$[-5, 5] \text{ by } [-2, 10]$$

In this window, it appears they cross twice, although a third crossing off-screen appears likely.

   (b)

x	change in $Y1$	change in $Y2$
1		
	3	2
2		
	5	4
3		
	7	8
4		

   (c) $x = -0.7667, x = 2, x = 4$

   (d) $(-0.7667, 2) \cup (4, \infty)$

41. $a = 3, k = 1.5$ **42.** $a = 0.5, k = 3$

1.4 Parametric Equations (pp. 26–31)

Quick Review 1.4

1. $y = -\dfrac{5}{3}x + \dfrac{29}{3}$ **2.** $y = -4$

3. $x = 2$

4. x-intercepts: $x = -3$ and $x = 3$
   y-intercepts: $y = -4$ and $y = 4$

5. x-intercepts: $x = -4$ and $x = 4$
   y-intercepts: None

6. x-intercept: $x = -1$
   y-intercepts: $y = -\dfrac{1}{\sqrt{2}}$ and $y = \dfrac{1}{\sqrt{2}}$

7. (a) Yes   **(b)** No
   (c) Yes

8. (a) Yes   **(b)** Yes
   (c) No

9. (a) $t = \dfrac{-2x - 5}{3}$ **(b)** $t = \dfrac{3y + 1}{2}$

10. (a) $a \geq 0$ **(b)** All reals
   (c) All reals

Section 1.4 Exercises

1. Graph (c).
   Window: $[-4, 4]$ by $[-3, 3], 0 \leq t \leq 2\pi$

2. Graph (a).
   Window: $[-2, 2]$ by $[-2, 2], 0 \leq t \leq 2\pi$

3. Graph (d).
   Window: $[-10, 10]$ by $[-10, 10], 0 \leq t \leq 2\pi$

4. Graph (b).
   Window: $[-15, 15]$ by $[-15, 15], 0 \leq t \leq 2\pi$

5. (a) The resulting graph appears to be the right half of a hyperbola in the first and fourth quadrants. The parameter a determines the x-intercept. The parameter b determines the shape of the hyperbola. If b is smaller, the graph has less steep slopes and appears "sharper." If b is larger, the slopes are steeper and the graph appears more "blunt."

   (b) This appears to be the left half of the same hyperbola.

   (c) Because both sec t and tan t are discontinuous at these points. This might cause the grapher to include extraneous lines (the asymptotes to the hyperbola) in its graph.

   (d) $\left(\dfrac{x}{a}\right)^2 - \left(\dfrac{y}{b}\right)^2 = (\sec t)^2 - (\tan t)^2 = 1$
   by a standard trigonometric identity.

   (e) This changes the orientation of the hyperbola. In this case, b determines the y-intercept of the hyperbola, and a determines the shape.

   The parameter interval $\left(-\dfrac{\pi}{2}, \dfrac{\pi}{2}\right)$ gives the upper half of the hyperbola. The parameter interval $\left(\dfrac{\pi}{2}, \dfrac{3\pi}{2}\right)$ gives the lower half.

   The same values of t cause discontinuities and may add extraneous lines to the graph.

6. (a) h determines the x-coordinate of the center of the circle. It causes a horizontal shift of the graph.

   (b) k determines the y-coordinate of the center of the circle. It causes a vertical shift of the graph.

   (c) $x = 5 \cos t + 2, y = 5 \sin t - 3, 0 \leq t \leq 2\pi$

   (d) $x = 5 \cos t - 3, y = 2 \sin t + 4, 0 \leq t \leq 2\pi$

7. (a)

$$[-3, 3] \text{ by } [-2, 2]$$

   Initial point: $(1, 0)$
   Terminal point: $(-1, 0)$

   (b) $x^2 + y^2 = 1$; upper half (or $y = \sqrt{1 - x^2}$; all)

8. (a)

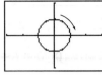

[−3, 3] by [−2, 2]

Initial and terminal point: (0, 1)

(b) $x^2 + y^2 = 1$; all

9. (a)

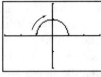

[−3, 3] by [−2, 2]

Initial point: (−1, 0)
Terminal point: (0, 1)

(b) $x^2 + y^2 = 1$; upper half (or $y = \sqrt{1 - x^2}$; all)

10. (a)

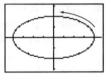

[−4.7, 4.7] by [−3.1, 3.1]

Initial and terminal point: (4, 0)

(b) $\left(\dfrac{x}{4}\right)^2 + \left(\dfrac{y}{2}\right)^2 = 1$; all

11. (a)

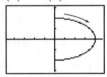

[−4.7, 4.7] by [−3.1, 3.1]

Initial point: (0, 2)
Terminal point: (0, −2)

(b) $\left(\dfrac{x}{4}\right)^2 + \left(\dfrac{y}{2}\right)^2 = 1$;
right half (or $x = 2\sqrt{4 - y^2}$; all)

12. (a)

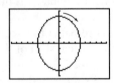

[−9, 9] by [−6, 6]

Initial and terminal point: (0, 5)

(b) $\left(\dfrac{x}{4}\right)^2 + \left(\dfrac{y}{5}\right)^2 = 1$; all

13. (a)

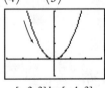

[−3, 3] by [−1, 3]

No initial or terminal point

(b) $y = x^2$; all

14. (a)

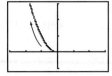

[−3, 3] by [−1, 3]

Initial point: (0, 0)
Terminal point: None

(b) $y = x^2$; left half (or $x = -\sqrt{y}$; all)

15. (a)

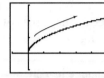

[−1, 5] by [−1, 3]

Initial point: (0, 0)
Terminal point: None

(b) $y = \sqrt{x}$; all (or $x = y^2$; upper half)

16. (a)

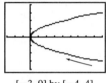

[−3, 9] by [−4, 4]

No initial or terminal point

(b) $x = y^2$; all

17. (a)

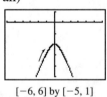

[−3, 3] by [−2, 2]

No initial or terminal point

(b) $x^2 - y^2 = 1$; left branch (or $x = -\sqrt{y^2 + 1}$;
all)

18. (a)

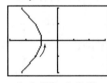

[−6, 6] by [−5, 1]

No initial or terminal point

(b) $\left(\dfrac{y}{2}\right)^2 - x^2 = 1$; lower branch
(or $y = -2\sqrt{x^2 + 1}$; all)

19. (a)

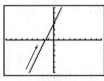

[−9, 9] by [−6, 6]

No initial or terminal point

(b) $y = 2x + 3$; all

20. (a)

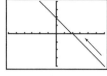

$[-6, 6]$ by $[-4, 4]$

No initial or terminal point

(b) $y = -x + 2$; all

21. (a)

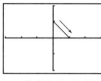

$[-3, 3]$ by $[-2, 2]$

Initial point: $(0, 1)$
Terminal point: $(1, 0)$

(b) $y = -x + 1$; $(0, 1)$ to $(1, 0)$

22. (a)

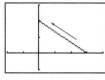

$[-2, 4]$ by $[-1, 3]$

Initial point: $(3, 0)$
Terminal point: $(0, 2)$

(b) $y = -\frac{2}{3}x + 2$; $(3, 0)$ to $(0, 2)$

23. (a)

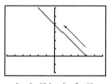

$[-6, 6]$ by $[-2, 6]$

Initial point: $(4, 0)$
Terminal point: None

(b) $y = -x + 4$; $x \leq 4$

24. (a)

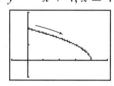

$[-1, 5]$ by $[-1, 3]$

Initial point: $(0, 2)$
Terminal point: $(4, 0)$

(b) $y = \sqrt{4 - x}$; $x \geq 0$

25. (a)

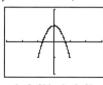

$[-3, 3]$ by $[-2, 2]$

The curve is traced and retraced in both directions, and there is no initial or terminal point.

(b) $y = -2x^2 + 1$; $-1 \leq x \leq 1$

26. (a)

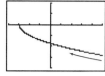

$[-4, 5]$ by $[-4, 2]$

Initial point: None
Terminal point: $(-3, 0)$

(b) $x = y^2 - 3$; lower half (or $y = -\sqrt{x + 3}$; all)

27. Possible answer:
$x = -1 + 5t, y = -3 + 4t, 0 \leq t \leq 1$

28. Possible answer:
$x = -1 + 4t, y = 3 - 5t, 0 \leq t \leq 1$

29. Possible answer:
$x = t^2 + 1, y = t, t \leq 0$

30. Possible answer:
$x = t, y = t^2 + 2t, t \leq -1$

31. Possible answer:
$x = 2 - 3t, y = 3 - 4t, t \geq 0$

32. Possible answer:
$x = -1 + t, y = 2 - 2t, t \geq 0$

33. $1 < t < 3$ **34.** $3 < t \leq 5$

35. $-5 \leq t < -3$ **36.** $-3 < t < 1$

37. Possible answer: $x = t, y = t^2 + 2t + 2, t > 0$

38. Possible answer: $x = t, y = \sqrt{t + 3}, t > 0$

39. Possible answers:
  (a) $x = a \cos t, y = -a \sin t, 0 \leq t \leq 2\pi$
  (b) $x = a \cos t, y = a \sin t, 0 \leq t \leq 2\pi$
  (c) $x = a \cos t, y = -a \sin t, 0 \leq t \leq 4\pi$
  (d) $x = a \cos t, y = a \sin t, 0 \leq t \leq 4\pi$

40. Possible answers:
  (a) $x = -a \cos t, y = b \sin t, 0 \leq t \leq 2\pi$
  (b) $x = -a \cos t, y = -b \sin t, 0 \leq t \leq 2\pi$
  (c) $x = -a \cos t, y = b \sin t, 0 \leq t \leq 4\pi$
  (d) $x = -a \cos t, y = -b \sin t, 0 \leq t \leq 4\pi$

41. $x = 2 \cot t, y = 2 \sin^2 t, 0 < t < \pi$

42. (a) If $x_2 = x_1$ then the line is a vertical line and the first parametric equation gives $x = x_1$, while the second will give all real values for y since it cannot be the case that $y_2 = y_1$ as well. Otherwise, solving the first equation for t gives
$$t = \frac{x - x_1}{x_2 - x_1}$$
Substituting that into the second equation for t gives
$$y = y_1 + \left[\frac{y_2 - y_1}{x_2 - x_1}\right](x - x_1)$$
which is the point-slope form of the equation for the line through (x_1, y_1) and (x_2, y_2).
Note that the first equation will cause x to take on all real values, because $x_2 - x_1$ is not zero. Therefore, all of the points on the line will be traced out.

(b) Use the equations for x and y given in part (a) with $0 \leq t \leq 1$.

1.5 Functions and Logarithms
(pp. 32–40)

Quick Review 1.5

1. 1   **2.** 5

3. $x^{2/3}$ **4.** $(x - 1)^{2/3} + 1$

5. Possible answer: $x = t, y = \dfrac{1}{t - 1}, t \geq 2$

6. Possible answer: $x = t, y = t, t < -3$

7. $(4, 5)$ **8.** $\left(\dfrac{8}{3}, -3\right) \approx (2.67, -3)$

9. (a) $(1.58, 3)$ **(b)** No intersection
10. (a) $(-1.39, 4)$ **(b)** No intersection

Section 1.5 Exercises

1. No   **2.** Yes
3. Yes   **4.** No
5. Yes   **6.** No
7. Yes   **8.** No
9. No   **10.** Yes
11. No   **12.** Yes

13. $f^{-1}(x) = \dfrac{x - 3}{2}$ **14.** $f^{-1}(x) = \dfrac{5 - x}{4}$

15. $f^{-1}(x) = (x + 1)^{1/3}$ or $\sqrt[3]{x + 1}$

16. $f^{-1}(x) = (x - 1)^{1/2}$ or $\sqrt{x - 1}$

17. $f^{-1}(x) = -x^{1/2}$ or $-\sqrt{x}$

18. $f^{-1}(x) = x^{3/2}$

19. $f^{-1}(x) = 2 - (-x)^{1/2}$ or $2 - \sqrt{-x}$

20. $f^{-1}(x) = x^{1/2} - 1$ or $\sqrt{x} - 1$

21. $f^{-1}(x) = \dfrac{1}{x^{1/2}}$ or $\dfrac{1}{\sqrt{x}}$ **22.** $f^{-1}(x) = \dfrac{1}{x^{1/3}}$ or $\dfrac{1}{\sqrt[3]{x}}$

23. $f^{-1}(x) = \dfrac{1 - 3x}{x - 2}$ **24.** $f^{-1}(x) = \dfrac{2x + 3}{x - 1}$

25.
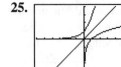
$[-6, 6]$ by $[-4, 4]$

26.

$[-6, 6]$ by $[-4, 4]$

27.

$[-4.5, 4.5]$ by $[-3, 3]$

28.
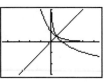
$[-4.5, 4.5]$ by $[-3, 3]$

29.
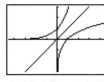
$[-4.5, 4.5]$ by $[-3, 3]$

30.

$[-4.5, 4.5]$ by $[-3, 3]$

31.

$[-3, 3]$ by $[-2, 2]$

32.

$[-6, 6]$ by $[-4, 4]$

33.
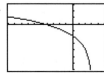
$[-10, 5]$ by $[-7, 3]$
Domain: $(-\infty, 3)$; Range: all reals

34.
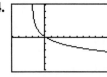
$[-5, 10]$ by $[-5, 5]$
Domain: $(-2, \infty)$; Range: all reals

35.
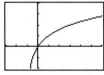
$[-3, 6]$ by $[-2, 4]$
Domain: $(-1, \infty)$; Range: all reals

36.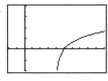

[−2, 10] by [−2, 4]

Domain: $(4, \infty)$; Range: all reals

37. $t = \dfrac{\ln 2}{\ln 1.045} \approx 15.75$

38. $t = \dfrac{\ln 3}{0.05} \approx 21.97$

39. $x = \ln\left(\dfrac{3 \pm \sqrt{5}}{2}\right) \approx -0.96$ or 0.96

40. $x = \log_2\left(\dfrac{5 \pm \sqrt{21}}{2}\right) \approx -2.26$ or 2.26

41. $y = e^{2t+4}$ **42.** $y = 2xe^x + 1$

43. $f^{-1}(x) = \log_2\left(\dfrac{x}{100 - x}\right)$

44. $f^{-1}(x) = \log_{1.1}\left(\dfrac{x}{50 - x}\right)$

45. (a) $f(f(x)) = \sqrt{1 - (f(x))^2}$

$= \sqrt{1 - (1 - x^2)}$

$= \sqrt{x^2}$

$= x$, since $x \geq 0$

(b) $f(f(x)) = f\left(\dfrac{1}{x}\right) = \dfrac{1}{1/x} = x$ for all $x \neq 0$

46. (a) Amount $= 8\left(\dfrac{1}{2}\right)^{t/12}$

(b) After 36 hours

47. About 14.936 years. (If the interest is only paid annually, it will take 15 years.)

48. After about 44.081 years

49. (a) $y = -2539.852 + 636.896 \ln x$

(b) 209.94 million metric tons

(c) When $x \approx 101.08$ in about 2001

50. (a) $y = -590.969 + 152.817 \ln x$

(b) 87.94

(c) When $x \approx 104.84$, in about 2005

51. (a) Suppose that $f(x_1) = f(x_2)$. Then $mx_1 + b = mx_2 + b$, which gives $x_1 = x_2$ since $m \neq 0$.

(b) $f^{-1}(x) = \dfrac{x - b}{m}$; the slopes are reciprocals.

(c) They are also parallel lines with non-zero slope.

(d) They are also perpendicular lines with non-zero slopes.

52. (a) y_2 is a vertical shift (upward) of y_1

(b) Each graph of y_3 is a horizontal line.

(c) The graphs of y_4 and $y = a$ are the same.

(d) $y_1 = \ln x - \ln a$

53. If the graph of $f(x)$ passes the horizontal line test, so will the graph of $g(x) = -f(x)$ since it's the same graph reflected about the x-axis.

54. Suppose that $g(x_1) = g(x_2)$. Then $\dfrac{1}{f(x_1)} = \dfrac{1}{f(x_2)}$, $f(x_1) = f(x_2)$, and $x_1 = x_2$ since f is one-to-one.

55. (a) Domain: All reals

Range: If $a > 0$, then (d, ∞)

If $a < 0$, then $(-\infty, d)$

(b) Domain: (c, ∞)

Range: All reals

56. (a) Suppose that $f(x_1) = f(x_2)$. Then cross multiplying, expanding and subtracting like terms leaves

$bcx_2 + adx_1 = adx_2 + bcx_1$.

This gives $(ad - bc)x_1 = (ad - bc)x_2$, which means that $x_1 = x_2$ since $(ad - bc) \neq 0$.

(b) $f^{-1}(x) = \dfrac{-dx + b}{cx - a}$

(c) Horizontal asymptote: $y = \dfrac{a}{c} \ (c \neq 0)$

Vertical asymptote: $x = -\dfrac{d}{c} \ (c \neq 0)$

(d) Horizontal asymptote: $y = -\dfrac{d}{c} \ (c \neq 0)$

Vertical asymptote: $x = \dfrac{a}{c} \ (c \neq 0)$

The horizontal asymptote of f becomes the vertical asymptote of f^{-1} and vice versa due to the reflection of the graph about the line $y = x$.

1.6 Trigonometric Functions (pp. 41–51)

Quick Review 1.6

1. $60°$

2. $-\left(\dfrac{450}{\pi}\right)° \approx -143.24°$

3. $-\dfrac{2\pi}{9}$

4. $\dfrac{\pi}{4}$

5. $x \approx 0.6435$, $x \approx 2.4981$

6. $x \approx 1.9823$, $x \approx 4.3009$

7. $x \approx 0.7854 \left(\text{or } \dfrac{\pi}{4}\right)$, $x \approx 3.9270 \left(\text{or } \dfrac{5\pi}{4}\right)$

8. $f(-x) = 2(-x)^2 - 3 = 2x^2 - 3 = f(x)$

The graph is symmetric about the y-axis because if a point (a, b) is on the graph, then so is the point $(-a, b)$.

9. $f(-x) = (-x)^3 - 3(-x) = -x^3 + 3x$
$= -(x^3 - 3x) = -f(x)$

The graph is symmetric about the origin because if a point (a, b) is on the graph, then so is the point $(-a, -b)$.

10. $x \geq 0$

Section 1.6 Exercises

1. $\dfrac{5\pi}{4}$

2. $\dfrac{72}{7\pi} \approx 3.274$

3. $\dfrac{1}{2}$ radian or $\approx 28.65°$

4. $\dfrac{\pi}{4}$ radian or $45°$

5. Possible answers are:
   (a) $[0, 4\pi]$ by $[-3, 3]$ (b) $[0, 4\pi]$ by $[-3, 3]$
   (c) $[0, 2\pi]$ by $[-3, 3]$

6. Possible answers are:
   (a) $[0, 4\pi]$ by $[-2, 2]$ (b) $[0, 4\pi]$ by $[-2, 2]$
   (c) $[0, 2\pi]$ by $[-3, 3]$

7. $\dfrac{\pi}{6}$ radian or $30°$

8. $-\dfrac{\pi}{4}$ radian or $-45°$

9. ≈ -1.3734 radians or $-78.6901°$

10. ≈ 0.7954 radian or $45.5730°$

11. (a) π (b) 1.5
     (c) $[-2\pi, 2\pi]$ by $[-2, 2]$

12. (a) $\dfrac{2\pi}{3}$ (b) 2
     (c) $\left[-\dfrac{2\pi}{3}, \dfrac{2\pi}{3}\right]$ by $[-4, 4]$

13. (a) π (b) 3
     (c) $[-2\pi, 2\pi]$ by $[-4, 4]$

14. (a) 4π (b) 5
     (c) $[-4\pi, 4\pi]$ by $[-10, 10]$

15. (a) 6 (b) 4
     (c) $[-3, 3]$ by $[-5, 5]$

16. (a) 2 (b) 1
     (c) $[-4, 4]$ by $[-2, 2]$

17. (a) $\dfrac{2\pi}{3}$

     (b) $x \neq \dfrac{k\pi}{3}$, for integers k

     (c) $(-\infty, -5] \cup [1, \infty)$

     (d)
     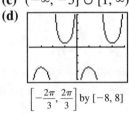
     $\left[-\dfrac{2\pi}{3}, \dfrac{2\pi}{3}\right]$ by $[-8, 8]$

18. (a) $\dfrac{\pi}{2}$ (b) All reals
     (c) $[1, 5]$

18. continued
   (d)
   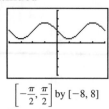
   $\left[-\dfrac{\pi}{2}, \dfrac{\pi}{2}\right]$ by $[-8, 8]$

19. (a) $\dfrac{\pi}{3}$

   (b) $x \neq \dfrac{k\pi}{6}$, for odd integers k

   (c) All reals

   (d)
   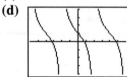
   $\left[-\dfrac{\pi}{2}, \dfrac{\pi}{2}\right]$ by $[-8, 8]$

20. (a) π (b) All reals
   (c) $[-2, 2]$
   (d)
   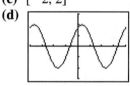
   $[-\pi, \pi]$ by $[-3, 3]$

21. $\cos\theta = \dfrac{15}{17}$ $\sin\theta = \dfrac{8}{17}$ $\tan\theta = \dfrac{8}{15}$

   $\sec\theta = \dfrac{17}{15}$ $\csc\theta = \dfrac{17}{8}$ $\cot\theta = \dfrac{15}{8}$

22. $\cos\theta = \dfrac{12}{13}$ $\sin\theta = -\dfrac{5}{13}$ $\tan\theta = -\dfrac{5}{12}$

   $\sec\theta = \dfrac{13}{12}$ $\csc\theta = -\dfrac{13}{5}$ $\cot\theta = -\dfrac{12}{5}$

23. $\cos\theta = -\dfrac{3}{5}$ $\sin\theta = \dfrac{4}{5}$ $\tan\theta = -\dfrac{4}{3}$

   $\sec\theta = -\dfrac{5}{3}$ $\csc\theta = \dfrac{5}{4}$ $\cot\theta = -\dfrac{3}{4}$

24. $\cos\theta = -\dfrac{1}{\sqrt{2}}$ $\sin\theta = \dfrac{1}{\sqrt{2}}$ $\tan\theta = -1$

   $\sec\theta = -\sqrt{2}$ $\csc\theta = \sqrt{2}$ $\cot\theta = -1$

25. $x \approx 1.190$ and $x \approx 4.332$

26. $x \approx 8.629$ and $x \approx 10.220$

27. $x = \dfrac{\pi}{6}$ and $x = \dfrac{5\pi}{6}$

28. $x \approx -1.911$ and $x \approx 1.911$

29. $x = \dfrac{7\pi}{6} + 2k\pi$ and $x = \dfrac{11\pi}{6} + 2k\pi$, k any integer

30. $x = \dfrac{3\pi}{4} + k\pi$, k any integer

31. $\dfrac{\sqrt{72}}{11} \approx 0.771$

32. $\dfrac{9}{\sqrt{88}} \approx 0.959$

33. (a) $y = 1.543 \sin (2468.635x - 0.494) + 0.438$

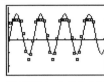

[0, 0.01] by [−2.5, 2.5]

(b) Frequency = 392.9, so it must be a "G."

34. (a) $b = \dfrac{\pi}{6}$

(b) It's half of the difference, so $a = 25$

(c) $k = 55$

(d) $h = 5$; $y = 25 \sin \left[\dfrac{\pi}{6}(t - 5) \right] + 55$

(e)

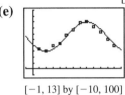

[−1, 13] by [−10, 100]

35. (a) 37   **(b)** 365
(c) 101   **(d)** 25

36. (a) Highest: 62°F; lowest: −12°F

(b) Average = 25°F. This is because the average of the highest and lowest values of the (unshifted) sine function is 0.

37. (a) $\cot (-x) = \dfrac{\cos (-x)}{\sin (-x)} = \dfrac{\cos (x)}{-\sin (x)} = -\cot (x)$

(b) Assume that f is even and g is odd.
Then $\dfrac{f(-x)}{g(-x)} = \dfrac{f(x)}{-g(x)} = -\dfrac{f(x)}{g(x)}$ so $\dfrac{f}{g}$ is odd.
The situation is similar for $\dfrac{g}{f}$.

38. (a) $\csc (-x) = \dfrac{1}{\sin (-x)} = \dfrac{1}{-\sin (x)} = -\csc (x)$

(b) Assume that f is odd.
Then $\dfrac{1}{f(-x)} = \dfrac{1}{-f(x)} = -\dfrac{1}{f(x)}$ so $\dfrac{1}{f}$ is odd.

39. Assume that f is even and g is odd.
Then $f(-x) g(-x) = f(x)[-g(x)] = -f(x)g(x)$
so fg is odd.

40. If (a, b) is the point on the unit circle corresponding to the angle θ, then $(-a, -b)$ is the point on the unit circle corresponding to the angle $(\theta + \pi)$ since it is exactly halfway around the circle. This means that both $\tan \theta$ and $\tan (\theta + \pi)$ have the same value, $\dfrac{b}{a}$.

41. (a) $y = 3.0014 \sin (0.9996x + 2.0012) + 2.9999$
(b) $y = 3 \sin (x + 2) + 3$

42. (a)

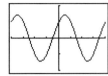

$[-2\pi, 2\pi]$ by $[-2, 2]$

The graph is a sine/cosine type graph, but it is shifted and has an amplitude greater than 1.

(b) Amplitude ≈ 1.414 or $\sqrt{2}$, period = 2π, horizontal shift ≈ -0.785 (that is, $-\dfrac{\pi}{4}$) or 5.498 (that is, $\dfrac{7\pi}{4}$), vertical shift = 0

(c) $\sin \left(x + \dfrac{\pi}{4} \right) = \sin (x) \cdot \dfrac{1}{\sqrt{2}} + \cos (x) \cdot \dfrac{1}{\sqrt{2}}$

$= \dfrac{1}{\sqrt{2}} (\sin x + \cos x)$

So, $\sin (x) + \cos (x) = \sqrt{2} \sin \left(x + \dfrac{\pi}{4} \right)$.

43. (a) $\sqrt{2} \sin \left(ax + \dfrac{\pi}{4} \right)$ **(b)** See part **(a)**.

(c) It works.

(d) $\sin \left(ax + \dfrac{\pi}{4} \right)$

$= \sin (ax) \cdot \dfrac{1}{\sqrt{2}} + \cos (ax) \cdot \dfrac{1}{\sqrt{2}}$

$= \dfrac{1}{\sqrt{2}} (\sin ax + \cos ax)$

So, $\sin (ax) + \cos (ax) = \sqrt{2} \sin \left(ax + \dfrac{\pi}{4} \right)$.

44. (a) One possible answer:

$y = \sqrt{a^2 + b^2} \sin \left(x + \tan^{-1} \dfrac{b}{a} \right)$

(b) See part **(a)**.   **(c)** It works.

(d) $\sin \left(x + \tan^{-1} \dfrac{b}{a} \right)$

$= \sin (x) \cos \left(\tan^{-1} \dfrac{b}{a} \right) + \cos (x) \sin \left(\tan^{-1} \dfrac{b}{a} \right)$

$= \sin (x) \dfrac{a}{\sqrt{a^2 + b^2}} + \cos (x) \dfrac{b}{\sqrt{a^2 + b^2}}$

$= \dfrac{1}{\sqrt{a^2 + b^2}} \cdot a \sin (x) + b \cos (x)$

and multiplying through by the square root gives the result.

45. Since $\sin (x)$ has period 2π, $(\sin (x + 2\pi))^3 = (\sin (x))^3$. This function has period 2π. A graph shows that no smaller number works for the period.

46. Since $\tan (x)$ has period π, $|\tan (x + \pi)| = |\tan (x)|$. This function has period π. A graph shows that no smaller number works for the period.

47. One possible graph:

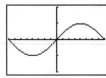

$\left[-\dfrac{\pi}{60}, \dfrac{\pi}{60}\right]$ by $[-2, 2]$

48. One possible graph:

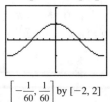

$\left[-\dfrac{1}{60}, \dfrac{1}{60}\right]$ by $[-2, 2]$

Chapter 1 Review Exercises
(pp. 52–53)

1. $y = 3x - 9$

2. $y = -\dfrac{1}{2}x + \dfrac{3}{2}$

3. $x = 0$

4. $y = -2x$

5. $y = 2$

6. $y = -\dfrac{2}{5}x + \dfrac{21}{5}$

7. $y = -3x + 3$

8. $y = 2x - 5$

9. $y = -\dfrac{4}{3}x - \dfrac{20}{3}$

10. $y = -\dfrac{5}{3}x - \dfrac{19}{3}$

11. $y = \dfrac{2}{3}x + \dfrac{8}{3}$

12. $y = \dfrac{5}{3}x - 5$

13. $y = -\dfrac{1}{2}x + 3$

14. $y = -\dfrac{2}{7}x - \dfrac{6}{7}$

15. Origin

16. y-axis

17. Neither

18. y-axis

19. Even

20. Odd

21. Even

22. Odd

23. Odd

24. Neither

25. Neither

26. Even

27. (a) Domain: all reals **(b)** Range: $[-2, \infty)$
(c)

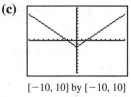

$[-10, 10]$ by $[-10, 10]$

28. (a) Domain: $(-\infty, 1]$ **(b)** Range: $[-2, \infty)$
(c)

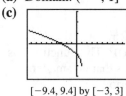

$[-9.4, 9.4]$ by $[-3, 3]$

29. (a) Domain: $[-4, 4]$ **(b)** Range: $[0, 4]$
(c)

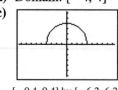

$[-9.4, 9.4]$ by $[-6.2, 6.2]$

30. (a) Domain: all reals **(b)** Range: $(1, \infty)$
(c)

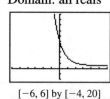

$[-6, 6]$ by $[-4, 20]$

31. (a) Domain: all reals **(b)** Range: $(-3, \infty)$
(c)

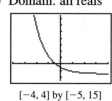

$[-4, 4]$ by $[-5, 15]$

32. (a) Domain: $x \neq \dfrac{k\pi}{4}$, for odd integers k

(b) Range: all reals
(c)

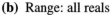
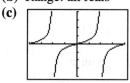

$\left[-\dfrac{\pi}{2}, \dfrac{\pi}{2}\right]$ by $[-8, 8]$

33. (a) Domain: all reals **(b)** Range: $[-3, 1]$
(c)

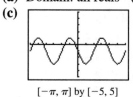

$[-\pi, \pi]$ by $[-5, 5]$

34. (a) Domain: all reals **(b)** Range: $[0, \infty)$
(c)

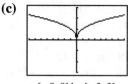

$[-8, 8]$ by $[-3, 3]$

35. (a) Domain: $(3, \infty)$ **(b)** Range: all reals
(c)

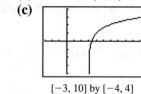

$[-3, 10]$ by $[-4, 4]$

36. (a) Domain: all reals **(b)** Range: all reals
(c)

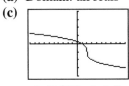

$[-10, 10]$ by $[-4, 4]$

37. (a) Domain: $[-4, 4]$ **(b)** Range: $[0, 2]$
(c)

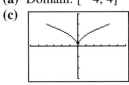

$[-6, 6]$ by $[-3, 3]$

38. (a) Domain: $[-2, 2]$ **(b)** Range: $[-1, 1]$
(c)

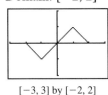

$[-3, 3]$ by $[-2, 2]$

39. $f(x) = \begin{cases} 1 - x, & 0 \le x < 1 \\ 2 - x, & 1 \le x \le 2 \end{cases}$

40. $f(x) = \begin{cases} \dfrac{5x}{2}, & 0 \le x < 2 \\ -\dfrac{5}{2}x + 10, & 2 \le x \le 4 \end{cases}$

41. (a) 1 **(b)** $\dfrac{1}{\sqrt{2.5}}\left(= \sqrt{\dfrac{2}{5}}\right)$

(c) $x, x \ne 0$

(d) $\dfrac{1}{\sqrt{1/\sqrt{x+2} + 2}}$

42. (a) 2 **(b)** 1

(c) x

(d) $\sqrt[3]{\sqrt[3]{x + 1} + 1}$

43. (a) $(f \circ g)(x) = -x, x \ge -2$
$(g \circ f)(x) = \sqrt{4 - x^2}$

(b) Domain $(f \circ g)$: $[-2, \infty)$
Domain $(g \circ f)$: $[-2, 2]$

(c) Range $(f \circ g)$: $(-\infty, 2]$
Range $(g \circ f)$: $[0, 2]$

44. (a) $(f \circ g)(x) = \sqrt[4]{1 - x}$
$(g \circ f)(x) = \sqrt{1 - \sqrt{x}}$

(b) Domain $(f \circ g)$: $(-\infty, 1]$
Domain $(g \circ f)$: $[0, 1]$

44. continued
(c) Range $(f \circ g)$: $[0, \infty)$
Range $(g \circ f)$: $[0, 1]$
45. (a)

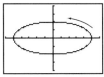

$[-6, 6]$ by $[-4, 4]$

Initial point: $(5, 0)$
Terminal point: $(5, 0)$

(b) $\left(\dfrac{x}{5}\right)^2 + \left(\dfrac{y}{2}\right)^2 = 1$; all

46. (a)

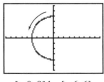

$[-9, 9]$ by $[-6, 6]$

Initial point: $(0, 4)$
Terminal point: $(0, -4)$

(b) $x^2 + y^2 = 16$; left half

47. (a)

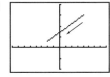

$[-8, 8]$ by $[-10, 20]$

Initial point: $(4, 15)$
Terminal point: $(-2, 3)$

(b) $y = 2x + 7$; from $(4, 15)$ to $(-2, 3)$

48. (a)

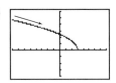

$[-8, 8]$ by $[-4, 6]$

Initial point: None
Terminal point: $(3, 0)$

(b) $y = \sqrt{6 - 2x}$; all

49. Possible answer:
$x = -2 + 6t, y = 5 - 2t, 0 \le t \le 1$

50. Possible answer:
$x = -3 + 7t, y = -2 + t, -\infty < t < \infty$

51. Possible answer:
$x = 2 - 3t, y = 5 - 5t, 0 \le t$

52. Possible answer:
$x = t, y = t(t - 4), t \le 2$

53. (a) $f^{-1}(x) = \dfrac{2 - x}{3}$

(b)

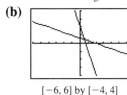

$[-6, 6]$ by $[-4, 4]$

54. (a) $f^{-1}(x) = \sqrt{x} - 2$

(b)

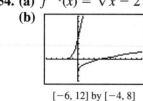

[−6, 12] by [−4, 8]

55. ≈0.6435 radians or 36.8699°

56. ≈−1.1607 radians or −66.5014°

57. $\cos \theta = \dfrac{3}{7}$ $\sin \theta = \dfrac{\sqrt{40}}{7}$ $\tan \theta = \dfrac{\sqrt{40}}{3}$

 $\sec \theta = \dfrac{7}{3}$ $\csc \theta = \dfrac{7}{\sqrt{40}}$ $\cot \theta = \dfrac{3}{\sqrt{40}}$

58. (a) $x \approx 3.3430$ and $x \approx 6.0818$

 (b) $x \approx 3.3430 + 2k\pi$ and $x \approx 6.0818 + 2k\pi$, k any integer

59. $x = -5 \ln 4$

60. (a)

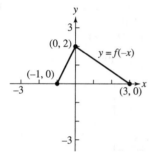

(b)

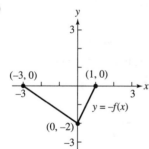

(c)

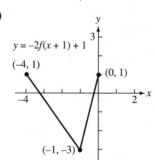

(d)

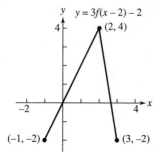

61. (a)

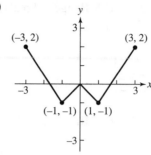

(b)

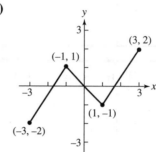

62. (a) $V = 100,000 - 10,000x$, $0 \le x \le 10$

 (b) After 4.5 years

63. (a) 90 units

 (b) $90 - 52 \ln 3 \approx 32.8722$ units

 (c)

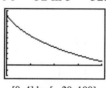

[0, 4] by [−20, 100]

64. After $\dfrac{\ln (10/3)}{\ln 1.08} \approx 15.6439$ years

 (If the bank only pays interest at the end of the year, it will take 16 years.)

65. (a) $N = 4 \cdot 2^t$

 (b) 4 days: 64; one week: 512

 (c) After $\dfrac{\ln 500}{\ln 2} \approx 8.9658$ days, or after nearly 9 days.

 (d) Because it suggests the number of guppies will continue to double indefinitely and become arbitrarily large, which is impossible due to the finite size of the tank and the oxygen supply in the water.

66. (a) $y = 20.627x + 338.622$

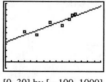

[0, 30] by [−100, 1000]

 (b) Approximately 957

 (c) Slope is 20.627. It represents the approximate arrival increase in number of doctorates earned by Hispanic Americans per year.

67. (a) $y = 14.60175 \cdot 1.00232^x$
    (b) Sometime during the year 2132
       (when $x \approx 232$)
    (c) 0.232%

Chapter 2
Limits and Continuity

2.1 Rates of Change and Limits
    (pp. 55–65)

Quick Review 2.1

1. 0   **2.** $\dfrac{11}{12}$

3. 0   **4.** $\dfrac{1}{3}$

5. $-4 < x < 4$ **6.** $-c^2 < x < c^2$
7. $-1 < x < 5$ **8.** $c - d^2 < x < c + d^2$

9. $x - 6$ **10.** $\dfrac{x}{x+1}$

Section 2.1 Exercises

1. (a) 3   **(b)** -2
   (c) No limit   **(d)** 1
2. (a) 5   **(b)** 2
   (c) No limit   **(d)** 2
3. (a) -4 **(b)** -4
   (c) -4 **(d)** -4
4. (a) 3   **(b)** 3
   (c) 3   **(d)** 3
5. (a) 4   **(b)** -3
   (c) No limit   **(d)** 4
6. (a) 1   **(b)** 1
   (c) 1   **(d)** 3

7. $-\dfrac{3}{2}$ **8.** 1

9. -15 **10.** 5
11. 0   **12.** 0
13. 4   **14.** $\sqrt{5}$
15. 1   **16.** 0
17. Expression not defined at $x = -2$. There is no limit.
18. Expression not defined at $x = 0$. There is no limit.
19. Expression not defined at $x = 0$. There is no limit.
20. Expression not defined at $x = 0$. Limit $= 8$.

21. $\dfrac{1}{2}$ **22.** $\dfrac{1}{4}$

23. $-\dfrac{1}{2}$ **24.** $-\dfrac{1}{4}$

25. 12   **26.** 2
27. -1 **28.** 2
29. 0   **30.** 4
31. (a) True   **(b)** True
   (c) False   **(d)** True

31. continued
   (e) True   **(f)** True
   (g) False   **(h)** False
   (i) False   **(j)** False
32. (a) True   **(b)** False
   (c) False   **(d)** True
   (e) True   **(f)** True
   (g) True   **(h)** True
   (i) True

33. (c)   **34.** (b)
35. (d)   **36.** (a)
37. 0   **38.** -1
39. 0   **40.** 1
41. 1   **42.** -1
43. (a) 6   **(b)** 0
   (c) 9   **(d)** -3
44. (a) 4   **(b)** -21
   (c) -12 **(d)** $-\dfrac{7}{3}$

45. (a)

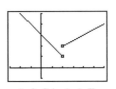

       $[-3, 6]$ by $[-1, 5]$

   (b) Right-hand: 2
       Left-hand: 1
   (c) No, because the two one-sided limits are different.

46. (a)

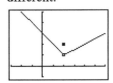

       $[-3, 6]$ by $[-1, 5]$

   (b) Right-hand: 1
       Left-hand: 1
   (c) Yes. The limit is 1.

47. (a)

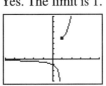

       $[-5, 5]$ by $[-4, 8]$

   (b) Right-hand: 4
       Left-hand: no limit
   (c) No, because the left-hand limit doesn't exist.

48. (a)

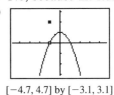

       $[-4.7, 4.7]$ by $[-3.1, 3.1]$

   (b) Right-hand: 0
       Left-hand: 0
   (c) Yes. The limit is 0.

49. (a)

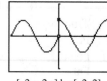

$[-2\pi, 2\pi]$ by $[-2, 2]$

(b) $(-2\pi, 0) \cup (0, 2\pi)$

(c) $c = 2\pi$ **(d)** $c = -2\pi$

50. (a)

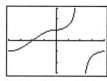

$[-\pi, \pi]$ by $[-3, 3]$

(b) $\left(-\pi, \dfrac{\pi}{2}\right) \cup \left(\dfrac{\pi}{2}, \pi\right)$

(c) $c = \pi$ **(d)** $c = -\pi$

51. (a)

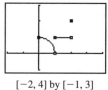

$[-2, 4]$ by $[-1, 3]$

(b) $(0, 1) \cup (1, 2)$ **(c)** $c = 2$

(d) $c = 0$

52. (a)

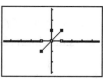

$[-4.7, 4.7]$ by $[-3.1, 3.1]$

(b) $(-\infty, -1) \cup (-1, 1) \cup (1, \infty)$

(c) None   **(d)** None

53. 0   **54.** 0

55. 0   **56.** 0

57. (a) 14.7 m/sec   **(b)** 29.4 m/sec

58. (a) $g = \dfrac{5}{4}$ **(b)** 5 m/sec

(c) 10 m/sec

59. (a)

x	-0.1	-0.01	-0.001	-0.0001
$f(x)$	-0.054402	-0.005064	-0.000827	-0.000031

(b)

x	0.1	0.01	0.001	0.0001
$f(x)$	-0.054402	-0.005064	-0.000827	-0.000031

The limit appears to be 0.

60. (a)

x	-0.1	-0.01	-0.001	-0.0001
$f(x)$	0.5440	0.5064	-0.8269	0.3056

(b)

x	0.1	0.01	0.001	0.0001
$f(x)$	-0.5440	-0.5064	0.8269	-0.3056

There is no clear indication of a limit.

61. (a)

x	-0.1	-0.01	-0.001	-0.0001
$f(x)$	2.0567	2.2763	2.2999	2.3023

(b)

x	0.1	0.01	0.001	0.0001
$f(x)$	2.5893	2.3293	2.3052	2.3029

The limit appears to be approximately 2.3.

62. (a)

x	-0.1	-0.01	-0.001	-0.0001
$f(x)$	0.074398	-0.009943	0.000585	0.000021

(b)

x	0.1	0.01	0.001	0.0001
$f(x)$	-0.074398	0.009943	-0.000585	-0.000021

The limit appears to be 0.

63. (a) Because the right-hand limit at zero depends only on the values of the function for positive x-values near zero.

(b) Use: area of triangle $= \left(\dfrac{1}{2}\right)$(base)(height)

area of circular sector $= \dfrac{(\text{angle})(\text{radius})^2}{2}$

(c) This is how the areas of the three regions compare.

(d) Multiply by 2 and divide by $\sin \theta$.

(e) Take reciprocals, remembering that all of the values involved are positive.

(f) The limits for $\cos \theta$ and 1 are both equal to 1. Since $\dfrac{\sin \theta}{\theta}$ is between them, it must also have a limit of 1.

(g) $\dfrac{\sin(-\theta)}{-\theta} = \dfrac{-\sin(\theta)}{-\theta} = \dfrac{\sin(\theta)}{\theta}$

(h) If the function is symmetric about the y-axis, and the right-hand limit at zero is 1, then the left-hand limit at zero must also be 1.

(i) The two one-sided limits both exist and are equal to 1.

64. (a) The limit can be found by substitution.

(b) One possible answer: $a = 1.75, b = 2.28$

(c) One possible answer: $a = 1.99, b = 2.01$

65. (a) $f\left(\dfrac{\pi}{6}\right) = \dfrac{1}{2}$

(b) One possible answer: $a = 0.305, b = 0.775$

(c) One possible answer: $a = 0.513, b = 0.535$

66. $\dfrac{1}{2}$

2.2 Limits Involving Infinity (pp. 65–73)

Quick Review 2.2

1. $f^{-1}(x) = \dfrac{x + 3}{2}$

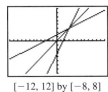

$[-12, 12]$ by $[-8, 8]$

2. $f^{-1}(x) = \ln(x)$

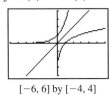

$[-6, 6]$ by $[-4, 4]$

3. $f^{-1}(x) = \tan(x), -\dfrac{\pi}{2} < x < \dfrac{\pi}{2}$

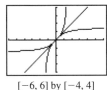

$[-6, 6]$ by $[-4, 4]$

4. $f^{-1}(x) = \cot(x), 0 < x < \pi$

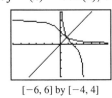

$[-6, 6]$ by $[-4, 4]$

5. $q(x) = \dfrac{2}{3}$

$r(x) = -3x^2 - \left(\dfrac{5}{3}\right)x + \dfrac{7}{3}$

6. $q(x) = 2x^2 + 2x + 1$

$r(x) = -x^2 - x - 2$

7. (a) $f(-x) = \cos x$

  (b) $f\left(\dfrac{1}{x}\right) = \cos\left(\dfrac{1}{x}\right)$

8. (a) $f(-x) = e^x$

  (b) $f\left(\dfrac{1}{x}\right) = e^{-1/x}$

9. (a) $f(-x) = -\dfrac{\ln(-x)}{x}$

  (b) $f\left(\dfrac{1}{x}\right) = -x \ln x$

10. (a) $f(-x) = \left(x + \dfrac{1}{x}\right)\sin x$

  (b) $f\left(\dfrac{1}{x}\right) = \left(\dfrac{1}{x} + x\right)\sin\left(\dfrac{1}{x}\right)$

Section 2.2 Exercises

1. (a) 1   **(b)** 1
  (c) $y = 1$
2. (a) 0   **(b)** 0
  (c) $y = 0$
3. (a) 0   **(b)** $-\infty$
  (c) $y = 0$
4. (a) ∞ **(b)** ∞
  (c) None
5. (a) 3   **(b)** -3
  (c) $y = 3, y = -3$
6. (a) 2   **(b)** -2
  (c) $y = 2, y = -2$
7. (a) 1   **(b)** -1
  (c) $y = 1, y = -1$
8. (a) 1   **(b)** 1
  (c) $y = 1$
9. ∞ **10.** $-\infty$
11. $-\infty$ **12.** $-\infty$
13. 0   **14.** ∞
15. ∞ **16.** $-\infty$
17. (a) $x = -2, x = 2$
  (b) Left-hand limit at -2 is ∞.
    Right-hand limit at -2 is $-\infty$.
    Left-hand limit at 2 is $-\infty$.
    Right-hand limit at 2 is ∞.
18. (a) $x = -2$
  (b) Left-hand limit at -2 is $-\infty$.
    Right-hand limit at -2 is ∞.
19. (a) $x = -1$
  (b) Left-hand limit at -1 is $-\infty$.
    Right-hand limit at -1 is ∞.
20. (a) $x = -\dfrac{1}{2}, x = 3$

  (b) Left-hand limit at $-\dfrac{1}{2}$ is ∞.
    Right hand limit at $-\dfrac{1}{2}$ is $-\infty$.
    Left-hand limit at 3 is ∞.

    Right-hand limit at 3 is $-\infty$.

21. (a) $x = k\pi$, k any integer
  (b) At each vertical asymptote:
    Left-hand limit is $-\infty$.
    Right-hand limit is ∞.
22. (a) $x = \dfrac{\pi}{2} + n\pi$, n any integer
  (b) If n is even:
    Left-hand limit is ∞.
    Right-hand limit is $-\infty$.
    If n is odd:
    Left-hand limit is $-\infty$.
    Right-hand limit is ∞.
23. Both are 1   **24.** Both arc 5
25. Both are 1   **26.** Both are 2
27. Both are 0   **28.** Both are 0
29. (a)   **30.** (c)
31. (d)   **32.** (b)

33. (a) $3x^2$ (b) None
34. (a) $-4x^3$ (b) None
35. (a) $\dfrac{1}{2x}$ (b) $y = 0$
36. (a) 3 (b) $y = 3$
37. (a) $4x^2$ (b) None
38. (a) $-x^2$ (b) None
39. (a) e^x (b) $-2x$
40. (a) x^2 (b) e^{-x}
41. (a) x (b) x
42. (a) x^2 (b) x^2
43. At ∞: ∞ **44.** At ∞: 0
At $-\infty$: 0 At $-\infty$: ∞
45. At ∞: 0 **46.** At ∞: 1
At $-\infty$: 0 At $-\infty$: 1
47. (a) 0 (b) -1
     (c) $-\infty$ (d) -1
48. (a) 1 (b) 0
     (c) 2 (d) ∞
49. One possible answer:

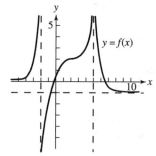

50. One possible answer:

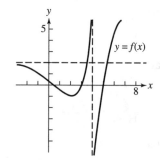

51. $\dfrac{f_1(x)/f_2(x)}{g_1(x)/g_2(x)} = \dfrac{f_1(x)/g_1(x)}{f_2(x)/g_2(x)}$

As x goes to infinity, $\dfrac{f_1}{g_1}$ and $\dfrac{f_2}{g_2}$ both approach 1.

Therefore, using the above equation, $\dfrac{f_1/f_2}{g_1/g_2}$ must

also approach 1.

52. Yes. The limit of $(f + g)$ will be the same as the limit of g. This is because adding numbers that are very close to a given real number L will not have a significant effect on the value of $(f + g)$ since the values of g are becoming arbitrarily large.

53. (a) Using 1980 as $x = 0$:
$$y = -2.2316x^3 + 54.7134x^2 - 351.0933x + 733.2224$$

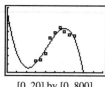

[0, 20] by [0, 800]

(b) Again using 1980 as $x = 0$:
$$y = 1.458561x^4 - 60.5740x^3 + 905.8877x^2 - 5706.0943x + 12967.6288$$

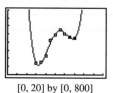

[0, 20] by [0, 800]

(c) Cubic: approximately -2256 dollars
Quartic: approximately 9979 dollars

(d) Cubic: End behavior model is $-2.2316x^3$. This model predicts that the grants will become negative by 1996.
   Quartic: End behavior model is $1.458561x^4$. This model predicts that the size of the grants will grow very rapidly after 1995.

Neither of these seem reasonable. There is no reason to expect the grants to disappear (become negative) based on the data. Similarly, the data give no indication that a period of rapid growth is about to occur.

54. (a) $f \to -\infty$ as $x \to 0^-$, $f \to \infty$ as $x \to 0^+$, $g \to 0$, $fg \to 1$
(b) $f \to \infty$ as $x \to 0^-$, $f \to -\infty$ as $x \to 0^+$, $g \to 0$, $fg \to -8$
(c) $f \to -\infty$ as $x \to 2^-$, $f \to \infty$ as $x \to 2^+$, $g \to 0$, $fg \to 0$
(d) $f \to \infty$, $g \to 0$, $fg \to \infty$
(e) Nothing — you need more information to decide.

55. (a) This follows from $x - 1 < \text{int } x \le x$ which is true for all x. Dividing by x gives the result.
(b) 1 (c) 1

56. For $x > 0$, $0 < e^{-x} < 1$, so $0 < \dfrac{e^{-x}}{x} < \dfrac{1}{x}$.
Since both 0 and $\dfrac{1}{x}$ approach zero as $x \to \infty$, the Sandwich Theorem states that $\dfrac{e^{-x}}{x}$ must also approach zero.

57. This is because as x approaches infinity, $\sin x$ continues to oscillate between 1 and -1 and doesn't approach any given real number.

58. Limit $= 2$, because $\dfrac{\ln x^2}{\ln x} = \dfrac{2 \ln x}{\ln x} = 2$.

59. Limit = ln(10),

since $\dfrac{\ln x}{\log x} = \dfrac{\ln x}{\ln x/\ln 10} = \ln 10.$

60. Limit = 1.

Since $\ln(x + 1) = \ln\ x\left(1 + \dfrac{1}{x}\right)$

$= \ln x + \ln\left(1 + \dfrac{1}{x}\right),$

$\dfrac{\ln(x + 1)}{\ln x} = \dfrac{\ln x + \ln(1 + 1/x)}{\ln x}$

$= 1 + \dfrac{\ln(1 + 1/x)}{\ln x}.$

But as $x \to \infty$, $1 + \dfrac{1}{x}$ approaches 1, so $\ln\left(1 + \dfrac{1}{x}\right)$

approaches $\ln(1) = 0$. Also, as $x \to \infty$, $\ln x$

approaches infinity. This means the second term

above approaches 0 and the limit is 1.

2.3 Continuity
(pp. 73–81)

Quick Review 2.3

1. 2

2. (a) -2 **(b)** -1
   (c) No limit   **(d)** -1

3. (a) 1   **(b)** 2
   (c) No limit   **(d)** 2

4. $(f \circ g)(x) = \dfrac{x + 2}{6x + 1}, x \neq 0$

   $(g \circ f)(x) = \dfrac{3x + 4}{2x - 1}, x \neq -5$

5. $g(x) = \sin x, x \geq 0$
   $(f \circ g)(x) = \sin^2 x, x \geq 0$

6. $f(x) = \dfrac{1}{x^2} + 1, x > 0$

   $(f \circ g)(x) = \dfrac{x}{x - 1}, x > 1$

7. $x = \dfrac{1}{2}, -5$ **8.** $x \approx 0.453$

9. $x = 1$ **10.** Any c in $[1, 2)$

Section 2.3 Exercises

1. $x = -2$, infinite discontinuity
2. $x = 1$ and $x = 3$, both infinite discontinuities
3. None   **4.** None
5. All points not in the domain, i.e., all $x < -\dfrac{3}{2}$
6. None
7. $x = 0$, jump discontinuity
8. $x = k\pi$ for all integers k, infinite discontinuity
9. $x = 0$, infinite discontinuity
10. All points not in the domain, i.e., all $x < -1$

11. (a) Yes   **(b)** Yes
   (c) Yes   **(d)** Yes

12. (a) Yes   **(b)** Yes
   (c) No   **(d)** No

13. (a) No   **(b)** No

14. Everywhere in $[-1, 3)$ except for $x = 0, 1, 2$

15. 0   **16.** 2

17. No, because the right-hand and left-hand limits are not the same at zero.

18. Yes. Assign the value 0 to $f(3)$.

19. (a) $x = 2$
   (b) Not removable, the one-sided limits are different.

20. (a) $x = 2$
   (b) Removable, assign the value 1 to $f(2)$.

21. (a) $x = 1$
   (b) Not removable, it's an infinite discontinuity.

22. (a) $x = -1$
   (b) Removable, assign the value 0 to $f(-1)$.

23. (a) All points not in the domain along with $x = 0, 1$
   (b) $x = 0$ is a removable discontinuity, assign $f(0) = 0$.
       $x = 1$ is not removable, the two-sided limits are different.

24. (a) All points not in the domain along with $x = 1, 2$
   (b) $x = 1$ is not removable, the one-sided limits are different.
       $x = 2$ is a removable discontinuity, assign $f(2) = 1$.

25. $y = x - 3$

26. $y = \dfrac{x^2 + x + 1}{x + 1}$

27. $y = \begin{cases} \dfrac{\sin x}{x}, & x \neq 0 \\ 1, & x = 0 \end{cases}$

28. $y = \begin{cases} \dfrac{\sin 4x}{x}, & x \neq 0 \\ 4, & x = 0 \end{cases}$

29. $y = \sqrt{x} + 2$

30. $y = \dfrac{x^2 - 2x - 15}{x + 2}$

Note: There are different ways to verify the continuity of the functions in 31–34. In each case, one possible answer is given.

31. Assume $y = x$, constant functions, and the square root function are continuous.
   Use the sum, composite, and quotient theorems.
   Domain: $(-2, \infty)$

32. Assume $y = x$, constant functions, and the cube root function are continuous.
Use the difference, composite, product, and sum theorems.
Domain: $(-\infty, \infty)$

33. Assume $y = x$ and the absolute value function are continuous.
Use the product, constant multiple, difference, and composite theorems.
Domain: $(-\infty, \infty)$

34. Assume $y = x$ and $y = 1$ are continuous.
Use the product, difference, and quotient theorems. One also needs to verify that the limit of this function as x approaches 1 is 2.
Domain: $(-\infty, \infty)$

35. One possible answer:

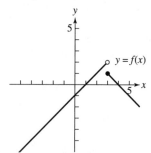

36. One possible answer:

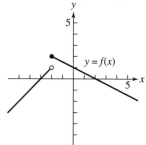

37. One possible answer:

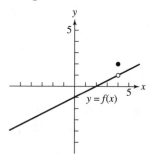

38. One possible answer:

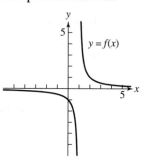

39. $x \approx -0.724$ and $x \approx 1.221$
40. $x \approx -1.521$
41. $a = \dfrac{4}{3}$

42. Consider $f(x) = x - e^{-x}$. f is continuous, $f(0) = -1$, and $f(1) = 1 - \dfrac{1}{e} > 0.5$. By the Intermediate Value Theorem, for some c in $(0, 1)$, $f(c) = 0$ and $e^{-c} = c$.

43. **(b)**

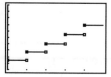

[0, 4.8] by [35000, 45000]

Continuous at all points in the domain $[0, 5)$ except at $t = 1, 2, 3, 4$.

44. **(a)** $f(x) = \begin{cases} -1.10 \text{ int } (-x), & 0 \le x \le 6 \\ 7.25, & 6 < x \le 24 \end{cases}$

(b)

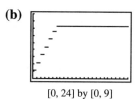

[0, 24] by [0, 9]

This is continuous at all values of x in the domain $[0, 24]$ except for $x = 0, 1, 2, 3, 4, 5, 6$.

45. **(a)** Domain of f: $(-\infty, -1) \cup (0, \infty)$
(b)

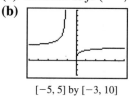

[-5, 5] by [-3, 10]

(c) Because f is undefined there due to division by 0.

(d) $x = 0$: removable, right-hand limit is 0
$x = -1$: not removable, infinite discontinuity

(e) 2.718 or e

46. This is because $\displaystyle\lim_{h \to 0} f(a + h) = \lim_{x \to a} f(x)$.

47. Suppose not. Then f would be negative somewhere in the interval and positive somewhere else in the interval. So, by the Intermediate Value Theorem, it would have to be zero somewhere in the interval, which contradicts the hypothesis.

48. Since the absolute value function is continuous, this follows from the theorem about continuity of composite functions.

49. For any real number a, the limit of this function as x approaches a cannot exist. This is because as x approaches a, the values of the function will continually oscillate between 0 and 1.

2.4 Rates of Change and Tangent Lines (pp. 82–90)

Quick Review 2.4

1. $\Delta x = 8, \Delta y = 3$
2. $\Delta x = a - 1, \Delta y = b - 3$
3. Slope $= -\dfrac{4}{7}$
4. Slope $= \dfrac{2}{3}$ 5. $y = \dfrac{3}{2}x + 6$
6. $y = -\dfrac{7}{3}x + \dfrac{25}{3}$ 7. $y = -\dfrac{3}{4}x + \dfrac{19}{4}$
8. $y = \dfrac{4}{3}x + \dfrac{8}{3}$ 9. $y = -\dfrac{2}{3}x + \dfrac{7}{3}$
10. $b = \dfrac{19}{3}$

Section 2.4 Exercises:

1. (a) 19   (b) 1
2. (a) 1
   (b) $\dfrac{7 - \sqrt{41}}{2} \approx 0.298$
3. (a) $\dfrac{1 - e^{-2}}{2} \approx 0.432$
   (b) $\dfrac{e^3 - e}{2} \approx 8.684$
4. (a) $\dfrac{\ln 4}{3} \approx 0.462$
   (b) $\dfrac{\ln(103/100)}{3} = \dfrac{\ln 1.03}{3} \approx 0.0099$
5. (a) $-\dfrac{4}{\pi} \approx -1.273$
   (b) $-\dfrac{3\sqrt{3}}{\pi} \approx -1.654$
6. (a) $-\dfrac{2}{\pi} \approx -0.637$
   (b) 0
7. Using $Q_1 = (10, 225)$, $Q_2 = (14, 375)$, $Q_3 = (16.5, 475)$, $Q_4 = (18, 550)$, and $P = (20, 650)$

   (a)
Secant	Slope
PQ_1	43
PQ_2	46
PQ_3	50
PQ_4	50

   Units are meters/second
   (b) Approximately 50 m/sec
8. Using $Q_1 = (5, 20)$, $Q_2 = (7, 38)$, $Q_3 = (8.5, 56)$, $Q_4 = (9.5, 72)$, and $P = (10, 80)$

   (a)
Secant	Slope
PQ_1	12
PQ_2	14
PQ_3	16
PQ_4	16

   Units are meters/second
   (b) Approximately 16 m/sec

9. (a) -4 (b) $y = -4x - 4$
   (c) $y = \dfrac{1}{4}x + \dfrac{9}{2}$
   (d)
   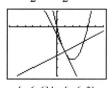
   $[-8, 7]$ by $[-1, 9]$
10. (a) -2 (b) $y = -2x - 1$
    (c) $y = \dfrac{1}{2}x - \dfrac{7}{2}$
    (d)
    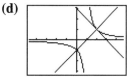
    $[-6, 6]$ by $[-6, 2]$
11. (a) -1 (b) $y = -x + 3$
    (c) $y = x - 1$
    (d)
    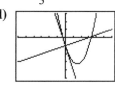
    $[-4.7, 4.7]$ by $[-3.1, 3.1]$
12. (a) -3 (b) $y = -3x - 1$
    (c) $y = \dfrac{1}{3}x - 1$
    (d)

    $[-6, 6]$ by $[-5, 3]$
13. (a) 1   (b) -1
14. -1
15. No. Slope from the left is -2; slope from the right is 2. The two-sided limit of the difference quotient doesn't exist.
16. Yes. The slope is -1.
17. Yes. The slope is $-\dfrac{1}{4}$.
18. No. The function is discontinuous at $x = \dfrac{3\pi}{4}$. The left-hand limit of the difference quotient doesn't exist.
19. (a) $2a$
    (b) The slope of the tangent steadily increases as a increases.
20. (a) $-\dfrac{2}{a^2}$
    (b) The slope of the tangent is always negative. The tangents are very steep near $x = 0$ and nearly horizontal as a moves away from the origin.

21. (a) $-\dfrac{1}{(a-1)^2}$

(b) The slope of the tangent is always negative. The tangents are very steep near $x = 1$ and nearly horizontal as a moves away from the origin.

22. (a) $-2a$

(b) The slope of the tangent steadily decreases as a increases.

23. 19.6 m/sec

24. 60 ft/sec   **25.** 6π in^2/in.

26. 16π in^3/in.   **27.** 3.72 m/sec

28. 45.76 m/sec   **29.** $(-2, -5)$

30. $(-2, 7)$

31. (a) At $x = 0$: $y = -x - 1$
At $x = 2$: $y = -x + 3$

(b) At $x = 0$: $y = x - 1$
At $x = 2$: $y = x - 1$

32. At $x = -1$: $y = 2x + 10$
At $x = 3$: $y = -6x + 18$

33. (a) 0.3 billion dollars per year

(b) 0.5 billion dollars per year

(c) $y = 0.0571x^2 - 0.1514x + 1.3943$

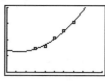

[0, 10] by [0, 4]

(d) 1993 to 1995: 0.31 billion dollars per year
1995 to 1997: 0.53 billion dollars per year

(e) 0.65 billion dollars per year

34. (a)

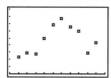

[7, 18] by [0, 900]

(b)

Q From Year	Slope
1988	23.9
1989	18.9
1990	24.3
1991	−8.8
1992	−48.8
1993	−80.8
1994	−70.3
1995	−80.0
1996	144.0

(c) As Q gets closer to 1997, the slopes do not seem to be approaching a limit value. The years 1995–97 seem to be very unusual and unpredictable.

35. (a) $\dfrac{e^{1+h} - e}{h}$

(b) Limit ≈ 2.718

(c) They're about the same.

35. continued

(d) Yes, it has a tangent whose slope is about e.

36. (a) $\dfrac{2^{1+h} - 2}{h}$

(b) Limit ≈ 1.386

(c) They're about the same.

(d) Yes, it has a tangent whose slope is about ln 4.

37. No   **38.** Yes

39. Yes   **40.** No

41. This function has a tangent with slope zero at the origin. It is sandwiched between two functions, $y = x^2$ and $y = -x^2$, both of which have slope zero at the origin.

Looking at the difference quotient,
$-h \le \dfrac{f(0 + h) - f(0)}{h} \le h$, so
the Sandwich Theorem tells us that the limit is 0.

42. This function does not have a tangent line at the origin. As the function oscillates between $y = x$ and $y = -x$ infinitely often near the origin, there are an infinite number of difference quotients (secant line slopes) with a value of 1 and with a value of -1. Thus the limit of the difference quotient doesn't exist.

The difference quotient is
$\dfrac{f(0 + h) - f(0)}{h} = \sin\left(\dfrac{1}{h}\right)$ which oscillates between 1 and -1 infinitely often near zero.

43. Slope ≈ 0.540

■ Chapter 2 Review Exercises (pp. 91–93)

1. -15 **2.** $\dfrac{5}{21}$

3. No limit   **4.** No limit

5. $-\dfrac{1}{4}$ **6.** $\dfrac{2}{5}$

7. $+\infty, -\infty$ **8.** $\dfrac{1}{2}$

9. 2   **10.** 0

11. 6   **12.** 5

13. 0   **14.** 1

15. Limit exists   **16.** Limit exists

17. Limit exists   **18.** Doesn't exist

19. Limit exists   **20.** Limit exists

21. Yes   **22.** No

23. No   **24.** Yes

25. (a) 1   **(b)** 1.5

(c) No

(d) g is discontinuous at $x = 3$ (and points not in domain).

25. continued

   (e) Yes, can remove discontinuity at $x = 3$ by assigning the value 1 to $g(3)$.

26. (a) 1.5   **(b)** 0

   (c) 0   **(d)** No

   (e) k is discontinuous at $x = 1$ (and points not in domain).

   (f) Discontinuity at $x = 1$ is not removable because the two one-sided limits are different.

27. (a) Vertical Asymp.: $x = -2$

   (b) Left-hand limit $= -\infty$

        Right-hand limit $= \infty$

28. (a) Vertical Asymp.: $x = 0$ and $x = -2$

   (b) At $x = 0$:

        Left-hand limit $= -\infty$

        Right-hand limit $= -\infty$

        At $x = -2$:

        Left-hand limit $= \infty$

        Right-hand limit $= -\infty$

29. (a) At $x = -1$:

        Left-hand limit $= 1$

        Right-hand limit $= 1$

        At $x = 0$:

        Left-hand limit $= 0$

        Right-hand limit $= 0$

        At $x = 1$:

        Left-hand limit $= -1$

        Right-hand limit $= 1$

   (b) At $x = -1$:

        Yes, the limit is 1.

        At $x = 0$:

        Yes, the limit is 0.

        At $x = 1$:

        No, the limit doesn't exist because the two one-sided limits are different.

   (c) At $x = -1$:

        Continuous because $f(-1) =$ the limit.

        At $x = 0$:

        Discontinuous because $f(0) \neq$ the limit.

        At $x = 1$:

        Discontinuous because limit doesn't exist.

30. (a) Left-hand limit $= 3$

        Right-hand limit $= -3$

   (b) No, because the two one-sided limits are different.

   (c) Every place except for $x = 1$

   (d) At $x = 1$

31. $x = -2$ and $x = 2$

32. There are no points of discontinuity.

33. (a) $\dfrac{2}{x}$ **(b)** $y = 0$ (x-axis)

34. (a) 2   **(b)** $y = 2$

35. (a) x^2 **(b)** None

36. (a) x **(b)** None

37. (a) e^x **(b)** x

38. (a) $\ln |x|$ **(b)** $\ln |x|$

39. $k = 8$ **40.** $k = \dfrac{1}{2}$

41. One possible answer:

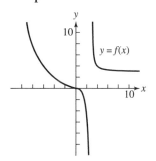

42. One possible answer:

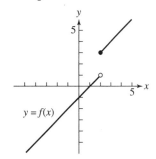

43. $\dfrac{2}{\pi}$ **44.** $\dfrac{2}{3}\pi aH$

45. $12a$ **46.** $2a - 1$

47. (a) -1 **(b)** $y = -x - 1$

   (c) $y = x - 3$

48. $\left(\dfrac{3}{2}, -\dfrac{9}{4}\right)$

49. (a) 25. Perhaps this is the number of bears placed in the reserve when it was established.

   (b) 200

   (c) Perhaps this is the maximum number of bears which the reserve can support due to limitations of food, space, or other resources. Or, perhaps the number is capped at 200 and excess bears are moved to other locations.

50. (a)

$$f(x) = \begin{cases} 3.20 - 1.35 \cdot \text{int}\,(-x + 1), & 0 < x \le 20 \\ 0, & x = 0 \end{cases}$$

   (b)

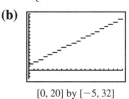

        $[0, 20]$ by $[-5, 32]$

        f is discontinuous at integer values of x: 0, 1, 2, ..., 19

51. (a) Cubic: $y = -1.644x^3 + 42.981x^2 - 254.369x + 300.232$

        Quartic: $y = 2.009x^4 - 102.081x^3 + 1884.997x^2 - 14918.180x + 43004.464$

   (b) Cubic: $-1.644x^3$, predicts spending will go to 0.

        Quartic: $2.009x^4$, predicts spending will go to ∞.

52. $\lim_{x \to c} f(x) = \frac{3}{2}$, $\lim_{x \to c} g(x) = \frac{1}{2}$

53. (a)

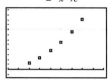

[3, 12] by [−2, 24]

(b)

Year of Q	Slope of PQ
1995	3.48
1996	3.825
1997	4.1
1998	4.45
1999	4.9

(c) Approximately 5 billion dollars per year

(d) $y = 0.3214x^2 - 1.3471x + 1.3857$
Predicted rate of change in 2000 is 5.081 billion dollars per year.

Chapter 3
Derivatives

3.1 Derivative of a Function (pp. 95–104)

Quick Review 3.1

1. 4

2. $\frac{5}{2}$

3. −1

4. 8

5. 0

6. $(-\infty, 0]$ and $[2, \infty)$

7. $\lim_{x \to 1^+} f(x) = 0$; $\lim_{x \to 1^-} f(x) = 3$

8. 0

9. No, the two one-sided limits are different.

10. No. f is discontinuous at $x = 1$ because the limit doesn't exist there.

Section 3.1 Exercises

1. (a) $y = 5x - 7$

(b) $y = -\frac{1}{5}x + \frac{17}{5}$

2. $-\frac{1}{9}$

3. $-\frac{1}{9}$

4. $f'(x) = 3$

5. $\frac{dy}{dx} = 7$

6. $2x$

7. (b)

8. (a)

9. (d)

10. (c)

11. $\frac{dy}{dx} = 4x - 13$, tangent line is $y = -x - 13$

12. (a) $y = 3x - 2$

(b) $y = -\frac{1}{3}x + \frac{4}{3}$

13. (ii)

14. (iv)

15. (a) Sometime around April 1. The rate then is approximately $\frac{1}{6}$ hour per day.

(b) Yes. Jan. 1 and July 1

(c) Positive: Jan 1. through July 1
Negative: July 1 through Dec. 31

16.

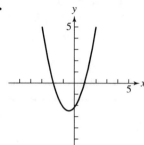

17. (a) 0 and 0

(b) 1700 and 1300

18. (a)

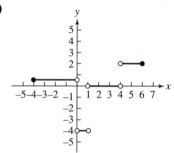

(b) $x = 0, 1, 4$

19. Graph of derivative:

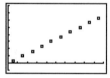

[0, 10] by [−10, 80]

(a) The speed of the skier

(b) Feet per second

(c) Approximately $D = 6.65t$

20. (a)

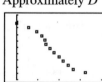

[−0.5, 4] by [700, 1700]

(b)

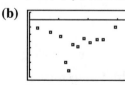

[0, 3.24] by [−800, 100]

(c) Feet per mile

(d) Feet per mile

(e) Look for the steepest part of the curve. This is where the elevation is dropping most rapidly, and therefore the most likely location for significant "rapids".

20. continued

    (f) Look for the lowest point on the graph. This is where the elevation is dropping most rapidly, and therefore the most likely location for significant "rapids".

21.

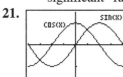

$[-\pi, \pi]$ by $[-1.5, 1.5]$

Cosine could be the derivative of sine. The values of cosine are positive where sine is increasing, zero where sine has horizontal tangents, and negative where sine is decreasing.

22. We show that the right-hand derivative at 1 does not exist.

$$\lim_{h \to 0^+} \frac{f(1 + h) - f(1)}{h} = \lim_{h \to 0^+} \frac{3(1 + h) - (1)^3}{h}$$

$$= \lim_{h \to 0^+} \frac{2 + 3h}{h} = \lim_{h \to 0^+} \left(\frac{2}{h} + 3\right) = \infty$$

23. $\displaystyle\lim_{h \to 0^+} \frac{f(0 + h) - f(0)}{h} = \lim_{h \to 0^+} \frac{\sqrt{h}}{h} = \lim_{h \to 0^+} \frac{1}{\sqrt{h}} = \infty$

Thus, the right-hand derivative at 0 does not exist.

24. Two parabolas are parallel if they have the same derivative at every value of x. This means their tangent lines are parallel at each value of x. Two such parabolas are given by $y = x^2$ and $y = x^2 + 4$. They are graphed below.

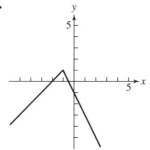

$[-4, 4]$ by $[-5, 20]$

The parabolas are "everywhere equidistant", as long as the distance between them is always measured along a vertical line.

25.

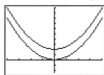

26. (a) $2x$ **(b)** 2

    (c) 2   **(d)** 2

    (e) Yes, the two one-sided limits exist and are the same.

    (f) 2

    (g) Does not exist

    (h) It does not exist because the right-hand derivative does not exist.

27. The y-intercept is $b - a$.

28. $k = -2$

29. (a) 0.992   **(b)** 0.008

    (c) If P is the answer to (b), then the probability of a shared birthday when there are four people is
$$1 - (1 - P)\frac{362}{365} \approx 0.016.$$

    (d) No. Clearly, February 29th is a much less likely birth date. Furthermore, census data do not support the assumption that the other 365 birth dates are equally likely. However, this simplifying assumption may still give us some insight into this problem even if the calculated probabilities aren't completely accurate.

3.2 Differentiability (pp. 105–112)

Quick Review 3.2

  1. Yes   **2.** No

  3. Yes   **4.** Yes

  5. No   **6.** All reals

  7. $[0, \infty)$ **8.** $[3, \infty)$

  9. 3.2   **10.** 5

Section 3.2 Exercises

  1. Left-hand derivative = 0

     Right-hand derivative = 1

  2. Left-hand derivative = 0

     Right-hand derivative = 2

  3. Left-hand derivative = $\dfrac{1}{2}$

     Right-hand derivative = 2

  4. Left-hand derivative = 1

     Right-hand derivative = -1

  5. (a) All points in $[-3, 2]$

    (b) None   **(c)** None

  6. (a) All points in $[-2, 3]$

    (b) None   **(c)** None

  7. (a) All points in $[-3, 3]$ except $x = 0$

    (b) None   **(c)** $x = 0$

  8. (a) All points in $[-2, 3]$ except $x = -1, 0, 2$

    (b) $x = -1$ **(c)** $x = 0, x = 2$

  9. (a) All points in $[-1, 2]$ except $x = 0$

    (b) $x = 0$ **(c)** None

10. (a) All points in $[-3, 3]$ except $x = -2, 2$

    (b) $x = -2, x = 2$ **(c)** None

11. Discontinuity   **12.** Cusp

13. Corner   **14.** Vertical tangent

15. Corner   **16.** Cusp

17. All reals except $x = -1, 5$

18. All reals except $x = 2$ **19.** All reals except $x = 0$

20. All reals   **21.** All reals except $x = 3$

22. All reals

23. (a) $x = 0$ is not in their domains, or, they are both discontinuous at $x = 0$.

    (b) For $\dfrac{1}{x}$: 1,000,000

        For $\dfrac{1}{x^2}$: 0

    (c) It returns an incorrect response because even though these functions are not defined at $x = 0$, they are defined at $x = \pm 0.001$.

24.

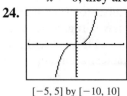

$[-5, 5]$ by $[-10, 10]$

$\dfrac{dy}{dx} = x^3$

25.

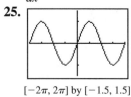

$[-2\pi, 2\pi]$ by $[-1.5, 1.5]$

$\dfrac{dy}{dx} = \sin x$

26.

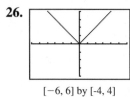

$[-6, 6]$ by $[-4, 4]$

$\dfrac{dy}{dx} = \text{abs}\,(x) \text{ or } |x|$

27.

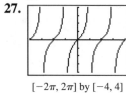

$[-2\pi, 2\pi]$ by $[-4, 4]$

$\dfrac{dy}{dx} = \tan x$

28.

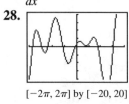

$[-2\pi, 2\pi]$ by $[-20, 20]$

Does not look like any basic function.

29. (a) $a + b = 2$ **(b)** $a = -3$ and $b = 5$

30. The function $f(x)$ does not have the intermediate value property. Choose some a in $(-1, 0)$ and b in $(0, 1)$. Then $f(a) = 0$ and $f(b) = 1$, but f does not take on any value between 0 and 1.

31. (a) Note that $-x \le x \sin \dfrac{1}{x} \le x$, for all x, so $\displaystyle\lim_{x \to 0} \left(x \sin \dfrac{1}{x} \right) = 0$ by the Sandwich Theorem. Therefore, f is continuous at $x = 0$.

    (b) $\dfrac{f(0 + h) - f(0)}{h} = \dfrac{h \sin \dfrac{1}{h} - 0}{h} = \sin \dfrac{1}{h}$

    (c) The limit does not exist because $\sin \dfrac{1}{h}$ oscillates between -1 and 1 an infinite number of times arbitrarily close to $h = 0$.

    (d) No

    (e) $\dfrac{g(0 + h) - g(0)}{h} = \dfrac{h^2 \sin \dfrac{1}{h} - 0}{h}$

                      $= h \sin \dfrac{1}{h}$

    As noted in part (a), the limit of this as x approaches zero is 0, so $g'(0) = 0$.

3.3 Rules for Differentiation (pp. 112–121)

Quick Review 3.3

1. $x + x^2 - 2x^{-1} - 2$ **2.** $x + x^{-1}$

3. $3x^2 - 2x^{-1} + 5x^{-2}$ **4.** $\dfrac{3}{2}x^2 - x + 2x^{-2}$

5. $x^{-3} + x^{-1} + 2x^{-2} + 2$ **6.** $x^2 + x$

7. Root: $x \approx 1.173$, $500x^6 \approx 1305$
    Root: $x \approx 2.394$, $500x^6 \approx 94{,}212$

8. (a) 7   **(b)** 7
    (c) 7   **(d)** 0

9. (a) 0   **(b)** 0
    (c) 0

10. (a) $f'(x) = \dfrac{1}{\pi}$ **(b)** $f'(x) = -\pi x^{-2}$

Section 3.3 Exercises

1. $\dfrac{dy}{dx} = -2x$, $\dfrac{d^2y}{dx^2} = -2$

2. $\dfrac{dy}{dx} = x^2 - 1$, $\dfrac{d^2y}{dx^2} = 2x$

3. $\dfrac{dy}{dx} = 2$, $\dfrac{d^2y}{dx^2} = 0$

4. $\dfrac{dy}{dx} = 2x + 1$, $\dfrac{d^2y}{dx^2} = 2$

5. $\dfrac{dy}{dx} = x^2 + x + 1$, $\dfrac{d^2y}{dx^2} = 2x + 1$

6. $\dfrac{dy}{dx} = -1 + 2x - 3x^2$, $\dfrac{d^2y}{dx^2} = 2 - 6x$

7. $\dfrac{dy}{dx} = 4x^3 - 21x^2 + 4x$, $\dfrac{d^2y}{dx^2} = 12x^2 - 42x + 4$

8. $\dfrac{dy}{dx} = 15x^2 - 15x^4$, $\dfrac{d^2y}{dx^2} = 30x - 60x^3$

9. $\dfrac{dy}{dx} = -8x^{-3} - 8,\ \dfrac{d^2y}{dx^2} = 24x^{-4}$

10. $\dfrac{dy}{dx} = -x^{-5} + x^{-4} - x^{-3} + x^{-2},$

$\dfrac{d^2y}{dx^2} = 5x^{-6} - 4x^{-5} + 3x^{-4} - 2x^{-3}$

11. **(a)** $3x^2 + 2x + 1$

    (b) $3x^2 + 2x + 1$

12. **(a)** $\dfrac{x(2x) - (x^2 + 3)}{x^2} = \dfrac{x^2 - 3}{x^2}$

    (b) $1 - \dfrac{3}{x^2}$

13. $-\dfrac{19}{(3x - 2)^2}$

14. $-\dfrac{5}{x^2} + \dfrac{2}{x^3}$

15. $\dfrac{3}{x^4}$

16. $\dfrac{x^2 - 2x - 1}{(1 + x^2)^2}$

17. $\dfrac{x^4 + 2x}{(1 - x^3)^2}$

18. $\dfrac{1}{\sqrt{x}(\sqrt{x} + 1)^2}$

19. $\dfrac{12 - 6x^2}{(x^2 - 3x + 2)^2}$

20. **(a)** Let $f(x) = x$.

$$\lim_{h \to 0} \frac{f(x + h) - f(x)}{h} = \lim_{h \to 0} \frac{(x + h) - x}{h}$$

$$= \lim_{h \to 0} \frac{h}{h} = \lim_{h \to 0} (1) = 1$$

    (b) Note that $u = u(x)$ is a function of x.

$$\lim_{h \to 0} \frac{-u(x + h) - [-u(x)]}{h}$$

$$= \lim_{h \to 0} \left(-\frac{u(x + h) - u(x)}{h} \right)$$

$$= -\lim_{h \to 0} \frac{u(x + h) - u(x)}{h} = -\frac{du}{dx}$$

21. $\dfrac{d}{dx}(c \cdot f(x)) = c \cdot \dfrac{d}{dx} f(x) + f(x) \cdot \dfrac{d}{dx} c$

$$= c \cdot \frac{d}{dx} f(x) + 0 = c \cdot \frac{d}{dx} f(x)$$

22. $-\dfrac{f'(x)}{[f(x)]^2}$

23. **(a)** 13 **(b)** -7

    (c) $\dfrac{7}{25}$ **(d)** 20

24. **(a)** 2 **(b)** -10

    (c) $\dfrac{10}{9}$ **(d)** -12

25. (iii)   **26.** (iii)

27. $y = -\dfrac{1}{9}x + \dfrac{29}{9}$

28. Slope is 4 at $x = \pm 1$:

    tangent at $x = -1$: $y = 4x + 2$

    tangent at $x = 1$: $y = 4x - 2$

    Smallest slope is 1 and occurs at $x = 0$.

29. $(-1, 27)$ and $(2, 0)$

30. x-intercept $= -\dfrac{4}{3}$, y-intercept $= 16$

31. At $(0, 0)$: $y = 4x$

    At $(1, 2)$: $y = 2$

32. $y = -\dfrac{1}{2}x + 2$

33. $-\dfrac{nRT}{(V - nb)^2} + \dfrac{2an^2}{V^3}$

34. $\dfrac{ds}{dt} = 9.8t,\ \dfrac{d^2s}{dt^2} = 9.8$ **35.** $\dfrac{dR}{dM} = CM - M^2$

36. If the radius of a circle is changed by a very small amount Δr, the change in the area can be thought of as a very thin strip with length given by the circumference, $2\pi r$, and width Δr. Therefore, the change in the area can be thought of as $(2\pi r)(\Delta r)$, which means that the change in the area divided by the change in the radius is just $2\pi r$.

37. If the radius of a sphere is changed by a very small amount Δr, the change in the volume can be thought of as $(4\pi r^2)(\Delta r)$, which means that the change in the volume divided by the change in the radius is just $4\pi r^2$.

38. 390 bushels of annual production per year.

39. It is going down approximately 20 cents per year. (rate ≈ -0.201 dollars/year)

40. **(a)** It is insignificant in the limiting case and can be treated as zero (and removed from the expression).

    (b) It was "rejected" because it is incomparably smaller than the other terms: $v\, du$ and $u\, dv$.

    (c) The product rule given in the text.

    (d) Because dx is "infinitely small," and this could be thought of as dividing by zero.

    (e) $d\left(\dfrac{u}{v}\right) = \dfrac{u + du}{v + dv} - \dfrac{u}{v}$

$$= \frac{(u + du)v - u(v + dv)}{(v + dv)v}$$

$$= \frac{uv + vdu - uv - udv}{v^2 + vdv}$$

$$= \frac{vdu - udv}{v^2}.$$

3.4 Velocity and Other Rates of Change (pp. 122-133)

Quick Review 3.4

1. Downward   **2.** y-intercept $= -256$

3. x-intercepts $= 2, 8$ **4.** $(-\infty, 144]$

5. $(5, 144)$ **6.** $x = 3, 7$

7. $x = \dfrac{15}{8}$ **8.** $(-\infty, 5)$

9. 64 **10.** -32

Section 3.4 Exercises

1. $3s^2$

2. **(a)** 10 m   **(b)** 2 m/sec

    (c) 5 m/sec   **(d)** 2 m/sec^2

    (e) At $t = \dfrac{3}{2}$ sec   **(f)** At $s = -\dfrac{1}{4}$ m

3. (a) vel$(t) = 24 - 1.6t$ m/sec,
accel$(t) = -1.6$ m/sec^2

(b) 15 seconds   **(c)** 180 meters

(d) About 4.393 seconds

(e) 30 seconds

4. Mars: $t \approx 4.462$ sec
Jupiter: $t \approx 0.726$ sec

5. About 29.388 meters

6. Moon: 320 seconds
Earth: 52 seconds

7. For the moon:
$$x_1(t) = 3(t < 160) + 3.1(t \geq 160)$$
$$y_1(t) = 832t - 2.6t^2$$
t-values: 0 to 320
window: [0, 6] by [$-10{,}000$, 70,000]
For the earth:
$$x_1(t) = 3(t < 26) + 3.1(t \geq 26)$$
$$y_1(t) = 832t - 16t^2$$
t-values: 0 to 52
window: [0, 6] by [-1000, 11,000]

8. At $t = 0$: 10,000 bacteria/hour
At $t = 5$: 0 bacteria/hour
At $t = 10$: $-10{,}000$ bacteria/hour

9. At the end of 10 minutes: 8000 gallons/minute
Average over first 10 minutes:
10,000 gallons/minute

10. (a) $110 per machine

(b) $80 per machine

(c) $79.90 for the 101st machine

11. (a)

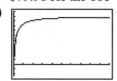

[0, 50] by [-500, 2200]

The values of x which make sense are the whole numbers, $x \geq 0$.

(b) $\dfrac{2000}{(x + 1)^2}$

(c) Approximately $55.56

(d) The limit is 0. This means that as x gets large, one reaches a point where very little extra revenue can be expected from selling more desks.

12. At $t = 1$: -6 m/sec^2 **13.** At $t = 1$: 0 m/sec
At $t = 3$: 6 m/sec^2 At $t = 2$: 1 m/sec

14. (a) $g'(x) = h'(x) = t'(x) = 3x^2$

(b)

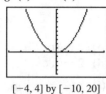

[-4, 4] by [-10, 20]

(c) $f(x)$ must be of the form $f(x) = x^3 + c$, where c is a constant.

(d) Yes. $f(x) = x^3$ **(e)** Yes. $f(x) = x^3 + 3$

15. (a)

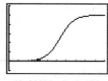

[0, 200] by [-2, 12]

(b) $x \geq 0$ (whole numbers)

(c)

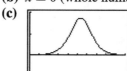

[0, 200] by [-0.1, 0.2]

P seems to be relatively sensitive to changes in x between approximately $x = 60$ and $x = 160$.

(d) The maximum occurs when $x \approx 106.44$. Since x must be an integer, $P(106) \approx 4.924$ thousand dollars or $4924.

(e) $13 per package sold, $165 per package sold, $118 per package sold, $31 per package sold, $6 per package sold, $P'(300) \approx 0$ (on the order of 10^{-6}, or $0.001 per package sold)

(f) The limit is 10. Maximum possible profit is $10,000 monthly.

(g) Yes. In order to sell more and more packages, the company might need to lower the price to a point where they won't make any additional profit.

16. (a) 190 ft/sec   **(b)** 2 seconds

(c) After 8 seconds, and its velocity was 0 ft/sec then

(d) After about 11 seconds, and it was falling 90 ft/sec then

(e) About 3 seconds

(f) Just before the engine stopped; from $t = 2$ to $t = 11$ while the rocket was in free fall

17. Possible answer:

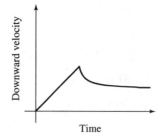

18. (a)

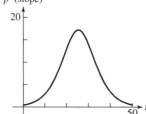

p' (slope)

horizontal axis: Days
vertical axis: Flies per day

(b) Fastest: Around the 25th day
Slowest: Day 50 or day 0

19. At $t \approx 2.83$

20. (a) It begins at the point $(-5, 2)$ moving in the positive direction. After a little more than one second, it has moved a bit past $(6, 2)$ and it turns back in the negative direction for approximately 2 seconds. At the end of that time, it is near $(-2, 2)$ and it turns back again in the positive direction. After that, it continues moving in the positive direction indefinitely, speeding up as it goes.

(b) Speeds up: $[1.153, 2.167]$ and $[3.180, \infty)$
slows down: $[0, 1.153]$ and $[2.167, 3.180]$

(c) At $t \approx 1.153$ sec and $t \approx 3.180$ sec

(d) At $t \approx 1.153$ sec and $t \approx 3.180$ sec
"instantaneously"

(e) The velocity starts out positive but decreasing, it becomes negative, then starts to increase, and becomes positive again and continues to increase.
The speed is decreasing, reaches 0 at $t \approx$ 1.15 sec, then increases until $t \approx 2.17$ sec, decreases until $t \approx 3.18$ when it is 0 again, and then increases after that.

(f) At about 0.745 sec, 1.626 sec, 4.129 sec

21. (a)

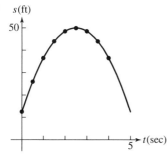

s (ft)

(b) $s'(1) = 18$, $s'(2.5) = 0$, $s'(3.5) = -12$

22. (a)

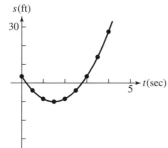

s (ft)

(b) $s'(1) = -6$, $s'(2.5) = 12$, $s'(3.5) = 24$

23. (a) At $t = 2$ and $t = 7$

(b) Between $t = 3$ and $t = 6$

(c)

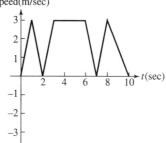

Speed(m/sec)

(d)

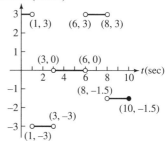

Acceleration (m/sec^2)

24. (a) Left: $2 < t < 3$, $5 < t \leq 6$
Right: $0 \leq t < 1$
Standing still: $1 < t < 2$, $3 < t < 5$

(b) Velocity graph:

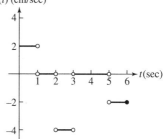

$v(t)$ (cm/sec)

Speed graph:

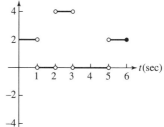

$|v(t)|$ (cm/sec)

25. (a) Move forward: $0 \leq t < 1$ and $5 < t < 7$
move backward: $1 < t < 5$
speed up: $1 < t < 2$ and $5 < t < 6$
slow down: $0 \leq t < 1$, $3 < t < 5$,
and $6 < t < 7$

(b) Positive: $3 < t < 6$
negative: $0 \leq t < 2$ and $6 < t < 7$
zero: $2 < t < 3$ and $7 < t \leq 9$

(c) At $t = 0$ and $2 < t < 3$

(d) $7 < t \leq 9$

26. (a) Velocity graph:

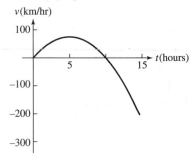

Acceleration:

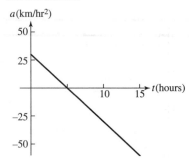

(b) $\dfrac{ds}{dt} = 30t - 3t^2$ and $\dfrac{d^2s}{dt^2} = 30 - 6t$.
The graphs are very similar.

27. (a) $\dfrac{4}{7}$ of a second. Average velocity = 280 cm/sec

(b) Velocity = 560 cm/sec;
acceleration = 980 cm/sec²

(c) About 28 flashes per second

28. Graph C is position, graph A is velocity, and graph B is acceleration.
A is the derivative of C because it is positive, negative, and zero where C is increasing, decreasing, and has horizontal tangents, respectively. The relationship between B and A is similar.

29. Graph C is position, graph B is velocity, and graph A is acceleration.
B is the derivative of C because it is negative and zero where C is decreasing and has horizontal tangents, respectively.
A is the derivative of B because it is positive, negative, and zero where B is increasing, decreasing, and has horizontal tangents, respectively.

30. (a) $\dfrac{dy}{dt} = \dfrac{t}{12} - 1$

(b) Fastest: at $t = 0$

slowest: at $t = 12$

At $t = 0$: $\dfrac{dy}{dt} = -1$

at $t = 12$: $\dfrac{dy}{dt} = 0$

30. continued

(c)

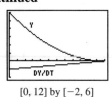

[0, 12] by [−2, 6]

y is decreasing and $\dfrac{dy}{dt}$ is negative over the entire interval. y decreases more rapidly early in the interval, and the magnitude of $\dfrac{dy}{dt}$ is larger then. $\dfrac{dy}{dt}$ is 0 at $t = 12$, where y seems to have a horizontal tangent.

31. (a) 16π cubic feet of volume per foot of radius
(b) By about 11.092 cubic feet

32. It will take 25 seconds, and the aircraft will have traveled approximately 694.444 meters.

33. Exit velocity $\approx$ 348.712 ft/sec $\approx$ 237.758 mi/h

34. By estimating the slope of the velocity graph at that point.

35. Since profit = revenue − cost, using Rule 4 (the "difference rule"), and taking derivatives, we see that marginal profit
= marginal revenue − marginal cost.

36. (a) 135 seconds

(b) $\dfrac{5}{73} \approx 0.068$ furlongs/sec

(c) $\dfrac{1}{13} \approx 0.077$ furlongs/sec

(d) During the last furlong (between the 9th and 10th furlong markers)

(e) During the first furlong (between markers 0 and 1)

37. (a) Assume that f is even. Then,

$$f'(-x) = \lim_{h \to 0} \frac{f(-x + h) - f(-x)}{h}$$

$$= \lim_{h \to 0} \frac{f(x - h) - f(x)}{h},$$

and substituting $k = -h$,

$$= \lim_{k \to 0} \frac{f(x + k) - f(x)}{-k}$$

$$= -\lim_{k \to 0} \frac{f(x + k) - f(x)}{k} = -f'(x)$$

So, f' is an odd function.

37. continued

(b) Assume that f is odd. Then,

$$f'(-x) = \lim_{h \to 0} \frac{f(-x + h) - f(-x)}{h}$$

$$= \lim_{h \to 0} \frac{-f(x - h) + f(x)}{h},$$
and substituting $k = -h$,

$$= \lim_{k \to 0} \frac{-f(x + k) + f(x)}{-k}$$

$$= \lim_{k \to 0} \frac{f(x + k) - f(x)}{k} = f'(x)$$

So, f' is an even function.

38. $\dfrac{d}{dx}fgh = \dfrac{df}{dx}gh + f\dfrac{dg}{dx}h + fg\dfrac{dh}{dx}$

3.5 Derivatives of Trigonometric Functions (pp. 134–141)

Quick Review 3.5

1. $\dfrac{3\pi}{4} \approx 2.356$

2. $\left(\dfrac{306}{\pi}\right)^{\circ} \approx 97.403°$

3. $\dfrac{\sqrt{3}}{2}$

4. Domain: all reals; range: $[-1, 1]$

5. Domain: $x \neq k\dfrac{\pi}{2}$, where k is an odd integer; range: all reals

6. 0

7. $\pm\dfrac{1}{\sqrt{2}}$

8. Multiply by $\dfrac{1 + \cos h}{1 + \cos h}$ and use $1 - \cos^2 h = \sin^2 h$.

9. $y = 12x - 35$ **10.** 12

Section 3.5 Exercises

1. $1 + \sin x$

2. $2 \cos x - \sec^2 x$

3. $-\dfrac{1}{x^2} + 5 \cos x$

4. $x \sec x \tan x + \sec x$

5. $-x^2 \cos x - 2x \sin x$

6. $3 + x \sec^2 x + \tan x$

7. $4 \sec x \tan x$

8. $\dfrac{1 + \cos x + x \sin x}{(1 + \cos x)^2}$

9. $-\dfrac{\csc^2 x}{(1 + \cot x)^2} = -\dfrac{1}{(\sin x + \cos x)^2}$

10. $-\dfrac{1}{1 + \sin x}$ **11.** $y = -x + \pi + 3$

12. Approximately $y = -1.081x + 2.122$

13. Approximately $y = -8.063x + 25.460$

14. $\displaystyle\lim_{h \to 0} \frac{\cos(x + h) - \cos(x)}{h}$

$$= \lim_{h \to 0} \frac{(\cos x \cos h - \sin x \sin h) - \cos x}{h}$$

$$= \lim_{h \to 0} \frac{(\cos x)(\cos h - 1) - \sin x \sin h}{h}$$

$$= (\cos x)\lim_{h \to 0}\left(\frac{\cos h - 1}{h}\right) - (\sin x)\left(\lim_{h \to 0}\frac{\sin h}{h}\right)$$

$$= \cos x\,(0) - \sin x\,(1) = -\sin x$$

15. (a) $\dfrac{d}{dx}\tan x = \dfrac{d}{dx}\dfrac{\sin x}{\cos x}$

$$= \frac{(\cos x)(\cos x) - (\sin x)(-\sin x)}{(\cos x)^2}$$

$$= \frac{\cos^2 x + \sin^2 x}{\cos^2 x}$$

$$= \frac{1}{\cos^2 x} = \sec^2 x$$

(b) $\dfrac{d}{dx}\sec x = \dfrac{d}{dx}\dfrac{1}{\cos x}$

$$= \frac{(\cos x)(0) - (1)(-\sin x)}{(\cos x)^2}$$

$$= \frac{\sin x}{(\cos x)^2} = \sec x \tan x$$

16. (a) $\dfrac{d}{dx}\cot x = \dfrac{d}{dx}\dfrac{\cos x}{\sin x}$

$$= \frac{(\sin x)(-\sin x) - (\cos x)(\cos x)}{(\sin x)^2}$$

$$= -\frac{\sin^2 x + \cos^2 x}{\sin^2 x}$$

$$= -\frac{1}{\sin^2 x} = -\csc^2 x$$

(b) $\dfrac{d}{dx}\csc x = \dfrac{d}{dx}\dfrac{1}{\sin x}$

$$= \frac{(\sin x)(0) - (1)(\cos x)}{(\sin x)^2}$$

$$= -\frac{\cos x}{(\sin x)^2} = -\csc x \cot x$$

17. $\dfrac{d}{dx}\sec x = \sec x \tan x$ which is 0 at $x = 0$, so the slope of the tangent line is 0.

$\dfrac{d}{dx}\cos x = -\sin x$ which is 0 at $x = 0$, so the slope of the tangent line is 0.

18. $\dfrac{d}{dx}\tan x = \sec^2 x$ which is never 0.

$\dfrac{d}{dx}\cot x = -\csc^2 x$ which is never 0.

19. Tangent: $y = -x + \dfrac{\pi}{4} + 1$

normal: $y = x + 1 - \dfrac{\pi}{4}$

20. $\left(-\dfrac{\pi}{4}, -1\right), \left(\dfrac{\pi}{4}, 1\right)$

21. (a) $y = -x + \dfrac{\pi}{2} + 2$

(b) $y = 4 - \sqrt{3}$

22. (a) $y = -4x + \pi + 4$
  (b) $y = 2$
23. (a) Velocity: $-2 \cos t$ m/sec
    Speed: $|2 \cos t|$ m/sec
    Accel.: $2 \sin t$ m/sec^2
    Jerk: $2 \cos t$ m/sec^3
  (b) Velocity: $-\sqrt{2}$ m/sec
    Speed: $\sqrt{2}$ m/sec
    Accel.: $\sqrt{2}$ m/sec^2
    Jerk: $\sqrt{2}$ m/sec^3
  (c) The body starts at 2, goes to 0 and then
    oscillates between 0 and 4.
    Speed: *Greatest* when $\cos t = \pm 1$ (or $t = k\pi$),
    at the center of the interval of motion.
    Zero when $\cos t = 0$ $\left(\text{or } t = \dfrac{k\pi}{2}, k \text{ odd}\right)$, at the
    endpoints of the interval of motion.

    Acceleration: *Greatest* (in magnitude) when
    $\sin t = \pm 1$ $\left(\text{or } t = \dfrac{k\pi}{2}, k \text{ odd}\right)$
    Zero when $\sin t = 0$ (or $t = k\pi$)

    Jerk: *Greatest* (in magnitude) when
    $\cos t = \pm 1$ (or $t = k\pi$)
    Zero when $\cos t = 0$ $\left(\text{or } t = \dfrac{k\pi}{2}, k \text{ odd}\right)$

24. (a) Velocity: $\cos t - \sin t$ m/sec
    Speed: $|\cos t - \sin t|$ m/sec
    Accel.: $-\sin t - \cos t$ m/sec^2
    Jerk: $-\cos t + \sin t$ m/sec^3
  (b) Velocity: 0 m/sec
    Speed: 0 m/sec
    Accel.: $-\sqrt{2}$ m/sec^2
    Jerk: 0 m/sec^3
  (c) The body starts at 1, goes to $\sqrt{2}$ and then
    oscillates between $\pm\sqrt{2}$.
    Speed:
    Greatest when $t = \dfrac{3\pi}{4} + k\pi$
    Zero when $t = \dfrac{\pi}{4} + k\pi$
    Acceleration:
    Greatest (in magnitude) when $t = \dfrac{\pi}{4} + k\pi$
    Zero when $t = \dfrac{3\pi}{4} + k\pi$
    Jerk:
    Greatest (in magnitude) when $t = \dfrac{3\pi}{4} + k\pi$
    Zero when $t = \dfrac{\pi}{4} + k\pi$

25. (a) The limit is $\dfrac{\pi}{180}$ because this is the conversion
    factor for changing from degrees to radians.
  (b) This limit is still 0.
  (c) $\dfrac{d}{dx} \sin x = \dfrac{\pi}{180} \cos x$
  (d) $\dfrac{d}{dx} \cos x = -\dfrac{\pi}{180} \sin x$
  (e) $\dfrac{d^2}{dx^2} \sin x = -\dfrac{\pi^2}{180^2} \sin x$
    $\dfrac{d^3}{dx^3} \sin x = -\dfrac{\pi^3}{180^3} \cos x$
    $\dfrac{d^2}{dx^2} \cos x = -\dfrac{\pi^2}{180^2} \cos x$
    $\dfrac{d^3}{dx^3} \cos x = \dfrac{\pi^3}{180^3} \sin x$
26. $y'' = \csc^3 x + \csc x \cot^2 x$
27. $y'' = \dfrac{2 + 2\theta \tan \theta}{\cos^2 \theta} = \dfrac{2 \cos \theta + 2\theta \sin \theta}{\cos^3 \theta}$
28. Continuous if $b = 1$, because this makes the two
    one-sided limits equal.
    Differentiable: No, because for $b = 1$, the
    left-hand derivative is 1 and the right-hand
    derivative is 0.(The left-hand derivative does not
    exist for other values of b).
29. $\sin x$ **30.** $\cos x$
31. $y = x$
32. (a) 0.12
  (b) $\sin (0.12) \approx 0.1197122$
    The approximation is within 0.0003 of the
    actual value.
33. $\dfrac{d}{dx} \sin 2x = \dfrac{d}{dx} 2 \sin x \cos x$
    $= 2 [(\sin x)(-\sin x) + (\cos x)(\cos x)]$
    $= 2 [\cos^2 x - \sin^2 x] = 2 \cos 2x$

34. $\dfrac{d}{dx} \cos 2x = \dfrac{d}{dx} [(\cos x)(\cos x) - (\sin x)(\sin x)]$
    $= [2(\cos x)(-\sin x) - 2(\sin x)(\cos x)]$
    $= -4 (\sin x)(\cos x) = -2(2 \sin x \cos x)$
    $= -2 \sin 2x$

35. $\displaystyle\lim_{h \to 0} \dfrac{\cos h - 1}{h} = \lim_{h \to 0} \dfrac{(\cos h - 1)(\cos h + 1)}{h(\cos h + 1)}$
    $= \displaystyle\lim_{h \to 0} \dfrac{\cos^2 h - 1}{h(\cos h + 1)}$
    $= \displaystyle\lim_{h \to 0} \dfrac{-\sin^2 h}{h(\cos h + 1)}$
    $= -\left(\displaystyle\lim_{h \to 0} \dfrac{\sin h}{h}\right)\left(\lim_{h \to 0} \dfrac{\sin h}{\cos h + 1}\right)$
    $= -(1)\left(\dfrac{0}{2}\right) = 0$

36. $A = -\dfrac{1}{2}, B = 0$

3.6 Chain Rule
(pp. 141–149)

Quick Review 3.6

1. $\sin (x^2 + 1)$ **2.** $\sin (49x^2 + 1)$
3. $49x^2 + 1$ **4.** $7x^2 + 7$
5. $\sin \dfrac{x^2 + 1}{7x}$ **6.** $g(f(x))$
7. $g(h(f(x)))$ **8.** $h(g(f(x)))$
9. $f(h(h(x)))$ **10.** $f(g(h(x)))$

Section 3.6 Exercises

1. $3 \cos (3x + 1)$ **2.** $-5 \cos (7 - 5x)$
3. $-\sqrt{3} \sin (\sqrt{3}x)$
4. $(2 - 3x^2) \sec^2 (2x - x^3)$
5. $\dfrac{10}{x^2} \csc^2 \left(\dfrac{2}{x}\right)$ **6.** $\dfrac{2 \sin x}{(1 + \cos x)^2}$
7. $-\sin (\sin x) \cos x$
8. $\sec (\tan x) \tan (\tan x) \sec^2 x$
9. $-2(x + \sqrt{x})^{-3}\left(1 + \dfrac{1}{2\sqrt{x}}\right)$
10. $\dfrac{\csc x}{\csc x + \cot x}$
11. $-5 \sin^{-6} x \cos x + 3 \cos^2 x \sin x$
12. $8x^3(2x - 5)^3 + 3x^2(2x - 5)^4$
$= x^2(2x - 5)^3(14x - 15)$
13. $4 \sin^3 x \sec^2 4x + 3 \sin^2 x \cos x \tan 4x$
14. $2 \sec x \sqrt{\sec x + \tan x}$
15. $-3(2x + 1)^{-3/2}$
16. $(1 + x^2)^{-3/2}$
17. $6 \sin (3x - 2) \cos (3x - 2) = 3 \sin (6x - 4)$
18. $-4(1 + \cos 2x) \sin 2x$
19. $-42(1 + \cos^2 7x)^2 \cos 7x \sin 7x$
20. $\dfrac{5}{2} (\tan 5x)^{-1/2} \sec^2 5x$

21. $3 \sin \left(\dfrac{\pi}{2} - 3t\right)$
22. $4t \sin (\pi - 4t) + \cos (\pi - 4t)$
23. $\dfrac{4}{\pi} \cos 3t - \dfrac{4}{\pi} \sin 5t$
24. $\dfrac{3\pi}{2} \cos \dfrac{3\pi t}{2} - \dfrac{7\pi}{4} \sin \dfrac{7\pi t}{4}$
25. $-\sec^2 (2 - \theta)$
26. $2 \sec^3 2\theta + 2 \sec 2\theta \tan^2 2\theta$
27. $\dfrac{\theta \cos \theta + \sin \theta}{2\sqrt{\theta \sin \theta}}$ **28.** $\sqrt{\sec \theta} \, (\theta \tan \theta + 2)$
29. $2 \sec^2 x \tan x$ **30.** $2 \csc^2 x \cot x$
31. $18 \csc^2 (3x - 1) \cot (3x - 1)$
32. $2 \sec^2 \dfrac{x}{3} \tan \dfrac{x}{3}$ **33.** $\dfrac{5}{2}$
34. 1 **35.** $-\dfrac{\pi}{4}$
36. 5π **37.** 0
38. -8
39. (a) $-6 \sin (6x + 2)$ **(b)** $-6 \sin (6x + 2)$

40. (a) $2x \cos (x^2 + 1)$ **(b)** $2x \cos (x^2 + 1)$
41. $y = -x + 2\sqrt{2}$ **42.** $y = \sqrt{3}x + 2$
43. $y = -\dfrac{1}{2}x - \dfrac{1}{2}$ **44.** $y = 2x - \sqrt{3}$
45. $y = x + \dfrac{1}{4}$ **46.** $y = x - 4$
47. $y = \sqrt{3}x + 2 - \dfrac{\pi}{\sqrt{3}}$ **48.** $y = 2$
49. (a) $\dfrac{\cos t}{2t + 1}$
(b) $\dfrac{d}{dt}\left(\dfrac{dy}{dx}\right) = -\dfrac{(2t + 1)(\sin t) + 2 \cos t}{(2t + 1)^2}$
(c) $\dfrac{d}{dx}\left(\dfrac{dy}{dx}\right) = -\dfrac{(2t + 1)(\sin t) + 2 \cos t}{(2t + 1)^3}$
(d) part (c)

50. Since the radius goes through $(0, 0)$ and $(2 \cos t, 2 \sin t)$, it has slope given by $\tan t$.
But $\dfrac{dy}{dx} = \dfrac{dy/dt}{dx/dt} = -\dfrac{\cos t}{\sin t} = -\cot t$, which is the negative reciprocal of $\tan t$. This means that the radius and the tangent are perpendicular.

51. 5 **52.** 3
53. $\dfrac{1}{2}$ **54.** $y = mx$

55. Tangent: $y = \pi x - \pi + 2$;
Normal: $y = -\dfrac{1}{\pi}x + \dfrac{1}{\pi} + 2$

56. (a) $\dfrac{2}{3}$ **(b)** $2\pi + 5$
(c) $15 - 8\pi$ **(d)** $\dfrac{37}{6}$
(e) -1 **(f)** $\dfrac{1}{12\sqrt{2}}$
(g) $\dfrac{5}{32}$ **(h)** $-\dfrac{5}{3\sqrt{17}}$

57. (a) 1 **(b)** 6
(c) 1 **(d)** $-\dfrac{1}{9}$
(e) $-\dfrac{40}{3}$ **(f)** -6
(g) $-\dfrac{4}{9}$

58. The slope of $y = \sin (2x)$ at the origin is 2. The slope of $y = -\sin \dfrac{x}{2}$ at the origin is $-\dfrac{1}{2}$. So the lines tangent to the two curves at the origin are perpendicular.

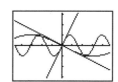

$[-4.7, 4.7]$ by $[-3.1, 3.1]$

59. Because the symbols $\dfrac{dy}{dx}, \dfrac{dy}{du}$, and $\dfrac{du}{dx}$ are not fractions. The individual symbols dy, du, and dx do not have numerical values.

60. The amplitude of the velocity is doubled. The amplitude of the acceleration is quadrupled. The amplitude of the jerk is multiplied by 8.

61. (a) On the 101st day (April 11th)
    (b) About 0.637 degrees per day

62. Velocity $= \dfrac{2}{5}$ m/sec
    acceleration $= -\dfrac{4}{125}$ m/sec^2

63. Acceleration $= \dfrac{dv}{dt} = \dfrac{dv}{ds}\dfrac{ds}{dt} = \dfrac{dv}{ds}v$
    $= \dfrac{k}{2\sqrt{s}}(k\sqrt{s}) = \dfrac{k^2}{2}$

64. Given: $v = \dfrac{k}{\sqrt{s}}$
    acceleration: $= \dfrac{dv}{dt} = \dfrac{dv}{ds}\dfrac{ds}{dt} = \dfrac{dv}{ds}v$
    $= \dfrac{-k}{2s^{3/2}}\dfrac{k}{\sqrt{s}} = -\dfrac{k^2}{2s^2}$

65. Acceleration $= \dfrac{dv}{dt} = \dfrac{d\,f(x)}{dt}$
    $= \left[\dfrac{d\,f(x)}{dx}\right]\left[\dfrac{dx}{dt}\right]$
    $= f'(x)f(x)$

66. $\dfrac{dT}{du} = \dfrac{dT}{dL}\dfrac{dL}{du}$
    $= \dfrac{\pi}{\sqrt{gL}}kL = k\pi\sqrt{\dfrac{L}{g}} = \dfrac{kT}{2}$

67. No, this does not contradict the Chain Rule. The Chain Rule states that if two functions are differentiable at the appropriate points, then their composite must also be differentiable. It does not say: If a composite is differentiable, then the functions which make up the composite must all be differentiable.

68. Yes. Either the graph of $y = g(x)$ must have a horizontal tangent at $x = 1$, or the graph of $y = f(u)$ must have a horizontal tangent at $u = g(1)$. This is because $\dfrac{d}{dx}f(g(x)) = f'(g(x))g'(x)$, so the slope of the tangent to the graph of $y = f(g(x)$ at $x = 1$ is given by $f'(g(1))g'(1)$. If this product is zero, then at least one of its factors must be zero.

69. As $h \to 0$, the second curve (the difference quotient) approaches the first $y = 2\cos 2x$. This is because $2\cos 2x$ is the derivative of $\sin 2x$, and the second curve is the difference quotient used to define the derivative of $\sin 2x$. As $h \to 0$, the difference quotient expression should be approaching the derivative.

70. As $h \to 0$, the second curve (the difference quotient) approaches the first ($y = -2x\sin(x^2)$). This is because $-2x\sin(x^2)$ is the derivative of $\cos(x^2)$, and the second curve is the difference quotient used to define the derivative of $\cos(x^2)$. As $h \to 0$, the difference quotient expression should be approaching the derivative.

71. (a) Let $f(x) = |x|$.
    Then $\dfrac{d}{dx}|u| = \dfrac{d}{dx}f(u) = f'(u)\dfrac{du}{dx}$
    $= f'(u)u' = \dfrac{u}{|u|}u'.$
    The derivative of the absolute value function is $+1$ for positive values, -1 for negative values, and undefined at 0. So $f'(u)$ should be $+1$ when $u > 0$ and -1 when $u < 0$. But this is exactly how the expression $\dfrac{u}{|u|}$ evaluates.

(b) $f'(x) = \dfrac{(2x)(x^2 - 9)}{|x^2 - 9|}$
    $g'(x) = |x|\cos x + \dfrac{x\sin x}{|x|}$

72. $\dfrac{dG}{dx} = \dfrac{d}{dx}\sqrt{uv} = \dfrac{d}{dx}\sqrt{x^2 + cx} = \dfrac{2x + c}{2\sqrt{x^2 + cx}}$
    $= \dfrac{x + \dfrac{c}{2}}{\sqrt{x^2 + cx}}$
    $= \dfrac{A}{G}$, since $A = x + \dfrac{c}{2}.$

3.7 Implicit Differentiation (pp. 149–157)

Quick Review 3.7

1. $y_1 = \sqrt{x}, y_2 = -\sqrt{x}$

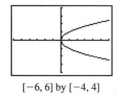

$[-6, 6]$ by $[-4, 4]$

2. $y_1 = \dfrac{2}{3}\sqrt{9 - x^2}, y_2 = -\dfrac{2}{3}\sqrt{9 - x^2}$

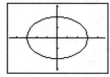

$[-4.7, 4.7]$ by $[-3.1, 3.1]$

3. $y_1 = \dfrac{x}{2}, y_2 = -\dfrac{x}{2}$

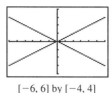

[−6, 6] by [−4, 4]

4. $y_1 = \sqrt{9 - x^2}, y_2 = -\sqrt{9 - x^2}$

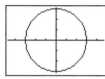

[−4.7, 4.7] by [−3.1, 3.1]

5. $y_1 = \sqrt{2x + 3 - x^2}, y_2 = -\sqrt{2x + 3 - x^2}$

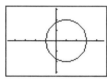

[−4.7, 4.7] by [−3.1, 3.1]

6. $y' = \dfrac{4x - y + 2xy}{x^2}$ **7.** $y' = \dfrac{y + x\cos x}{\sin x - x}$

8. $y' = \dfrac{xy^2}{x^2 - y + x}$ **9.** $x^{3/2} - x^{5/6}$

10. $x^{-1/2} + x^{-5/6}$

Section 3.7 Exercises

1. $\dfrac{9}{4}x^{5/4}$ **2.** $-\dfrac{3}{5}x^{-8/5}$

3. $\dfrac{1}{3}x^{-2/3}$ **4.** $\dfrac{1}{4}x^{-3/4}$

5. $-(2x + 5)^{-3/2}$ **6.** $-4(1 - 6x)^{-1/3}$

7. $x^2(x^2 + 1)^{-1/2} + (x^2 + 1)^{1/2}$

8. $(x^2 + 1)^{-3/2}$ **9.** $-\dfrac{2xy + y^2}{2xy + x^2}$

10. $\dfrac{6y - x^2}{y^2 - 6x}$ **11.** $\dfrac{1}{y(x + 1)^2}$

12. $\dfrac{y}{x} - (x + y)^2$ or $\dfrac{1 - 3x^2 - 2xy}{x^2 + 1}$

13. $-\dfrac{1}{4}(1 - x^{1/2})^{-1/2}x^{-1/2}$ **14.** $x^{-3/2}(2x^{-1/2} + 1)^{-4/3}$

15. $-\dfrac{9}{2}(\csc x)^{3/2} \cot x$

16. $\dfrac{5}{4}[\sin (x + 5)]^{1/4} \cos (x + 5)$

17. $\cos^2 y$ **18.** $\sec y$

19. $-\dfrac{1}{x}\cos^2 (xy) - \dfrac{y}{x}$ **20.** $\dfrac{1 - y}{x - \cos y}$

21. (b), (c), and (d)   **22.** (a) and (c)

23. $\dfrac{dy}{dx} = -\dfrac{x}{y}$

$\dfrac{d^2y}{dx^2} = -\dfrac{(x^2 + y^2)}{y^3} = -\dfrac{1}{y^3}$

24. $\dfrac{dy}{dx} = -\left(\dfrac{y}{x}\right)^{1/3}$

$\dfrac{d^2y}{dx^2} = \dfrac{x^{2/3} + y^{2/3}}{3x^{4/3}y^{1/3}} = \dfrac{1}{3x^{4/3}y^{1/3}}$

25. $\dfrac{dy}{dx} = \dfrac{x + 1}{y}$

$\dfrac{d^2y}{dx^2} = \dfrac{y^2 - (x + 1)^2}{y^3} = -\dfrac{1}{y^3}$

26. $\dfrac{dy}{dx} = \dfrac{1}{y + 1}$ **27. (a)** $y = \dfrac{7}{4}x - \dfrac{1}{2}$

$\dfrac{d^2y}{dx^2} = -\dfrac{1}{(y + 1)^3}$ **(b)** $y = -\dfrac{4}{7}x + \dfrac{29}{7}$

28. (a) $y = \dfrac{3}{4}x - \dfrac{25}{4}$ **29. (a)** $y = 3x + 6$

(b) $y = -\dfrac{4}{3}x$ **(b)** $y = -\dfrac{1}{3}x + \dfrac{8}{3}$

30. (a) $y = -x - 1$ **31. (a)** $y = \dfrac{6}{7}x + \dfrac{6}{7}$

(b) $y = x + 3$ **(b)** $y = -\dfrac{7}{6}x - \dfrac{7}{6}$

32. (a) $y = 2$ **33. (a)** $y = -\dfrac{\pi}{2}x + \pi$

(b) $x = \sqrt{3}$ **(b)** $y = \dfrac{2}{\pi}x - \dfrac{2}{\pi} + \dfrac{\pi}{2}$

34. (a) $y = 2x$ **35. (a)** $y = 2\pi x - 2\pi$

(b) $y = -\dfrac{1}{2}x + \dfrac{5\pi}{8}$ **(b)** $y = -\dfrac{x}{2\pi} + \dfrac{1}{2\pi}$

36. (a) $y = \pi$ **(b)** $x = 0$

37. (a) At $\left(\dfrac{\sqrt{3}}{4}, \dfrac{\sqrt{3}}{2}\right)$: Slope = -1;

at $\left(\dfrac{\sqrt{3}}{4}, \dfrac{1}{2}\right)$: Slope = $\sqrt{3}$

(b)

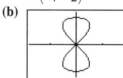

[−1.8, 1.8] by [−1.2, 1.2]

Parameter interval:
$-1 \le t \le 1$

38. (a) Tangent: $y = 2x - 1$

normal: $y = -\dfrac{1}{2}x + \dfrac{3}{2}$

(b) One way is to graph the equations

$y = \pm\sqrt{\dfrac{x^3}{2 - x}}.$

39. (a) $(-1)^3(1)^2 = \cos(\pi)$ is true since both sides equal: -1.

(b) The slope is $\dfrac{3}{2}$.

40. (a) There are three values: $1, \dfrac{-1 \pm \sqrt{5}}{2}$

(b) $f'(2) = 1, f''(2) = -4$

41. The points are $(\pm\sqrt{7}, 0)$.

$$\frac{dy}{dx} = -\frac{2x + y}{2y + x}$$

At both points, $\frac{dy}{dx} = -2$

42. (a) $\left(\sqrt{\dfrac{7}{3}}, -2\sqrt{\dfrac{7}{3}}\right)$ and $\left(-\sqrt{\dfrac{7}{3}}, 2\sqrt{\dfrac{7}{3}}\right)$

(b) $\left(-2\sqrt{\dfrac{7}{3}}, \sqrt{\dfrac{7}{3}}\right)$ and $\left(2\sqrt{\dfrac{7}{3}}, -\sqrt{\dfrac{7}{3}}\right)$

43. First curve: $\dfrac{dy}{dx} = -\dfrac{2x}{3y}$

second curve: $\dfrac{dy}{dx} = \dfrac{3x^2}{2y}$

At $(1, 1)$, the slopes are $-\dfrac{2}{3}$ and $\dfrac{3}{2}$ respectively.

At $(1, -1)$, the slopes are $\dfrac{2}{3}$ and $-\dfrac{3}{2}$ respectively.
In both cases, the tangents are perpendicular.

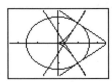

$[-2.4, 2.4]$ by $[-1.6, 1.6]$

44. Velocity $= 36$ m/sec;

acceleration $= \dfrac{27}{4}$ m/sec^2

45. Acceleration $= \dfrac{dv}{dt} = 4(s - t)^{-1/2}(v - 1)$

$= 32$ ft/sec^2

46. At $(3, 2)$: $\dfrac{27}{8}$;

at $(-3, 2)$: $-\dfrac{27}{8}$;

at $(-3, -2)$: $\dfrac{27}{8}$;

at $(3, -2)$: $-\dfrac{27}{8}$

47. (a) At $(4, 2)$: $\dfrac{5}{4}$;

at $(2, 4)$: $\dfrac{4}{5}$

(b) At $(3\sqrt[3]{2}, 3\sqrt[3]{4}) \approx (3.780, 4.762)$

(c) At $(3\sqrt[3]{4}, 3\sqrt[3]{2}) \approx (4.762, 3.780)$

48. $(3, -1)$

49. At $(-1, -1)$: $y = -2x - 3$;
at $(3, -3)$: $y = -2x + 3$

50. The normal at the point (b^2, b) is:

$y = -2bx + 2b^3 + b$.

This line intersects the x-axis at $x = b^2 + \dfrac{1}{2}$, which

must be greater than $\dfrac{1}{2}$ if $b \neq 0$.

The two normals are perpendicular when

$a = \dfrac{3}{4}$.

51. (a) $\dfrac{dy}{dx} = -\dfrac{b^2 x}{a^2 y}$

The tangent line is $y - y_1 = -\dfrac{b^2 x_1}{a^2 y_1}(x - x_1)$.

This gives: $a^2 y_1 y - a^2 y_1{}^2 = -b^2 x_1 x + b^2 x_1{}^2$,

$\qquad\qquad a^2 y_1 y + b^2 x_1 x = a^2 y_1{}^2 + b^2 x_1{}^2$.

But $a^2 y_1{}^2 + b^2 x_1{}^2 = a^2 b^2$ since (x_1, y_1) is on
the ellipse.

Therefore, $a^2 y_1 y + b^2 x_1 x = a^2 b^2$, and dividing

by $a^2 b^2$ gives $\dfrac{x_1 x}{a^2} + \dfrac{y_1 y}{b^2} = 1$.

(b) $\dfrac{x_1 x}{a^2} - \dfrac{y_1 y}{b^2} = 1$.

52. (a) Solve for y.

(b) Because the limit of $\dfrac{f(x)}{g(x)}$ as $x \to \infty$ is 1.

(c) Because the limit of $\dfrac{f(x)}{g(x)}$ as $x \to \infty$ is 1.

3.8 Derivatives of Inverse Trigonometric Functions (pp. 157–163)

Quick Review 3.8

1. Domain: $[-1, 1]$

Range: $\left[-\dfrac{\pi}{2}, \dfrac{\pi}{2}\right]$

At 1: $\dfrac{\pi}{2}$

2. Domain: $[-1, 1]$

Range: $[0, \pi]$

At 1: 0

3. Domain: all reals

Range: $\left(-\dfrac{\pi}{2}, \dfrac{\pi}{2}\right)$

At 1: $\dfrac{\pi}{4}$

4. Domain: $(-\infty, -1] \cup [1, \infty)$

Range: $\left[0, \dfrac{\pi}{2}\right) \cup \left(\dfrac{\pi}{2}, \pi\right]$

At 1: 0

5. Domain: all reals
Range: all reals
At 1: 1

6. $f^{-1}(x) = \dfrac{x + 8}{3}$

7. $f^{-1}(x) = x^3 - 5$

8. $f^{-1}(x) = \dfrac{8}{x}$

9. $f^{-1}(x) = \dfrac{2}{3 - x}$

10. $f^{-1}(x) = 3 \tan x$, $-\dfrac{\pi}{2} < x < \dfrac{\pi}{2}$

Section 3.8 Exercises

1. $-\dfrac{2x}{\sqrt{1 - x^4}}$

2. $\dfrac{1}{|x|\sqrt{x^2 - 1}}$

3. $\dfrac{\sqrt{2}}{\sqrt{1-2t^2}}$

4. $-\dfrac{1}{\sqrt{2t-t^2}}$

5. $\dfrac{1}{|2s+1|\sqrt{s^2+s}}$

6. $\dfrac{1}{|s|\sqrt{25s^2-1}}$

7. $-\dfrac{2}{(x^2+1)\sqrt{x^2+2}}$

8. $-\dfrac{2}{|x|\sqrt{x^2-4}}$

9. $-\dfrac{1}{\sqrt{1-t^2}}$

10. $-\dfrac{6}{t\sqrt{t^4-9}}$

11. $-\dfrac{1}{2\sqrt{t}(t+1)}$

12. $-\dfrac{1}{2t\sqrt{t-1}}$

13. $-\dfrac{2s^2}{\sqrt{1-s^2}}$

14. $\dfrac{s|s|-1}{|s|\sqrt{s^2-1}}$

15. $0, x > 1$

16. $0, x \neq 0$

17. $\sin^{-1} x$

18. $-\dfrac{2}{(\sin^{-1}2x)^2\sqrt{1-4x^2}}$

19. (a) $y = 2x - \dfrac{\pi}{2} + 1$

   (b) $y = \dfrac{1}{2}x - \dfrac{1}{2} + \dfrac{\pi}{4}$

20. (a) $f(1) = 3, f'(1) = 12$

   (b) $f^{-1}(3) = 1, (f^{-1})'(3) = \dfrac{1}{12}$

21. (a) $f'(x) = 3 - \sin x$ and $f'(x) \neq 0$. So f has a differentiable inverse by Theorem 3.

   (b) $f(0) = 1, f'(0) = 3$

   (c) $f^{-1}(1) = 0, (f^{-1})'(1) = \dfrac{1}{3}$

22.

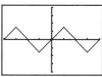

$[-2\pi, 2\pi]$ by $[-4, 4]$

   (a) All reals

   (b) $\left[-\dfrac{\pi}{2}, \dfrac{\pi}{2}\right]$

   (c) At the points $x = k\dfrac{\pi}{2}$, where k is an odd integer.

   (d)

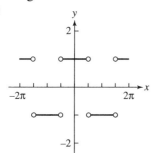

   (e) $f'(x) = \dfrac{\cos x}{\sqrt{1 - \sin^2 x}}$, which is ± 1 depending on whether $\cos x$ is positive or negative.

23. (a) $v(t) = \dfrac{dx}{dt} = \dfrac{1}{1+t^2}$ which is always positive.

   (b) $a(t) = \dfrac{dv}{dt} = -\dfrac{2t}{(1+t^2)^2}$ which is always negative.

   (c) $\dfrac{\pi}{2}$

24. $\dfrac{d}{dx}\cos^{-1}(x) = \dfrac{d}{dx}\left(\dfrac{\pi}{2} - \sin^{-1}x\right)$

   $= 0 - \dfrac{d}{dx}\sin^{-1}x$

   $= -\dfrac{1}{\sqrt{1-x^2}}$

25. $\dfrac{d}{dx}\cot^{-1}x = \dfrac{d}{dx}\left(\dfrac{\pi}{2} - \tan^{-1}x\right)$

   $= 0 - \dfrac{d}{dx}\tan^{-1}x$

   $= -\dfrac{1}{1+x^2}$

26. $\dfrac{d}{dx}\csc^{-1}(x) = \dfrac{d}{dx}\left(\dfrac{\pi}{2} - \sec^{-1}x\right)$

   $= 0 - \dfrac{d}{dx}\sec^{-1}x$

   $= -\dfrac{1}{|x|\sqrt{x^2-1}}$

27. (a) $y = \dfrac{\pi}{2}$ **(b)** $y = -\dfrac{\pi}{2}$

   (c) None

28. (a) $y = 0$ **(b)** $y = \pi$

   (c) None

29. (a) $y = \dfrac{\pi}{2}$ **(b)** $y = \dfrac{\pi}{2}$

   (c) None

30. (a) $y = 0$ **(b)** $y = 0$

   (c) None

31. (a) None   **(b)** None

   (c) None

32. (a) None   **(b)** None

   (c) None

33. (a)

   $\alpha = \cos^{-1}x, \beta = \sin^{-1}x$

   So $\dfrac{\pi}{2} = \alpha + \beta = \cos^{-1}x + \sin^{-1}x$.

   (b)

   $\alpha = \tan^{-1}x, \beta = \cot^{-1}x$

   So $\dfrac{\pi}{2} = \alpha + \beta = \tan^{-1}x + \cot^{-1}x$.

   (c)

   $\alpha = \sec^{-1}x, \beta = \csc^{-1}x$

   So $\dfrac{\pi}{2} = \alpha + \beta = \sec^{-1}x + \csc^{-1}x$.

34. The "straight angle" with the arrows in it is the sum of three angles. Call them A, B, and C, moving clockwise from the upper left to the lower right.

A is equal to $\tan^{-1} 3$ since the opposite side is 3 times as long as the adjacent side.
B is equal to $\tan^{-1} 2$ since the side opposite it is 2 units and the adjacent side is one unit.
C is equal to $\tan^{-1} 1$ since both the opposite and adjacent sides are one unit long.
But the sum of these three angles is the "straight angle," which has measure π radians.

35. If s is the length of a side of the square, and let α, β, γ denote the angles labeled $\tan^{-1} 1$, $\tan^{-1} 2$, and $\tan^{-1} 3$, respectively.

$\tan \alpha = \dfrac{s}{s} = 1$, so $\alpha = \tan^{-1} 1$ and

$\tan \beta = \dfrac{s}{\frac{s}{2}} = 2$, so $\beta = \tan^{-1} 2$.

$\gamma = \pi - \alpha - \beta = \pi - \tan^{-1} 1 - \tan^{-1} 2$

$= \tan^{-1} 3$.

3.9 Derivatives of Exponential and Logarithmic Functions (pp. 163–171)

Quick Review 3.9

1. $\dfrac{\ln 8}{\ln 5}$ **2.** $e^{x \ln 7}$

3. $\tan x$ **4.** $\ln (x - 2)$

5. $3x - 15$ **6.** $\dfrac{5}{4}$

7. $\ln (4x^4)$ **8.** $x = \dfrac{\ln 19}{\ln 3} \approx 2.68$

9. $x = \dfrac{\ln 18 - \ln (\ln 5)}{\ln 5} \approx 1.50$

10. $x = \dfrac{\ln 3}{\ln 2 - \ln 3} \approx -2.71$

Section 3.9 Exercises

1. $2e^x$ **2.** $2e^{2x}$
3. $-e^{-x}$ **4.** $-5e^{-5x}$
5. $\dfrac{2}{3} e^{2x/3}$ **6.** $-\dfrac{1}{4} e^{-x/4}$
7. $e^2 - e^x$ **8.** $x^2 e^x + x e^x - e^x$
9. $\dfrac{e^{\sqrt{x}}}{2\sqrt{x}}$ **10.** $2x e^{(x^2)}$
11. $\pi x^{\pi - 1}$ **12.** $(1 + \sqrt{2}) x^{\sqrt{2}}$
13. $-\sqrt{2} x^{-\sqrt{2} - 1}$ **14.** $(1 - e) x^{-e}$
15. $8^x \ln 8$ **16.** $-9^{-x} \ln 9$

17. $-3^{\csc x} (\ln 3)(\csc x \cot x)$
18. $-3^{\cot x} (\ln 3)(\csc^2 x)$ **19.** $\dfrac{2 x^{\ln x} \ln x}{x}$
20. $0, x > 0$ **21.** $\dfrac{2}{x}$
22. $\dfrac{2 \ln x}{x}$ **23.** $-\dfrac{1}{x}, x > 0$
24. $-\dfrac{1}{x}, x > 0$ **25.** $\dfrac{1}{x + 2}, x > -2$
26. $\dfrac{1}{x + 1}, x > -1$ **27.** $\dfrac{\sin x}{2 - \cos x}$
28. $\dfrac{2x}{x^2 + 1}$ **29.** $\dfrac{1}{x \ln x}$
30. $\ln x$ **31.** $\dfrac{2}{x \ln 4} = \dfrac{1}{x \ln 2}$
32. $\dfrac{1}{2x \ln 5}, x > 0$ **33.** $\dfrac{3}{(3x + 1) \ln 2}, x > -\dfrac{1}{3}$
34. $\dfrac{1}{2(x + 1) \ln 10}, x > -1$ **35.** $-\dfrac{1}{x \ln 2}, x > 0$
36. $-\dfrac{1}{x (\ln 2)(\log_2 x)^2}$ **37.** $\dfrac{1}{x}, x > 0$
38. $\dfrac{1}{1 + x \ln 3}, x > -\dfrac{1}{\ln 3}$ **39.** $\dfrac{1}{\ln 10}$
40. $\ln 10$ **41.** $y = ex$
42. $y = -x$
43. $(\sin x)^x [x \cot x + \ln (\sin x)]$
44. $x^{\tan x} \left[\dfrac{\tan x}{x} + (\ln x)(\sec^2 x) \right]$

45.
$\left(\dfrac{(x - 3)^4(x^2 + 1)}{(2x + 5)^3} \right)^{1/5} \left(\dfrac{4}{5(x - 3)} + \dfrac{2x}{5(x^2 + 1)} - \dfrac{6}{5(2x + 5)} \right)$

46. $\left(\dfrac{x\sqrt{x^2 + 1}}{(x + 1)^{2/3}} \right)\left(\dfrac{1}{x} + \dfrac{x}{x^2 + 1} - \dfrac{2}{3(x + 1)} \right)$
47. rate ≈ 0.098 grams/day
48. **(a)** $\dfrac{d}{dx} \ln (kx) = \dfrac{1}{kx} \dfrac{d}{dx} kx = \dfrac{k}{kx} = \dfrac{1}{x}$

(b) $\dfrac{d}{dx} \ln (kx) = \dfrac{d}{dx} (\ln k + \ln x)$
$= 0 + \dfrac{d}{dx} \ln x = \dfrac{1}{x}$

49. **(a)** $\ln 2$ **(b)** $f'(0) = \lim\limits_{h \to 0} \dfrac{2^h - 1}{h}$
(c) $\ln 2$ **(d)** $\ln 7$
50. Recall that a point (a, b) is on the graph of $y = e^x$ if and only if the point (b, a) is on the graph of $y = \ln x$. Since there are points (x, e^x) on the graph of $y = e^x$ with arbitrarily large x-coordinates, there will be points $(x, \ln x)$ on the graph of $y = \ln x$ with arbitrarily large y-coordinates.
51. **(a)** The graph of y_4 is a horizontal line at $y = a$.
(b) The graph of y_3 is a horizontal line at $y = \ln a$.
(c) $\dfrac{d}{dx} a^x = a^x$ if and only if $y_3 = \dfrac{y_2}{y_1} = 1$.
So if $y_3 = \ln a$, then $\dfrac{d}{dx} a^x$ will equal a^x if and only if $\ln a = 1$, or $a = e$.

51. continued

(d) $y_2 = \dfrac{d}{dx} a^x = a^x \ln a$. This will equal $y_1 = a^x$ if and only if $\ln a = 1$, or $a = e$.

52. $\dfrac{d}{dx}\left(-\dfrac{1}{2}x^2 + k\right) = -x$ and $\dfrac{d}{dx}(\ln x + c) = \dfrac{1}{x}$.

Therefore, at any given value of x, these two curves will have perpendicular tangent lines.

53. (a) $y = \dfrac{1}{e}x$

(b) Because the graph of $\ln x$ lies below the graph of the line for all positive $x \neq e$.

(c) Multiplying by e, $e(\ln x) < x$, or $\ln x^e < x$.

(d) Exponentiate both sides of the inequality in (c).

(e) Let $x = \pi$ to see that $\pi^e < e^\pi$.

■ Chapter 3 Review Exercises (pp. 172–175)

1. $5x^4 - \dfrac{x}{4} + \dfrac{1}{4}$

2. $-21x^2 + 21x^6$

3. $-2\cos^2 x + 2\sin^2 x = 2\cos 2x$

4. $-\dfrac{4}{(2x-1)^2}$

5. $2\sin(1 - 2t)$

6. $\dfrac{2}{t^2}\csc^2\dfrac{2}{t}$

7. $\dfrac{1}{2\sqrt{x}} - \dfrac{1}{2x^{3/2}}$

8. $\dfrac{3x+1}{\sqrt{2x+1}}$

9. $3\sec(1 + 3\theta)\tan(1 + 3\theta)$

10. $-4\theta\tan(3 - \theta^2)\sec^2(3 - \theta^2)$

11. $-5x^2\csc 5x \cot 5x + 2x\csc 5x$

12. $\dfrac{1}{2x}, x > 0$

13. $\dfrac{e^x}{1 + e^x}$

14. $-xe^{-x} + e^{-x}$

15. e

16. $\cot x$, where x is in an interval of the form $(k\pi, (k+1)\pi)$, k even

17. $-\dfrac{1}{\cos^{-1}x\sqrt{1 - x^2}}$

18. $\dfrac{2}{\theta \ln 2}$

19. $\dfrac{1}{(t-7)\ln 5}, t > 7$

20. $-8^{-t}\ln 8$

21. $\dfrac{2(\ln x)x^{\ln x}}{x}$

22. $\dfrac{(2\cdot 2^x)[x^3\ln 2 + x\ln 2 + 1]}{(x^2 + 1)^{3/2}}$ or

$\dfrac{(2x)2^x}{\sqrt{x^2 + 1}}\left(\dfrac{1}{x} + \ln 2 - \dfrac{x}{x^2 + 1}\right)$

23. $\dfrac{e^{\tan^{-1}}}{1 + x^2}$

24. $-\dfrac{u}{\sqrt{u^2 - u^4}} = -\dfrac{u}{|u|\sqrt{1 - u^2}}$

25. $\dfrac{t}{|t|\sqrt{t^2 - 1}} + \sec^{-1}t - \dfrac{1}{2t}$

26. $-\dfrac{2 + 2t^2}{1 + 4t^2} + 2t\cot^{-1}2t$

27. $\cos^{-1}z$

28. $-\dfrac{1}{x} + \dfrac{\csc^{-1}\sqrt{x}}{\sqrt{x - 1}}$

29. $-\dfrac{\sin x}{|\sin x|} = -\text{sign}(\sin x), x \neq \dfrac{\pi}{2}, \pi, \dfrac{3\pi}{2}$;

or $\begin{cases} -1, & 0 \leq x < \pi, \quad x \neq \dfrac{\pi}{2} \\ 1, & \pi < x \leq 2\pi, \quad x \neq \dfrac{3\pi}{2} \end{cases}$

30. $2\left(\dfrac{1 + \sin\theta}{1 - \cos\theta}\right)\left(\dfrac{\cos\theta - \sin\theta - 1}{(1 - \cos\theta)^2}\right)$

31. For all $x \neq 0$

32. For all real x

33. For all $x < 1$

34. For all $x \neq \dfrac{7}{2}$

35. $-\dfrac{y+2}{x+3}$

36. $-\dfrac{1}{3}(xy)^{-1/5}$

37. $-\dfrac{y}{x}$ or $-\dfrac{1}{x^2}$

38. $\dfrac{1}{2y(x + 1)^2}$

39. $-\dfrac{2x}{y^5}$

40. $-\dfrac{1 + 2xy^2}{x^4y^3}$

41. $-2\dfrac{(3y^2 + 1)^2\cos x + 12y\sin^2 x}{(3y^2 + 1)^3}$

42. $\dfrac{2}{3}x^{-4/3}y^{1/3} + \dfrac{2}{3}x^{-5/3}y^{2/3} = \dfrac{8}{3}x^{-5/3}y^{1/3}$

43. $y' = 2x^3 - 3x - 1$,

$y'' = 6x^2 - 3$,

$y''' = 12x$,

$y^{(4)} = 12$, and the rest are all zero.

44. $y' = \dfrac{x^4}{24}$,

$y'' = \dfrac{x^3}{6}$,

$y''' = \dfrac{x^2}{2}$,

$y^{(4)} = x$,

$y^{(5)} = 1$, and the rest are all zero.

45. (a) $y = \dfrac{2}{\sqrt{3}}x - \sqrt{3}$

(b) $y = -\dfrac{\sqrt{3}}{2}x + \dfrac{5\sqrt{3}}{2}$

46. (a) $y = -x + \dfrac{\pi}{2} + 2$

(b) $y = x - \dfrac{\pi}{2} + 2$

47. (a) $y = -\dfrac{1}{4}x + \dfrac{9}{4}$

(b) $y = 4x - 2$

48. (a) $y = -\dfrac{5}{4}x + 6$

(b) $y = \dfrac{4}{5}x - \dfrac{11}{5}$

49. $y = x - 2\sqrt{2}$

50. $y = \dfrac{4}{3}x + 4\sqrt{2}$

51. $y = \dfrac{10}{3}x - 5\sqrt{3}$

52. $y = (1 + \sqrt{2})x - \sqrt{2} - 1 - \dfrac{\pi}{4}$

or $y \approx 2.414x - 3.200$

53. (a)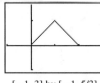

[−1, 3] by [−1, 5/3]

(b) Yes, because both of the one-sided limits as $x \to 1$ are equal to $f(1) = 1$.

(c) No, because the left-hand derivative at $x = 1$ is $+1$ and the right-hand derivative at $x = 1$ is -1.

54. (a) The function is continuous for all values of m, because the right-hand limit as $x \to 0$ is equal to $f(0) = 0$ for any value of m.

(b) The left-hand derivative at $x = 0$ is 2, and the right-hand derivative at $x = 0$ is m, so in order for the function to be differentiable at $x = 0$, m must be 2.

55. (a) For all $x \neq 0$ **(b)** At $x = 0$
    (c) Nowhere

56. (a) For all x **(b)** Nowhere
    (c) Nowhere

57. (a) $[-1, 0) \cup (0, 4]$ **(b)** At $x = 0$
    (c) Nowhere in its domain

58. (a) $[-2, 0) \cup (0, 2]$ **(b)** Nowhere
    (c) Nowhere in its domain

59.

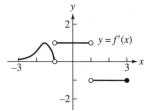

60.

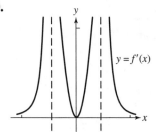

61. (a) iii   **(b)** i
    (c) ii

62.

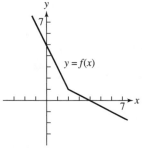

63.

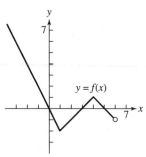

64. Answer is **D**: **i** and **iii** only could be true

65. (a)

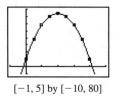

[−1, 5] by [−10, 80]

(b)

t interval	avg. vel.
[0, 0.5]	56
[0.5, 1]	40
[1, 1.5]	24
[1.5, 2]	8
[2, 2.5]	−8
[2.5, 3]	−24
[3, 3.5]	−40
[3.5, 4]	−56

(c)

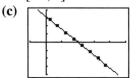

[−1, 5] by [−80, 80]

(d) Average velocity is a good approximation to velocity.

66. (a) $-\dfrac{13}{10}$ **(b)** $-\dfrac{1}{3}$

    (c) $\dfrac{1}{10}$ **(d)** -1

    (e) $-\dfrac{2}{3}$ **(f)** -12

67. (a) 5   **(b)** 0
    (c) 8   **(d)** 2
    (e) 6   **(f)** −1

68. $\sqrt{3}$

69. $-\dfrac{1}{6}$

70. (a) One possible answer:

$$x(t) = 10 \cos\left(t + \frac{\pi}{4}\right)$$

$$y(t) = 1$$

(b) $5\sqrt{2}$

(c) $s = -10$ and $s = 10$

(d) At $t = \dfrac{\pi}{4}$:

Velocity $= -10$

Speed $= 10$

Acceleration $= 0$

71. (a) $\dfrac{ds}{dt} = 64 - 32t$

$\dfrac{d^2s}{dt^2} = -32$

(b) 2 sec

(c) 64 ft/sec

(d) $\dfrac{64}{5.2} \approx 12.3$ sec;

$5\left(\dfrac{64}{5.2}\right) \approx 393.8$ ft

72. (a) $\dfrac{4}{7}$ sec; 280 cm/sec

(b) 560 cm/sec; 980 cm/sec^2

73. $\pi(20x - x^2)$

74. (a) $r(x) = \left(3 - \dfrac{x}{40}\right)^2 x = 9x - \dfrac{3}{20}x^2 + \dfrac{1}{1600}x^3$

(b) 40 people; $4.00

(c) One possible answer:
Probably not, since the company charges less overall for 60 passengers than it does for 40 passengers.

75. (a) -0.6 km/sec

(b) $\dfrac{18}{\pi} \approx 5.73$ revolutions/min

76. Yes

77. $y'(r) = -\dfrac{1}{2r^2l}\sqrt{\dfrac{T}{\pi d}}$, so increasing r decreases the frequency.

$y'(l) = -\dfrac{1}{2rl^2}\sqrt{\dfrac{T}{\pi d}}$, so increasing l decreases the frequency.

$y'(d) = -\dfrac{1}{4rl}\sqrt{\dfrac{T}{\pi d^3}}$, so increasing d decreases the frequency.

$y'(T) = \dfrac{1}{4rl\sqrt{\pi Td}}$, so increasing T increases the frequency.

78. (a) $P(0) \approx 1.339$, so initially, one student was infected

(b) 200

(c) After 5 days, when the rate is 50 students/day

79. (a) $x \neq k\dfrac{\pi}{4}$, where k is an odd integer

79. continued

(b) $\left(-\dfrac{\pi}{2}, \dfrac{\pi}{2}\right)$

(c) Where it's not defined, at $x = k\dfrac{\pi}{4}$, k an odd integer

(d) It has period $\dfrac{\pi}{2}$ and continues to repeat the pattern seen in this window.

80. $-\dfrac{1}{3\sqrt{3}}$

Chapter 4
Applications of Derivatives

4.1 Extreme Values of Functions (pp. 177–185)

Quick Review 4.1

1. $\dfrac{-1}{2\sqrt{4-x}}$

2. $\dfrac{3}{4}x^{-1/4}$

3. $\dfrac{2x}{(9-x^2)^{3/2}}$

4. $\dfrac{-2x}{3(x^2-1)^{4/3}}$

5. $\dfrac{2x}{x^2+1}$

6. $-\dfrac{\sin(\ln x)}{x}$

7. $2e^{2x}$

8. 1

9. ∞

10. ∞

11. (a) 1

(b) 1

(c) Undefined

12. (a) $x \neq 2$

(b) $f'(x) = \begin{cases} 3x^2 - 2, & x < 2 \\ 1, & x > 2 \end{cases}$

Section 4.1 Exercises

1. Maximum at $x = b$, minimum at $x = c_2$;
Extreme Value Theorem applies, so both the max and min exist.

2. Maximum at $x = c$, minimum at $x = b$;
Extreme Value Theorem applies, so both the max and min exist.

3. Maximum at $x = c$, no minimum;
Extreme Value Theorem doesn't apply, since the function isn't defined on a closed interval.

4. No maximum, no minimum;
Extreme Value Theorem doesn't apply, since the function isn't continuous or defined on a closed interval.

5. Maximum at $x = c$, minimum at $x = a$;
Extreme Value Theorem doesn't apply, since the function isn't continuous.

6. Maximum at $x = a$, minimum at $x = c$;
Extreme Value Theorem doesn't apply, since the function isn't continuous.

7. Local minimum at $(-1, 0)$, local maximum at $(1, 0)$

8. Minima at $(-2, 0)$ and $(2, 0)$, maximum at $(0, 2)$

9. Maximum at $(0, 5)$

10. Local maximum at $(-3, 0)$, local minimum at $(2, 0)$, maximum at $(1, 2)$, minimum at $(0, -1)$

11. Maximum value is $\frac{1}{4} + \ln 4$ at $x = 4$;

minimum value is 1 at $x = 1$;

local maximum at $\left(\frac{1}{2}, 2 - \ln 2\right)$

12. Maximum value is e at $x = -1$;

minimum value is $\frac{1}{e}$ at $x = 1$.

13. Maximum value is $\ln 4$ at $x = 3$;
minimum value is 0 at $x = 0$.

14. Maximum value is 1 at $x = 0$

15. Maximum value is 1 at $x = \frac{\pi}{4}$;

minimum value is -1 at $x = \frac{5\pi}{4}$;

local minimum at $\left(0, \frac{1}{\sqrt{2}}\right)$;

local maximum at $\left(\frac{7\pi}{4}, 0\right)$

16. Local minimum at $(0, 1)$;
local maximum at $(\pi, -1)$

17. Maximum value is $3^{2/5}$ at $x = -3$;
minimum value is 0 at $x = 0$

18. Maximum value is $3^{3/5}$ at $x = 3$

19. Minimum value is 1 at $x = 2$.

20. Local maximum at

$$\left(-\sqrt{\frac{2}{3}}, 4 + \frac{4\sqrt{6}}{9}\right) \approx (-0.816, 5.089);$$

Local minimum at

$$\left(\sqrt{\frac{2}{3}}, 4 - \frac{4\sqrt{6}}{9}\right) \approx (0.816, 2.911)$$

21. Local maximum at $(-2, 17)$;

local minimum at $\left(\frac{4}{3}, -\frac{41}{27}\right)$

22. There are none.

23. Minimum value is 0 at $x = -1$ and $x = 1$.

24. Local maximum at $(0, -1)$

25. Minimum value is 1 at $x = 0$.

26. Local minimum at $(0, 1)$

27. Maximum value is 2 at $x = 1$;
minimum value is 0 at $x = -1$ and $x = 3$.

28. Minimum value is $-\frac{115}{2}$ at $x = -3$;

local maximum at $(0, 10)$;

local minimum at $\left(1, \frac{13}{2}\right)$

29. Maximum value is $\frac{1}{2}$ at $x = 1$;

minimum value is $-\frac{1}{2}$ at $x = -1$.

30. Maximum value is $\frac{1}{2}$ at $x = 0$;

minimum value is $-\frac{1}{2}$ at $x = -2$.

31. Maximum value is 11 at $x = 5$;
minimum value is 5 on the interval $[-3, 2]$;
local maximum at $(-5, 9)$

32. Maximum value is 4 on the interval $[5, 7]$;
minimum value is -4 on the interval $[-2, 1]$.

33. Maximum value is 5 on the interval $[3, \infty)$;
minimum value is -5 on the interval $(-\infty, -2]$.

34. Minimum value is 4 on the interval $[-1, 3]$.

35. (a) No

(b) The derivative is defined and nonzero for $x \neq 2$. Also, $f(2) = 0$, and $f(x) > 0$ for all $x \neq 2$.

(c) No, because $(-\infty, \infty)$ is not a closed interval.

(d) The answers are the same as (a) and (b) with 2 replaced by a.

36. (a) No   **(b)** No

(c) No

(d) Minimum value is 0 at $x = -3$, $x = 0$, and $x = 3$;
local maxima at $(-\sqrt{3}, 6\sqrt{3})$ and $(\sqrt{3}, 6\sqrt{3})$

37.

crit. pt.	derivative	extremum	value
$x = -\dfrac{4}{5}$	0	local max	$\dfrac{12}{25}10^{1/3} \approx 1.034$
$x = 0$	undefined	local min	0

38.

crit. pt.	derivative	extremum	value
$x = -1$	0	minimum	-3
$x = 0$	undefined	local max	0
$x = 1$	0	minimum	-3

39.

crit. pt.	derivative	extremum	value
$x = -2$	undefined	local max	0
$x = -\sqrt{2}$	0	minimum	-2
$x = \sqrt{2}$	0	maximum	2
$x = 2$	undefined	local min	0

40.

crit. pt.	derivative	extremum	value
$x = 0$	0	minimum	0
$x = \dfrac{12}{5}$	0	local max	$\dfrac{144}{125}15^{1/2} \approx 4.462$
$x = 3$	undefined	minimum	0

41.

crit. pt.	derivative	extremum	value
$x = 1$	undefined	minimum	2

42.

crit. pt.	derivative	extremum	value
$x = 0$	undefined	local min	3
$x = 1$	0	local max	4

43.

crit. pt.	derivative	extremum	value
$x = -1$	0	maximum	5
$x = 1$	undefined	local min	1
$x = 3$	0	maximum	5

44.

crit. pt.	derivative	extremum	value
$x = -1$	0	local max	4
$x \approx 3.155$	0	local max	≈ -3.079

45. (c)   **46.** (b)
47. (d)   **48.** (a)
49. (a) Maximum value is 144 at $x = 2$.
    (b) The largest volume of the box is 144 cubic units and it occurs when $x = 2$.
50. (a) Minimum value is 40 at $x = 10$.
    (b) The smallest perimeter of the rectangle is 40 units and it occurs when $x = 10$, which makes it a 10 by 10 square.
51. (a) $f'(x) = 3ax^2 + 2bx + c$ is a quadratic, so it can have 0, 1, or 2 zeros, which would be the critical points of f. Examples:

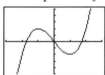

[−3, 3] by [−5, 5]
The function $f(x) = x^3 - 3x$ has two critical points at $x = -1$ and $x = 1$.

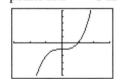

[−3, 3] by [−5, 5]
The function $f(x) = x^3 - 1$ has one critical point at $x = 0$.

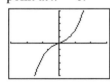

[−3, 3] by [−5, 5]
The function $f(x) = x^3 + x$ has no critical points.
    (b) Two or none
52. (a) By definition of local maximum, there is an open interval containing c where $f(x) \leq f(c)$, so $f(x) - f(c) \leq 0$.
    (b) Because $x \to c^+$, $(x - c) > 0$, and the sign of the quotient must be negative (or zero). This means the limit is nonpositive.

52. continued
    (c) Because as $x \to c^-$, $(x - c) < 0$, and the sign of the quotient must be positive (or zero). This means the limit is nonnegative.
    (d) Assuming that $f'(c)$ exists, the one-sided limits in (b) and (c) above must exist and be equal. Since one is nonpositive and one is nonnegative, the only possible common value is 0.
    (e) There will be an open interval containing c where $f(x) - f(c) \geq 0$.
The difference quotient for the left-hand derivative will have to be negative (or zero), and the difference quotient for the right-hand derivative will have to be positive (or zero). Taking the limit, the left-hand derivative will be nonpositive, and the right-hand derivative will be nonnegative. Therefore, the only possible value for $f'(c)$ is 0.

53. (a)

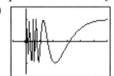

[−0.1, 0.6] by [−1.5, 1.5]
$f(0) = 0$ is not a local extreme value because in any open interval containing $x = 0$, there are infinitely many points where $f(x) = 1$ and where $f(x) = -1$.
    (b) One possible answer, on the interval [0, 1]:

$$f(x) = \begin{cases} (1 - x)\cos\dfrac{1}{1 - x}, & 0 \leq x < 1 \\ 0, & x = 1 \end{cases}$$

This function has no local extreme value at $x = 1$. Note that it is continuous on [0, 1].

4.2 Mean Value Theorem (pp. 186–194)

Quick Review 4.2

1. $(-\sqrt{3}, \sqrt{3})$
2. $(-\infty, -\sqrt{2}) \cup (\sqrt{2}, \infty)$
3. $[-2, 2]$
4. For all x in its domain, or, $[-2, 2]$
5. On $(-2, 2)$ **6.** $x \neq \pm 1$
7. For all x in its domain, or, for all $x \neq \pm 1$
8. For all x in its domain, or, for all $x \neq \pm 1$
9. $C = 3$ **10.** $C = -4$

Section 4.2 Exercises

1. (a) Local maximum at $\left(\dfrac{5}{2}, \dfrac{25}{4}\right)$
    (b) On $\left(-\infty, \dfrac{5}{2}\right]$ (c) On $\left[\dfrac{5}{2}, \infty\right)$

2. (a) Local minimum at $\left(\frac{1}{2}, -\frac{49}{4}\right)$

   (b) On $\left[\frac{1}{2}, \infty\right)$ **(c)** On $\left(-\infty, \frac{1}{2}\right)$

3. (a) None   **(b)** None
   (c) On $(-\infty, 0)$ and $(0, \infty)$

4. (a) None   **(b)** On $(-\infty, 0)$
   (c) On $(0, \infty)$

5. (a) None   **(b)** On $(-\infty, \infty)$
   (c) None

6. (a) None   **(b)** None
   (c) On $(-\infty, \infty)$

7. (a) Local maximum at $(-2, 4)$
   (b) None   **(c)** On $[-2, \infty)$

8. (a) Local maximum at $(0, 9)$;
   local minima at $(-\sqrt{5}, -16)$
   and $(\sqrt{5}, -16)$
   (b) On $[-\sqrt{5}, 0]$ and $[\sqrt{5}, \infty)$
   (c) On $(-\infty, -\sqrt{5}]$ and $[0, \sqrt{5}]$

9. (a) Local maximum at
   $\approx (2.67, 3.08)$;
   local minimum at $(4, 0)$
   (b) On $\left(-\infty, \frac{8}{3}\right]$ **(c)** On $\left[\frac{8}{3}, 4\right]$

10. (a) Local minimum at $\approx (-2, -7.56)$
   (b) On $[-2, \infty)$ **(c)** On $(-\infty, -2]$

11. (a) Local maximum at $\left(-2, \frac{1}{4}\right)$;
   local minimum at $\left(2, -\frac{1}{4}\right)$
   (b) On $(-\infty, -2]$ and $[2, \infty)$
   (c) On $[-2, 2]$

12. (a) None   **(b)** None
   (c) On $(-\infty, -2)$, $(-2, 2)$, and $(2, \infty)$

13. (a) Local maximum at $\approx (-1.126, -0.036)$;
   local minimum at $\approx (0.559, -2.639)$
   (b) On $(-\infty, -1.126]$ and $[0.559, \infty)$
   (c) On $[-1.126, 0.559]$

14. (a) None   **(b)** On $(-\infty, \infty)$
   (c) None

15. (a) f is continuous on $[0, 1]$ and differentiable on $(0, 1)$.
   (b) $c = \frac{1}{2}$

16. (a) f is continuous on $[0, 1]$ and differentiable on $(0, 1)$.
   (b) $c = \frac{8}{27}$

17. (a) f is continuous on $[-1, 1]$ and differentiable on $[-1, 1]$.
   (b) $c \approx \pm 0.771$

18. (a) f is continuous on $[2, 4]$ and differentiable on $(2, 4)$.
   (b) $c \approx 2.820$

19. (a) $y = \frac{5}{2}$ **(b)** $y = 2$

20. (a) $y = \frac{1}{\sqrt{2}}x - \frac{1}{\sqrt{2}}$, or $y \approx 0.707x - 0.707$
   (b) $y = \frac{1}{\sqrt{2}}x - \frac{1}{2\sqrt{2}}$, or $y \approx 0.707x - 0.354$

21. (a) Not differentiable at $x = 0$
   (b)
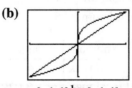
   $[-1, 1]$ by $[-1, 1]$
   (c) $c = \pm 3^{-3/2} \approx \pm 0.192$

22. (a) Not differentiable at $x = 1$
   (b)
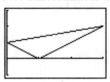
   $[0, 3]$ by $[-1, 3]$
   (c) There are none.

23. (a) Not differentiable at $x = 0$
   (b)
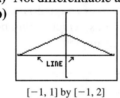
   $[-1, 1]$ by $[-1, 2]$
   (c) There are none

24. (a) Not differentiable at $x = 0$
   (b)
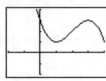
   $[-\pi, \pi]$ by $[-1, 2]$
   (c) $c \approx -2.818, -0.324, 1.247$

25. $\frac{x^2}{2} + C$ **26.** $2x + C$

27. $x^3 - x^2 + x + C$ **28.** $-\cos x + C$

29. $e^x + C$ **30.** $\ln (x - 1) + C$

31. $\frac{1}{x} + \frac{1}{2}, x > 0$ **32.** $x^{1/4} - 3$

33. $\ln (x + 2) + 3$ **34.** $x^2 + x - \sin x + 3$

35. Possible answers:
   (a)
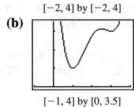
   $[-2, 4]$ by $[-2, 4]$
   (b)
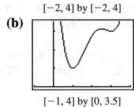
   $[-1, 4]$ by $[0, 3.5]$

35. continued

(c)

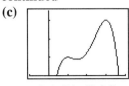

[−1, 4] by [0, 3.5]

36. Possible answers:

(a)

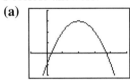

[−1, 5] by [−2, 4]

(b)

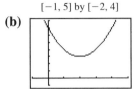

[−1, 5] by [−1, 8]

(c)

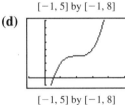

[−1, 5] by [−1, 8]

(d)

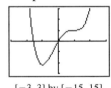

[−1, 5] by [−1, 8]

37. One possible answer:

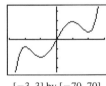

[−3, 3] by [−15, 15]

38. One possible answer:

[−3, 3] by [−70, 70]

39. Because the trucker's average speed was 79.5 mph, and by the Mean Value Theorem, the trucker must have been going that speed at least once during the trip.

40. Let $f(t)$ denote the temperature indicated after t seconds. We assume that $f'(t)$ is defined and continuous for $0 \le t \le 20$. The average rate of change is 10.6°F/sec. Therefore, by the Mean Value Theorem, $f'(c) = 10.6$°F/sec for some value of c in [0, 20]. Since the temperature was constant before $t = 0$, we also know that $f'(0) = 0$°F/min. But f' is continuous, so by the Intermediate Value Theorem, the rate of change $f'(t)$ must have been 10.1°F/sec at some moment during the interval.

41. Because its average speed was approximately 7.667 knots, and by the Mean Value Theorem, it must have been going that speed at least once during the trip.

42. The runner's average speed for the marathon was approximately 11.909 mph. Therefore, by the Mean Value Theorem, the runner must have been going that speed at least once during the marathon. Since the initial speed and final speed are both 0 mph and the runner's speed is continuous, by the Intermediate Value Theorem, the runner's speed must have been 11 mph at least twice.

43. (a) 48 m/sec   **(b)** 720 meters
   (c) After about 27.604 seconds, and it will be going about 48.166 m/sec

44. (a) 14 m/sec

   (b) $10\sqrt{2}$ m/sec, or, about 14.142 m/sec

45. Because the function is not continuous on [0, 1].

46. Because the Mean Value Theorem applies to the function $y = \sin x$ on any interval, and $y = \cos x$ is the derivative of $\sin x$. So, between any two zeros of $\sin x$, its derivative, $\cos x$, must be zero at least once.

47. $f(x)$ must be zero at least once between a and b by the Intermediate Value Theorem.
   Now suppose that $f(x)$ is zero twice between a and b. Then by the Mean Value Theorem, $f'(x)$ would have to be zero at least once between the two zeros of $f(x)$, but this can't be true since we are given that $f'(x) \ne 0$ on this interval.
   Therefore, $f(x)$ is zero once and only once between a and b.

48. Let $f(x) = x^4 + 3x + 1$. Then $f(x)$ is continuous and differentiable everywhere. $f'(x) = 4x^3 + 3$, which is never zero between $x = -2$ and $x = -1$. Since $f(-2) = 11$ and $f(-1) = -1$, exercise 47 applies, and $f(x)$ has exactly one zero between $x = -2$ and $x = -1$.

49. Let $f(x) = x + \ln(x + 1)$. Then $f(x)$ is continuous and differentiable everywhere on $[0, 3]$.

$f'(x) = 1 + \dfrac{1}{x + 1}$, which is never zero on $[0, 3]$.

Now $f(0) = 0$, so $x = 0$ is one solution of the equation. If there were a second solution, $f(x)$ would be zero twice in $[0, 3]$, and by the Mean Value Theorem, $f'(x)$ would have to be zero somewhere between the two zeros of $f(x)$. But this can't happen, since $f'(x)$ is never zero on $[0, 3]$. Therefore, $f(x) = 0$ has exactly one solution in the interval $[0, 3]$.

50. Consider the function $k(x) = f(x) - g(x)$. $k(x)$ is continuous and differentiable on $[a, b]$, and since $k(a) = f(a) - g(a) = 0$ and $k(b) = f(b) - g(b) = 0$, by the Mean Value Theorem, there must be a point c in (a, b) where $k'(c) = 0$. But since $k'(c) = f'(c) - g'(c)$, this means that $f'(c) = g'(c)$, and c is a point where the graphs of f and g have parallel or identical tangent lines.

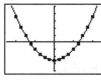

51. (a) Increasing: $[-2, -1.3]$ and $[1.3, 2]$;
   decreasing: $[-1.3, 1.3]$;
   local max: $x \approx -1.3$
   local min: $x \approx 1.3$
(b) Regression equation: $y = 3x^2 - 5$

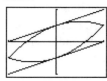

   $[-2.5, 2.5]$ by $[-8, 10]$
(c) $f(x) = x^3 - 5x$
52. (a) Toward: $0 < t < 2$ and $5 < t < 8$;
   away: $2 < t < 5$
(b) A local extremum in this problem is a time/place where Priya changes the direction of her motion.
(c) Regression equation:
   $y = -0.0820x^3 + 0.9163x^2 - 2.5126x$
       $+ 3.3779$

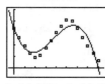

   $[-0.5, 8.5]$ by $[-0.5, 5]$
(d) $f'(t) = -0.2459t^2 + 1.8324t - 2.5126$
   toward: $0 < t < 1.81$ and $5.64 < t < 8$;
   away: $1.81 < t < 5.64$

53. $\dfrac{f(b) - f(a)}{b - a} = \dfrac{\dfrac{1}{b} - \dfrac{1}{a}}{b - a} = -\dfrac{1}{ab}$

$f'(c) = -\dfrac{1}{c^2}$, so $-\dfrac{1}{c^2} = -\dfrac{1}{ab}$ and $c^2 = ab$.

Thus, $c = \sqrt{ab}$.

54. $\dfrac{f(b) - f(a)}{b - a} = \dfrac{b^2 - a^2}{b - a} = b + a$

$f'(c) = 2c$, so $2c = b + a$ and $c = \dfrac{a + b}{2}$.

55. By the Mean Value Theorem,
$\sin b - \sin a = (\cos c)(b - a)$ for some c between a and b. Taking the absolute value of both sides and using $|\cos c| \le 1$ gives the result.

56. Apply the Mean Value Theorem to f on $[a, b]$.
Since $f(b) < f(a)$, $\dfrac{f(b) - f(a)}{b - a}$ is negative, and
hence $f'(x)$ must be negative at some point
between a and b.

57. Let $f(x)$ be a monotonic function defined on an interval D. For any two values in D, we may let x_1 be the smaller value and let x_2 be the larger value, so $x_1 < x_2$. Then either $f(x_1) < f(x_2)$ (if f is increasing), or $f(x_1) > f(x_2)$ (if f is decreasing), which means $f(x_1) \ne f(x_2)$. Therefore, f is one-to-one.

4.3 Connecting f' and f'' with the Graph of f
(pp. 194–206)

Quick Review 4.3

1. $(-3, 3)$ **2.** $(-2, 0) \cup (2, \infty)$
3. f: all reals **4.** f: all reals
   f': all reals f': $x \ne 0$
5. f: $x \ne 2$ **6.** f: all reals
   f': $x \ne 2$ f': $x \ne 0$
7. $y = 0$ **8.** $y = 0$
9. $y = 0$ and $y = 200$ **10.** $y = 0$ and $y = 375$

Section 4.3 Exercises

1. (a) Zero: $x = \pm 1$;
   positive: $(-\infty, -1)$ and $(1, \infty)$;
   negative: $(-1, 1)$
(b) Zero: $x = 0$;
   positive: $(0, \infty)$;
   negative: $(-\infty, 0)$
2. (a) Zero: $x \approx 0, \pm 1.25$;
   positive: $(-1.25, 0)$ and $(1.25, \infty)$;
   negative: $(-\infty, -1.25)$ and $(0, 1.25)$
(b) Zero: $x \approx \pm 0.7$;
   positive: $(-\infty, -0.7)$ and $(0.7, \infty)$;
   negative: $(-0.7, 0.7)$

3. (a) $(-\infty, -2]$ and $[0, 2]$
  (b) $[-2, 0]$ and $[2, \infty)$
  (c) Local maxima: $x = -2$ and $x = 2$;
     local minimum: $x = 0$
4. (a) $[-2, 2]$ **(b)** $(-\infty, -2]$ and $[2, \infty)$
  (c) Local maximum: $x = 2$;
     local minimum: $x = -2$
5. (a) $[0, 1]$, $[3, 4]$, and $[5.5, 6]$
  (b) $[1, 3]$ and $[4, 5.5]$
  (c) Local maxima: $x = 1$, $x = 4$
     (if f is continuous at $x = 4$), and $x = 6$;
     local minima: $x = 0$, $x = 3$, and $x = 5.5$
6. If f is continuous on the interval $[0, 3]$:
  (a) $[0, 3]$ **(b)** Nowhere
  (c) Local maximum: $x = 3$;
     local minimum: $x = 0$
7. (a) $\left[\dfrac{1}{2}, \infty\right)$ **(b)** $\left(-\infty, \dfrac{1}{2}\right]$
  (c) $(-\infty, \infty)$ **(d)** Nowhere
  (e) Local minimum at $\left(\dfrac{1}{2}, -\dfrac{5}{4}\right)$
  (f) None
8. (a) $[0, 2]$ **(b)** $(-\infty, 0]$ and $[2, \infty)$
  (c) $(-\infty, 1)$ **(d)** $(1, \infty)$
  (e) Local maximum: $(2, 5)$;
     local minimum: $(0, -3)$
  (f) At $(1, 1)$
9. (a) $[-1, 0]$ and $[1, \infty)$
  (b) $(-\infty, -1]$ and $[0, 1]$
  (c) $\left(-\infty, -\dfrac{1}{\sqrt{3}}\right)$ and $\left(\dfrac{1}{\sqrt{3}}, \infty\right)$
  (d) $\left(-\dfrac{1}{\sqrt{3}}, \dfrac{1}{\sqrt{3}}\right)$
  (e) Local maximum: $(0, 1)$;
     local minima: $(-1, -1)$ and $(1, -1)$
  (f) $\left(\pm\dfrac{1}{\sqrt{3}}, -\dfrac{1}{9}\right)$
10. (a) $(-\infty, 0)$ and $[1, \infty)$
  (b) $(0, 1]$ **(c)** $(0, \infty)$
  (d) $(-\infty, 0)$ **(e)** Local minimum: $(1, e)$
  (f) None
11. (a) $[-2, 2]$
  (b) $[-\sqrt{8}, -2]$ and $[2, \sqrt{8}]$
  (c) $(-\sqrt{8}, 0)$ **(d)** $(0, \sqrt{8})$
  (e) Local maxima: $(-\sqrt{8}, 0)$ and $(2, 4)$;
     local minima: $(-2, -4)$ and $(\sqrt{8}, 0)$
  (f) $(0, 0)$
12. (a) $(-\infty, 0)$ and $[0, \infty)$ **(b)** None
  (c) $(0, \infty)$ **(d)** $(-\infty, 0)$
  (e) Local minimum: $(0, 1)$
  (f) None
13. (a) $(-\infty, -2]$ and $\left[-\dfrac{3}{2}, \infty\right)$
  (b) $\left[-2, -\dfrac{3}{2}\right]$ **(c)** $\left(-\dfrac{7}{4}, \infty\right)$

13. continued
  (d) $\left(-\infty, -\dfrac{7}{4}\right)$
  (e) Local maximum: $(-2, -40)$;
     local minimum: $\left(-\dfrac{3}{2}, -\dfrac{161}{4}\right)$
  (f) $\left(-\dfrac{7}{4}, -\dfrac{321}{8}\right)$
14. (a) $(-\infty, -0.53]$ and $[0.65, 2.88]$
  (b) $[-0.53, 0.65]$ and $[2.88, \infty)$
  (c) $(0, 2)$ **(d)** $(-\infty, 0)$ and $(2, \infty)$
  (e) Local maxima: $(-0.53, 2.45)$ and
     $(2.88, 16.23)$;
     local minimum: $(0.65, -0.68)$
  (f) $(0, 1)$ and $(2, 9)$
15. (a) $(-\infty, \infty)$ **(b)** None
  (c) $(-\infty, 0)$ **(d)** $(0, \infty)$
  (e) None   **(f)** $(0, 3)$
16. (a) None   **(b)** $(-\infty, \infty)$
  (c) $(0, \infty)$ **(d)** $(-\infty, 0)$
  (e) None   **(f)** $(0, 5)$
17. (a) $(-\infty, \infty)$ **(b)** None
  (c) $(-\infty, 5 \ln 3) \approx (-\infty, 5.49)$
  (d) $(5 \ln 3, \infty) \approx (5.49, \infty)$
  (e) None
  (f) $\left(5 \ln 3, \dfrac{5}{2}\right) \approx (5.49, 2.50)$
18. (a) $(-\infty, \infty)$ **(b)** None
  (c) $\left(-\infty, 2 \ln \dfrac{5}{2}\right) \approx (-\infty, 1.83)$
  (d) $\left(2 \ln \dfrac{5}{2}, \infty\right) \approx (1.83, \infty)$
  (e) None
  (f) $\left(2 \ln \dfrac{5}{2}, 2\right) \approx (1.83, 2)$
19. (a) $(-\infty, 1)$ **(b)** $[1, \infty)$
  (c) None   **(d)** $(1, \infty)$
  (e) None   **(f)** None
20. (a) $[0, 2\pi]$ **(b)** None
  (c) $(0, 2\pi)$ **(d)** None
  (e) Local maximum: $(2\pi, e^{2\pi})$
     local minimum: $(0, 1)$
  (f) None
21. (a) $(-\infty, -\sqrt{2}]$ and $[\sqrt{2}, \infty)$
  (b) $[-\sqrt{2}, 0)$ and $(0, \sqrt{2}]$
  (c) $(0, \infty)$ **(d)** $(-\infty, 0)$
  (e) Local maximum:
     $(-\sqrt{2}, -\sqrt{2e}) \approx (-1.41, -2.33)$;
     local minimum: $(\sqrt{2}, \sqrt{2e}) \approx (1.41, 2.33)$
  (f) None
22. (a) $[-3, -\sqrt{6}]$ and $[0, \sqrt{6}]$ or, $\approx [-3, -2.45]$
     and $[0, 2.45]$
  (b) $[-\sqrt{6}, 0]$ and $[\sqrt{6}, 3]$ or, $\approx [-2.45, 0]$ and
     $[2.45, 3]$
  (c) Approximately $(-1.56, 1.56)$
  (d) Approximately $(-3, -1.56)$ and $(1.56, 3)$

22. continued

   (e) Local maxima: $(\pm\sqrt{6}, 6\sqrt{3})$

       $\approx (\pm2.45, 10.39)$;

       local minima: $(0, 0)$ and $(\pm3, 0)$

   (f) $\approx(\pm1.56, 6.25)$

23. (a) $(-\infty, \infty)$ **(b)** None

   (c) $(-\infty, 0)$ **(d)** $(0, \infty)$

   (e) None   **(f)** $(0, 0)$

24. (a) $\left[0, \dfrac{15}{7}\right]$ **(b)** $\left[\dfrac{15}{7}, \infty\right)$

   (c) None   **(d)** $(0, \infty)$

   (e) Local maximum:

     $\left(\dfrac{15}{7}, \left(\dfrac{15}{7}\right)^{3/4} \cdot \dfrac{20}{7}\right) \approx \left(\dfrac{15}{7}, 5.06\right)$;

     local minimum: $(0, 0)$

   (f) None

25. (a) $[1, \infty)$ **(b)** $(-\infty, 1]$

   (c) $(-\infty, -2)$ and $(0, \infty)$

   (d) $(-2, 0)$

   (e) Local minimum: $(1, -3)$

   (f) $\approx (-2, 7.56)$ and $(0, 0)$

26. (a) $[0, \infty)$ **(b)** None

   (c) $\left(\dfrac{9}{5}, \infty\right)$ **(d)** $\left(0, \dfrac{9}{5}\right)$

   (e) Local minimum: $(0, 0)$

   (f) $\approx \left(\dfrac{9}{5}, 5.56\right)$

27. (a) Approximately $[0.15, 1.40]$ and $[2.45, \infty)$

   (b) Approximately $(-\infty, 0.15]$, $[1.40, 2)$,

     and $(2, 2.45]$

   (c) $(-\infty, 1)$ and $(2, \infty)$ **(d)** $(1, 2)$

   (e) Local maximum: $\approx(1.40, 1.29)$;

     local minima: $\approx(0.15, 0.48)$ and $(2.45, 9.22)$

   (f) $(1, 1)$

28. (a) $[-1, 1]$

   (b) $(-\infty, -1]$ and $[1, \infty)$

   (c) $(-\sqrt{3}, 0)$ and $(\sqrt{3}, \infty)$

   (d) $(-\infty, -\sqrt{3})$ and $(0, \sqrt{3})$

   (e) Local maximum: $\left(1, \dfrac{1}{2}\right)$;

     local minimum: $\left(-1, -\dfrac{1}{2}\right)$

   (f) $(0, 0)$, $\left(\sqrt{3}, \dfrac{\sqrt{3}}{4}\right)$, and $\left(-\sqrt{3}, -\dfrac{\sqrt{3}}{4}\right)$

29. (a) None   **(b)** At $x = 2$

   (c) At $x = 1$ and $x = \dfrac{5}{3}$

30. (a) At $x = 2$ **(b)** At $x = 4$

   (c) At $x = 1$, $x \approx 1.63$, $x \approx 3.37$

31.

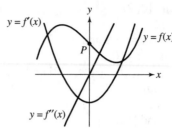

32.

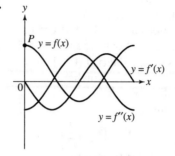

33. (a) Absolute maximum at $(1, 2)$;

     absolute minimum at $(3, -2)$

   (b) None

   (c) One possible answer:

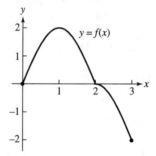

34. (a) Absolute maximum at $(0, 2)$;

     absolute minimum at $(2, -1)$ and $(-2, -1)$

   (b) At $(1, 0)$ and $(-1, 0)$

   (c) One possible answer:

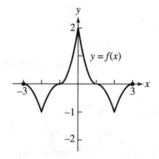

   (d) $f(3) = f(-3)$, and $-1 < f(3) \leq 0$.

35.

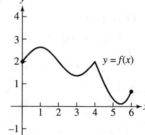

36.

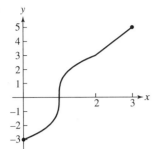

37. (a) $v(t) = 2t - 4$ **(b)** $a(t) = 2$
   (c) It begins at position 3 moving in a negative direction. It moves to position -1 when $t = 2$, and then changes direction, moving in a positive direction thereafter.

38. (a) $v(t) = -2 - 2t$ **(b)** $a(t) = -2$
   (c) It begins at position 6 and moves in the negative direction thereafter.

39. (a) $v(t) = 3t^2 - 3$ **(b)** $a(t) = 6t$
   (c) It begins at position 3 moving in a negative direction. It moves to position 1 when $t = 1$, and then changes direction, moving in a positive direction thereafter.

40. (a) $v(t) = 6t - 6t^2$ **(b)** $a(t) = 6 - 12t$
   (c) It begins at position 0. It starts moving in the positive direction until it reaches position 1 when $t = 1$, and then it changes direction. It moves in the negative direction thereafter.

41. (a) $t = 2.2, 6, 9.8$ **(b)** $t = 4, 8, 11$
42. (a) $t = -0.2, 4, 12$ **(b)** $t = 1.5, 5.2, 8, 11, 13$
43. No. f must have a horizontal tangent line at that point, but it could be increasing (or decreasing) on both sides of the point, and there would be no local extremum.
44. No. $f''(x)$ could still be positive (or negative) on both sides of $x = c$, in which case the concavity of the function wouldn't change at $x = c$.
45. One possible answer:

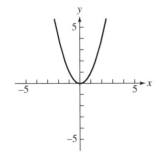

46. One possible answer:

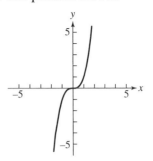

47. One possible answer:

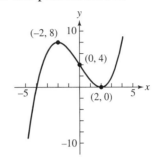

48. One possible answer:

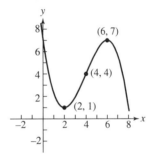

49. (a) Regression equation:
$$y = \frac{2161.4541}{1 + 28.1336e^{-0.8627x}}$$

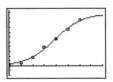

[0, 8] by [−400, 2300]
   (b) At approximately $x = 3.868$ (late in 1996), when the sales are about 1081 million dollars/year
   (c) 2161.45 million dollars/year

50. (a) In exercise 13, $a = 4$ and $b = 21$, so $-\dfrac{b}{3a} = -\dfrac{7}{4}$, which is the x-value where the point of inflection occurs. The local extrema are at $x = -2$ and $x = -\dfrac{3}{2}$, which are symmetric about $x = -\dfrac{7}{4}$.

50. continued

(b) In exercise 8, $a = -2$ and $b = 6$, so

$-\dfrac{b}{3a} = 1$, which is the x-value where the point of inflection occurs. The local extrema are at $x = 0$ and $x = 2$, which are symmetric about $x = 1$.

(c) $f'(x) = 3ax^2 + 2bx + c$ and
$f''(x) = 6ax + 2b$.
The point of inflection will occur where $f''(x) = 0$, which is at $x = -\dfrac{b}{3a}$.
If there are local extrema, they will occur at the zeros of $f'(x)$. Since $f'(x)$ is quadratic, its graph is a parabola and any zeros will be symmetric about the vertex which will also be where $f''(x) = 0$.

51. (a) $f'(x) = \dfrac{abce^{bx}}{(e^{bx} + a)^2}$, so the sign of $f'(x)$ is the same as the sign of the product abc.

(b) $f''(x) = -\dfrac{ab^2ce^{bx}(e^{bx} - a)}{(e^{bx} + a)^3}$. Since $a > 0$, this changes sign when $x = \dfrac{\ln a}{b}$ due to the $e^{bx} - a$ factor in the numerator, and there is a point of inflection at that location.

52. (a) Since $f''(x)$ is quadratic it must have 0, 1, or 2 zeros. If $f''(x)$ has 0 or 1 zeros, it will not change sign and the concavity of $f(x)$ will not change, so there is no point of inflection. If $f''(x)$ has 2 zeros, it will change sign twice, and $f(x)$ will have 2 points of inflection.

(b) $f(x)$ has two points of inflection if and only if $3b^2 > 8ac$.

4.4 Modeling and Optimization (pp. 206–220)

Quick Review 4.4

1. None

2. Local maximum: $(-2, 17)$;
local minimum: $(1, -10)$

3. $\dfrac{200\pi}{3}$ cm^3

4. $r \approx 4.01$ cm and $h \approx 19.82$ cm, or,
$r \approx 7.13$ cm and $h \approx 6.26$ cm

5. $-\sin \alpha$ **6.** $\cos \alpha$

7. $\sin \alpha$ **8.** $-\cos \alpha$

9. $x = 1$ and $y = \sqrt{3}$, or, $x = -1$ and $y = -\sqrt{3}$

10. $x = 0$ and $y = 3$, or, $x = -\dfrac{24}{13}$ and $y = \dfrac{15}{13}$

Section 4.4 Exercises

1. (a) As large as possible: 0 and 20;
as small as possible: 10 and 10

(b) As large as possible: $\dfrac{79}{4}$ and $\dfrac{1}{4}$;
as small as possible: 0 and 20

2. Largest area $= \dfrac{25}{4}$, dimensions are $\dfrac{5}{\sqrt{2}}$ cm by $\dfrac{5}{\sqrt{2}}$ cm

3. Smallest perimeter $= 16$ in., dimensions are 4 in. by 4 in.

4. $A(x) = x(4 - x)$, $0 < x < 4$. $A'(x) = 4 - 2x$, so there is an absolute maximum at $x = 2$. If $x = 2$, then the length of the second side is also 2, so the rectangle with the largest area is a square.

5. (a) $y = 1 - x$ (b) $A(x) = 2x(1 - x)$

(c) Largest area $= \dfrac{1}{2}$, dimensions are 1 by $\dfrac{1}{2}$

6. Largest area $= 32$, dimensions are 4 by 8

7. Largest volume is $\dfrac{2450}{27} \approx 90.74$ in^3;
dimensions: $\dfrac{5}{3}$ in. by $\dfrac{14}{3}$ in. by $\dfrac{35}{3}$ in.

8. Since $a^2 + b^2 = 400$, Area $= \dfrac{1}{2}a(400 - a^2)^{1/2}$.
$\dfrac{d}{da}$Area $= \dfrac{200 - a^2}{(400 - a^2)^{1/2}}$.
Thus the maximum area occurs when $a^2 = 200$, but then $b^2 = 200$ as well, so $a = b$.

9. Largest area $= 80{,}000$ m^2;
dimensions: 200 m (perpendicular to river) by 400 m (parallel to river)

10. Dimensions: 12 m (divider is this length) by 18 m; total length required: 72 m

11. (a) 10 ft by 10 ft by 5 ft

(b) Assume that the weight is minimized when the total area of the bottom and the 4 sides is minimized.

12. (a) $x = 15$ ft and $y = 5$ ft

(b) The material for the tank costs 5 dollars/sq ft and the excavation charge is 10 dollars for each square foot of the cross-sectional area of one wall of the hole.

13. 18 in. high by 9 in. wide

14. (a) 96 ft/sec

(b) 256 feet at $t = 3$ seconds

(c) -128 ft/sec

15. $\theta = \dfrac{\pi}{2}$

16. Radius $=$ height $= 10\pi^{-1/3}$ cm ≈ 6.83 cm
In Example 2, because of the top on the can, the "best" design is less big around and taller.

17. $\dfrac{8}{\pi}$ to 1

18. (a) $V(x) = 2x^3 - 25x^2 + 75x$

(b) Domain: $(0, 5)$

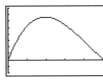

[0, 5] by [−20, 80]

(c) Maximum volume ≈ 66.02 in^3 when $x \approx 1.96$ in.

(d) $V'(x) = 6x^2 - 50x + 75$, so the critical point is at $x = \dfrac{25 - 5\sqrt{7}}{6}$, which confirms the result in (c).

19. (a) $V(x) = 2x(24 - 2x)(18 - 2x)$

(b) Domain: $(0, 9)$

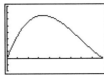

[0, 9] by [−400, 1600]

(c) Maximum volume ≈ 1309.95 in^3 when $x \approx 3.39$ in.

(d) $V'(x) = 24x^2 - 336x + 864$, so the critical point is at $x = 7 - \sqrt{13}$, which confirms the result in (c).

(e) $x = 2$ in. or $x = 5$ in.

(f) The dimensions of the resulting box are $2x$ in., $(24 - 2x)$ in., and $(18 - 2x)$ in. Each of these measurements must be positive, so that gives the domain of $(0, 9)$.

20. $\dfrac{4}{\sqrt{21}} \approx 0.87$ miles down the shoreline from the point nearest her boat.

21. Dimensions: width ≈ 3.44, height ≈ 2.61; maximum area ≈ 8.98

22. Dimensions: Radius $= 10\sqrt{\dfrac{2}{3}} \approx 8.16$ cm, height $= \dfrac{20}{\sqrt{3}} \approx 11.55$ cm; maximum volume $= \dfrac{4000\pi}{3\sqrt{3}} \approx 2418.40$ cm^3

23. (a) At $x = 1$

(b)

a	b	A
0.1	3.72	0.33
0.2	2.86	0.44
0.3	2.36	0.46
0.4	2.02	0.43
0.5	1.76	0.38
0.6	1.55	0.31
0.7	1.38	0.23
0.8	1.23	0.15
0.9	1.11	0.08
1.0	1.00	0.00

(c)

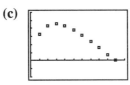

[0, 1.1] by [−0.2, 0.6]

(d) Quadratic:
$A \approx -0.91a^2 + 0.54a + 0.34$

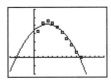

[−0.5, 1.5] by [−0.2, 0.6]

Cubic:
$A \approx 1.74a^3 - 3.78a^2 + 1.86a + 0.19$

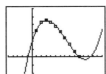

[−0.5, 1.5] by [−0.2, 0.6]

Quartic:
$A \approx -1.92a^4 + 5.96a^3 - 6.87a^2 + 2.71a + 0.12$

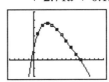

[−0.5, 1.5] by [−0.2, 0.6]

(e) Quadratic: $A \approx 0.42$; cubic: $A \approx 0.45$; quartic: $A \approx 0.46$

24. (a) $f'(x)$ is a quadratic polynomial, and as such it can have 0, 1, or 2 zeros. If it has 0 or 1 zeros, then its sign never changes, so $f(x)$ has no local extrema.
If $f'(x)$ has 2 zeros, then its sign changes twice, and $f(x)$ has 2 local extrema at those points.

24. continued

(b) Possible answers:
No local extrema: $y = x^3$;
2 local extrema: $y = x^3 - 3x$

25. 18 in. by 18 in. by 36 in.

26. (a) $x = 12$ cm and $y = 6$ cm
(b) $x = 12$ cm and $y = 6$ cm

27. Radius $= \sqrt{2}$ m, height $= 1$ m, volume $\dfrac{2\pi}{3}$ m³

28. (a) $a = 16$ (b) $a = -1$

29. $f'(x) = \dfrac{2x^3 - a}{x^2}$, so the only sign change in $f'(x)$ occurs at $x = \left(\dfrac{a}{2}\right)^{1/3}$, where the sign changes from negative to positive. This means there is a local minimum at that point, and there are no local maxima.

30. (a) $a = -3$ and $b = -9$
(b) $a = -3$ and $b = -24$

31. $\dfrac{32\pi}{3}$ cubic units

32. (a) $4\sqrt{3}$ in. wide by $4\sqrt{6}$ in. deep

(b)

[0, 12] by [−100, 800]

(c)
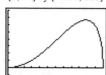
[0, 12] by [−100, 800]

Changing the value of k changes the maximum strength, but not the dimensions of the strongest beam. The graphs for different values of k look the same except that the vertical scale is different.

33. (a) 6 in. wide by $6\sqrt{3}$ in. deep

(b)
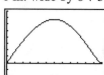
[0, 12] by [−2000, 8000]

33. continued

(c)
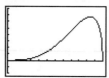
[0, 12] by [−2000, 8000]

$y = x^3(144 - x^2)^{1/2}$

Changing the value of k changes the maximum stiffness, but not the dimensions of the stiffest beam. The graphs for different values of k look the same except that the vertical scale is different.

34. (a) Maximum speed $= 10\pi$ cm/sec;
maximum speed is at $t = \dfrac{1}{2}, \dfrac{3}{2}, \dfrac{5}{2}, \dfrac{7}{2}$ seconds;
position at those times is $s = 0$ cm (rest position);
acceleration at those times is 0 cm/sec²

(b) The magnitude of the acceleration is greatest when the cart is at positions $s = \pm 10$ cm;
The speed of the cart is 0 cm/sec at those times.

35. $2\sqrt{2}$ amps

36. The minimum distance is $\dfrac{\sqrt{5}}{2}$.

37. The minimum distance is 2.

38. No. It has an absolute minimum at the point $\left(\dfrac{1}{2}, \dfrac{3}{4}\right)$.

39. (a) Because $f(x)$ is periodic with period 2π.
(b) No. It has an absolute minimum at the point $(\pi, 0)$.

40. (a) Whenever t is an integer multiple of π sec.
(b) The distance is greatest when $t = \dfrac{2\pi}{3}$ and $\dfrac{4\pi}{3}$ sec. The distance at those times is $\dfrac{3\sqrt{3}}{2}$ m.

41. (a) At $t = \dfrac{\pi}{3}$ sec and at $t = \dfrac{4\pi}{3}$ sec
(b) The maximum distance between particles is 1 m.
(c) Near $t = \dfrac{\pi}{3}$ sec and near $t = \dfrac{4\pi}{3}$ sec

42. $\theta = \dfrac{\pi}{6}$

43. (a) Answers will vary. (b) $x = \dfrac{51}{8} = 6.375$ in.
(c) Minimum length ≈ 11.04 in.

44. $M = \dfrac{C}{2}$ **45.** $x = \dfrac{c + 100}{2} = 50 + \dfrac{c}{2}$

46. Let P be the foot of the perpendicular from A to the mirror, and Q be the foot of the perpendicular from B to the mirror. Suppose the light strikes the mirror at point R on the way from A to B. Let:

a = distance from A to P
b = distance from B to Q
c = distance from P to Q
x = distance from P to R

To minimize the time is to minimize the total distance the light travels going from A to B. The total distance is

$$D(x) = (x^2 + a^2)^{1/2} + ((c - x)^2 + b^2)^{1/2}.$$

Then $D'(x) = 0$ and $D(x)$ has it minimum when

$x = \dfrac{ac}{a + b}$, or, $\dfrac{x}{a} = \dfrac{c}{a + b}$. It follows that

$c - x = \dfrac{bc}{a + b}$, or $\dfrac{c - x}{b} = \dfrac{c}{a + b}$. This means that the two triangles APR and BQR are similar, and the two angles must be equal.

47. The rate v is maximum when $x = \dfrac{a}{2}$.

The rate then is $\dfrac{ka^2}{4}$.

48. (a) $\dfrac{dv}{dr} = cr\,(2r_0 - 3r)$ which is zero when

$r = \dfrac{2}{3}\,r_0$.

(b)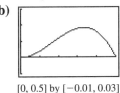

[0, 0.5] by [−0.01, 0.03]

49. 67 people

50. (a) $q = \sqrt{\dfrac{2km}{h}}$

(b) $q = \sqrt{\dfrac{2\text{ km}}{h}}$ (the same amount as in (a))

51. $p(x) = 6x - (x^3 - 6x^2 + 15x), x \ge 0$. This function has its maximum value at the points $(0, 0)$ and $(3, 0)$.

52. $x = 10$ items

53. (a) $y'(0) = 0$ **(b)** $y'(-L) = 0$

(c) $y(0) = 0$, so $d = 0$. $y'(0) = 0$, so $c = 0$.

Then $y(-L) = -aL^3 + bL^2 = H$ and

$y'(-L) = 3aL^2 - 2bL = 0$.

Solving, $a = 2\dfrac{H}{L^3}$ and $b = 3\dfrac{H}{L^2}$, which gives the equation shown.

54. (a) $V(x) = \dfrac{\pi}{3}\left(\dfrac{2\pi a - x}{2\pi}\right)^2 \sqrt{a^2 - \left(\dfrac{2\pi a - x}{2\pi}\right)^2}$

(b) When $a = 4$: $r = \dfrac{4\sqrt{6}}{3}, h = \dfrac{4\sqrt{3}}{3}$;

when $a = 5$: $r = \dfrac{5\sqrt{6}}{3}, h = \dfrac{5\sqrt{3}}{3}$;

when $a = 6$: $r = 2\sqrt{6}, h = 2\sqrt{3}$;

when $a = 8$: $r = \dfrac{8\sqrt{6}}{3}, h = \dfrac{8\sqrt{3}}{3}$

(c) $\dfrac{r}{h} = \sqrt{2}$

55. (a) The x- and y-intercepts of the line through R and T are $x - \dfrac{a}{f'(x)}$ and $a - xf'(x)$ respectively.

The area of the triangle is the product of these two values.

(b) Domain: $(0, 10)$

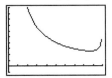

[0, 10] by [−100, 1000]

The vertical asymptotes at $x = 0$ and $x = 10$ correspond to horizontal or vertical tangent lines, which do not form triangles.

(c) Height = 15, which is 3 times the y-coordinate of the center of the ellipse.

(d) Part (a) remains unchanged.

The domain is $(0, C)$ and the graph is similar.

The minimum area occurs when $x^2 = \dfrac{3C^2}{4}$.

From this, it follows that the triangle has minimum area when its height is $3B$.

4.5 Linearization and Newton's Method (pp. 220–232)

Quick Review 4.5

1. $2x \cos (x^2 + 1)$

2. $\dfrac{1 - \cos x - (x + 1) \sin x}{(x + 1)^2}$

3. $x \approx -0.567$ **4.** $x \approx -0.322$

5. $y = x + 1$ **6.** $y = 2ex + e + 1$

7. (a) $x = -1$ **(b)** $x = -\dfrac{e + 1}{2e} \approx -0.684$

8.

x	$f(x)$	$g(x)$
0.7	-1.457	-1.7
0.8	-1.688	-1.8
0.9	-1.871	-1.9
1.0	-2	-2
1.1	-2.069	-2.1
1.2	-2.072	-2.2
1.3	-2.003	-2.3

9.

$[0, \pi]$ by $[-0.2, 1.3]$

10.

$[-1, 7]$ by $[-2, 2]$

Section 4.5 Exercises

1. (a) $L(x) = 10x - 13$
  (b) Differs from the true value in absolute value by less than 10^{-1}

2. (a) $L(x) = -\dfrac{4}{5}x + \dfrac{9}{5}$
  (b) Differs from the true value in absolute value by less than 10^{-3}

3. (a) $L(x) = 2$
  (b) Differs from the true value in absolute value by less than 10^{-2}

4. (a) $L(x) = x$
  (b) Differs from the true value in absolute value by less than 10^{-2}

5. (a) $L(x) = x - \pi$
  (b) Differs from the true value in absolute value by less than 10^{-3}

6. (a) $L(x) = -x + \dfrac{\pi}{2}$
  (b) Differs from the true value in absolute value by less than 10^{-3}

7. $f(0) = 1$. Also, $f'(x) = k(1 + x)^{k-1}$, so $f'(0) = k$. This means the linearization at $x = 0$ is $L(x) = 1 + kx$.

8. (a) $1 - 6x$ **(b)** $2 + 2x$
  (c) $1 - \dfrac{x}{2}$ **(d)** $\sqrt{2}\left(1 + \dfrac{x^2}{4}\right)$
  (e) $4^{1/3}\left(1 + \dfrac{x}{4}\right)$ **(f)** $1 - \dfrac{2}{6 + 3x}$

9. The linearization is $1 + \dfrac{3x}{2}$. It is the sum of the two individual linearizations.

10. (a) ≈ 1.2, $\left|1.002^{100} - 1.2\right| < 10^{-1}$
  (b) ≈ 1.003, $\left|\sqrt[3]{1.009} - 1.003\right| < 10^{-5}$

11. Center $= -1$, $L(x) = -5$

12. Center $= 8$, $L(x) = \dfrac{x}{12} + \dfrac{4}{3}$

13. Center $= 1$, $L(x) = \dfrac{x}{4} + \dfrac{1}{4}$, or
  Center $= 1.5$, $L(x) = \dfrac{4x}{25} + \dfrac{9}{25}$

14. Center $= \dfrac{\pi}{2}$, $L(x) = -x + \dfrac{\pi}{2}$

15. $x \approx 0.682328$

16. $x \approx -1.452627, 1.164035$

17. $x \approx 0.386237, 1.961569$

18. $x \approx \pm 1.189207$

19. (a) $dy = (3x^2 - 3)\, dx$
  (b) $dy = 0.45$ at the given values

20. (a) $dy = \dfrac{2 - 2x^2}{(1 + x^2)^2}\, dx$
  (b) $dy = -0.024$ at the given values

21. (a) $dy = (2x \ln x + x)\, dx$
  (b) $dy = 0.01$ at the given values

22. (a) $dy = \dfrac{1 - 2x^2}{(1 - x^2)^{1/2}}\, dx$
  (b) $dy = -0.2$ at the given values

23. (a) $dy = (\cos x)\, e^{\sin x}\, dx$
  (b) $dy = 0.1$ at the given values

24. (a) $dy = \csc\left(1 - \dfrac{x}{3}\right) \cot\left(1 - \dfrac{x}{3}\right) dx$
  (b) $dy \approx 0.205525$ at the given values

25. (a) $dy = \dfrac{dx}{(x + 1)^2}$
  (b) $dy = 0.01$ at the given values

26. (a) $dy = 2x \sec(x^2 - 1) \tan(x^2 - 1)\, dx$
  (b) $dy \approx 1.431663$ at the given values

27. (a) 0.21   **(b)** 0.2
  (c) 0.01

28. (a) 0.231   **(b)** 0.2
  (c) 0.031

29. (a) $-\dfrac{2}{11}$ **(b)** $-\dfrac{1}{5}$
  (c) $\dfrac{1}{55}$

30. (a) 0.04060401   **(b)** 0.04
  (c) 0.00060401

31. $4\pi a^2\, dr$ **32.** $8\pi a\, dr$

33. $3a^2\, dx$ **34.** $12a\, dx$

35. $2\pi ah\, dr$ **36.** $2\pi r\, dh$

37. (a) $x + 1$ **(b)** $f(0.1) \approx 1.1$
  (c) The actual value is less than 1.1, since the derivative is decreasing over the interval $[0, 0.1]$.

38. (a) $0.08\pi \approx 0.2513$ **(b)** 2%

39. The diameter grew $\dfrac{2}{\pi} \approx 0.6366$ in.
  The cross section area grew about 10 in^2.

40. 3%

41. The side should be measured to within 1%.

42. $180\pi \approx 565.5$ in^3

43. The angle should be measured to within 0.76%. This is also ±0.01 radian or ≈ ±0.57 degree.

44. The height should be measured to within $\frac{1}{3}$%

45. (a) Within 0.5%   **(b)** Within 5%

46. The variation of the radius should not exceed $\frac{1}{2000}$ of the ideal radius, that is, 0.05% of the ideal radius.

47. About 37.87 to 1

48. (a) $dT = -\pi L^{1/2} g^{-3/2}\, dg$
   (b) If g increases, T decreases and the clock speeds up. This can be seen from the fact that dT and dg have opposite signs.
   (c) $dg \approx -0.9765$, so $g \approx 979.0235$

49. If $f'(x_1) \neq 0$, then x_2 and all later approximations are equal to x_1.

50. If $x_1 = h$, then $f'(x_1) = \dfrac{1}{2h^{1/2}}$ and $x_2 = h - \dfrac{h^{1/2}}{\frac{1}{2h^{1/2}}}$

$= h - 2h = -h$. If $x_1 = -h$,

then $f'(x_1) = -\dfrac{1}{2h^{1/2}}$ and $x_2 = -h + 2h = h$.

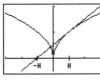

[−3, 3] by [−0.5, 2]

51. $x_2 = -2$, $x_3 = 4$, $x_4 = -8$, and $x_5 = 16$;
$|x_n| = 2^{n-1}$.

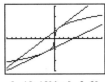

[−10, 10] by [−3, 3]

52. (a) $b_0 = f(a)$, $b_1 = f'(a)$, and $b_2 = \dfrac{f''(a)}{2}$.

   (b) $1 + x + x^2$

   (c) As one zooms in, the two graphs quickly become indistinguishable. They appear to be identical.

   (d) The quadratic approximation is $1 - (x - 1) + (x - 1)^2$.
   As one zooms in, the two graphs quickly become indistinguishable. They appear to be identical.

   (e) The quadratic approximation is $1 + \dfrac{x}{2} - \dfrac{x^2}{8}$.
   As one zooms in, the two graphs quickly become indistinguishable. They appear to be identical.

52. continued

   (f) For f: $1 + x$;
   for g: $1 - (x - 1) = 2 - x$;
   for h: $1 + \dfrac{x}{2}$

53. Just multiply the corresponding derivative formulas by dx.

54. $\lim\limits_{x \to 0} \dfrac{\tan x}{x} = \lim\limits_{x \to 0} \dfrac{\sin x / \cos x}{x}$

$= \lim\limits_{x \to 0} \left(\dfrac{1}{\cos x} \cdot \dfrac{\sin x}{x} \right)$

$= \left(\lim\limits_{x \to 0} \dfrac{1}{\cos x} \right)\left(\lim\limits_{x \to 0} \dfrac{\sin x}{x} \right)$

$= (1)(1) = 1$.

55. $g(a) = c$, so if $E(a) = 0$, then $g(a) = f(a)$ and $c = f(a)$. Then
$E(x) = f(x) - g(x) = f(x) - f(a) - m(x - a)$.
Thus, $\dfrac{E(x)}{x - a} = \dfrac{f(x) - f(a)}{x - a} - m$.

$\lim\limits_{x \to a} \dfrac{f(x) - f(a)}{x - a} = f'(a)$, so if the limit of $\dfrac{E(x)}{x - a}$ is zero, then $m = f'(a)$ and $g(x) = L(x)$.

4.6 Related Rates (pp. 232–241)

Quick Review 4.6

1. $\sqrt{74}$ **2.** $\sqrt{a^2 + b^2}$

3. $\dfrac{1 - 2y}{2x + 2y - 1}$ **4.** $-\dfrac{y + \sin y}{x + x \cos y}$

5. $2x \cos^2 y$ **6.** $2x + 2y - 1$

7. One possible answer:
$x = -2 + 6t$, $y = 1 - 4t$, $0 \leq t \leq 1$.

8. One possible answer:
$x = 5t$, $y = -4 + 4t$, $0 \leq t \leq 1$.

9. One possible answer:
$\dfrac{\pi}{2} \leq t \leq \dfrac{3\pi}{2}$

10. One possible answer:
$\dfrac{3\pi}{2} \leq t \leq 2\pi$

Section 4.6 Exercises

1. $\dfrac{dA}{dt} = 2\pi r \dfrac{dr}{dt}$ **2.** $\dfrac{dS}{dt} = 8\pi r \dfrac{dr}{dt}$

3. (a) $\dfrac{dV}{dt} = \pi r^2 \dfrac{dh}{dt}$ **(b)** $\dfrac{dV}{dt} = 2\pi r h \dfrac{dr}{dt}$

   (c) $\dfrac{dV}{dt} = \pi r^2 \dfrac{dh}{dt} + 2\pi r h \dfrac{dr}{dt}$

160 Section 4.6

4. (a) $\dfrac{dP}{dt} = 2RI\dfrac{dI}{dt} + I^2\dfrac{dR}{dt}$

(b) $0 = 2RI\dfrac{dI}{dt} + I^2\dfrac{dR}{dt}$, or,

$$\dfrac{dR}{dt} = \left(-\dfrac{2R}{I}\right)\left(\dfrac{dI}{dt}\right) = \left(-\dfrac{2P}{I^3}\right)\left(\dfrac{dI}{dt}\right)$$

5. $\dfrac{ds}{dt} = \dfrac{x\dfrac{dx}{dt} + y\dfrac{dy}{dt} + z\dfrac{dz}{dt}}{\sqrt{x^2 + y^2 + z^2}}$

6. $\dfrac{dA}{dt} = \dfrac{1}{2}\left(b\sin\theta\dfrac{da}{dt} + a\sin\theta\dfrac{db}{dt} + ab\cos\theta\dfrac{d\theta}{dt}\right)$

7. (a) 1 volt/sec   **(b)** $-\dfrac{1}{3}$ amp/sec

(c) $\dfrac{dV}{dt} = I\dfrac{dR}{dt} + R\dfrac{dI}{dt}$

(d) $\dfrac{dR}{dt} = \dfrac{3}{2}$ ohms/sec. R is increasing since $\dfrac{dR}{dt}$ is positive.

8. π cm^2/sec

9. (a) $\dfrac{dA}{dt} = 14$ cm^2/sec   **(b)** $\dfrac{dP}{dt} = 0$ cm/sec

(c) $\dfrac{dD}{dt} = -\dfrac{14}{13}$ cm/sec

(d) The area is increasing, because its derivative is positive.
The perimeter is not changing, because its derivative is zero.
The diagonal length is decreasing, because its derivative is negative.

10. (a) 2 m^3/sec   **(b)** 0 m^2/sec

(c) 0 m/sec

11. $\dfrac{dx}{dt} = \dfrac{3000}{\sqrt{51}}$ mph ≈ 420.08 mph

12. $\dfrac{1}{16}$ ft/min

13. (a) 12 ft/sec   **(b)** $-\dfrac{119}{2}$ ft^2/sec

(c) -1 radian/sec

14. 20 ft/sec

15. $\dfrac{19\pi}{2500} \approx 0.0239$ in^3/min

16. (a) $\dfrac{1125}{32\pi} \approx 11.19$ cm/min

(b) $\dfrac{375}{8\pi} \approx 14.92$ cm/min

17. (a) $\dfrac{32}{9\pi} \approx 1.13$ cm/min

(b) $-\dfrac{80}{3\pi} \approx -8.49$ cm/min

18. (a) $-\dfrac{1}{24\pi} \approx -0.01326$ m/min

or $-\dfrac{25}{6\pi} \approx -1.326$ cm/min

(b) $r = \sqrt{169 - (13 - y)^2} = \sqrt{26y - y^2}$

18. continued

(c) $-\dfrac{5}{288\pi} \approx -0.00553$ m/min

or $-\dfrac{125}{72\pi} \approx -0.553$ cm/min

19. $V = \dfrac{4}{3}\pi r^3$, so $\dfrac{dV}{dt} = 4\pi r^2\dfrac{dr}{dt}$. But $S = 4\pi r^2$, so we are given that $\dfrac{dV}{dt} = kS = 4k\pi r^2$. Substituting,

$4k\pi r^2 = 4\pi r^2\dfrac{dr}{dt}$ which gives $\dfrac{dr}{dt} = k$.

20. (a) 1 ft/min   **(b)** 40π ft^2/min

21. (a) $\dfrac{5}{2}$ ft/sec   **(b)** $-\dfrac{3}{20}$ radian/sec

22. 11 ft/sec

23. (a) $\dfrac{dc}{dt} = 0.3, \dfrac{dr}{dt} = 0.9, \dfrac{dp}{dt} = 0.6$

(b) $\dfrac{dc}{dt} = -1.5625, \dfrac{dr}{dt} = 3.5, \dfrac{dp}{dt} = 5.0625$

24. (a) $\dfrac{10}{9\pi} \approx 0.354$ in./min

(b) $\dfrac{8}{5\pi} \approx 0.509$ in./min

25. $\dfrac{dy}{dt} = \dfrac{466}{1681} \approx 0.277$ L/min^2

26. 1 radian/sec   **27.** $\dfrac{2}{5}$ radian/sec

28. -5 m/sec   **29.** -3 ft/sec

30. -1500 ft/sec

31. In front: 2 radians/sec;

Half second later: 1 radian/sec

32. 1.6 cm^2/min   **33.** 80 mph
34. 7.1 in./min   **35.** -6 deg/sec
36. 29.5 knots

37. (a) $\dfrac{24}{5}$ cm/sec   **(b)** 0 cm/sec

(c) $-\dfrac{1200}{160,801} \approx -0.00746$ cm/sec

38. (a) -46 cm/sec   **(b)** 2 cm/sec
(c) -88 cm/sec

39. (a) The point being plotted would correspond to a point on the edge of the wheel as the wheel turns.

(b) One possible answer:
$\theta = 16\pi t$, where t is in seconds.

39. continued

   (c) Assuming counterclockwise motion, the rates are as follows.

$$\theta = \frac{\pi}{4}: \quad \frac{dx}{dt} \approx -71.086 \text{ ft/sec}$$

$$\frac{dy}{dt} \approx 71.086 \text{ ft/sec}$$

$$\theta = \frac{\pi}{2}: \quad \frac{dx}{dt} \approx -100.531 \text{ ft/sec}$$

$$\frac{dy}{dt} = 0 \text{ ft/sec}$$

$$\theta = \pi: \quad \frac{dx}{dt} = 0 \text{ ft/sec}$$

$$\frac{dy}{dt} \approx -100.531 \text{ ft/sec}$$

40. (a) One possible answer:
$x = 30 \cos \theta, \ y = 40 + 30 \sin \theta$

   (b) Assuming counterclockwise motion, the rates are as follows.

$$\text{When } t = 5: \quad \frac{dx}{dt} = 0 \text{ ft/sec}$$

$$\frac{dy}{dt} \approx -18.850 \text{ ft/sec}$$

$$\text{When } t = 8: \quad \frac{dx}{dt} \approx 17.927 \text{ ft/sec}$$

$$\frac{dy}{dt} \approx 5.825 \text{ ft/sec}$$

41. (a) 9% per year
   (b) Increasing at 1% per year

Chapter 4 Review Exercises (pp. 242–245)

1. Maximum: $\frac{4\sqrt{6}}{9}$ at $x = \frac{4}{3}$;
minimum: -4 at $x = -2$

2. No global extrema

3. (a) $[-1, 0)$ and $[1, \infty)$
   (b) $(-\infty, -1]$ and $(0, 1]$
   (c) $(-\infty, 0)$ and $(0, \infty)$
   (d) None
   (e) Local minima at $(1, e)$ and $(-1, e)$
   (f) None

4. (a) $[-\sqrt{2}, \sqrt{2}]$
   (b) $[-2, -\sqrt{2}]$ and $[\sqrt{2}, 2]$
   (c) $(-2, 0)$ **(d)** $(0, 2)$
   (e) Local max: $(-2, 0)$ and $(\sqrt{2}, 2)$;
local min: $(2, 0)$ and $(-\sqrt{2}, -2)$
   (f) $(0, 0)$

5. (a) Approximately $(-\infty, 0.385]$
   (b) Approximately $[0.385, \infty)$
   (c) None   **(d)** $(-\infty, \infty)$
   (e) Local maximum at $\approx (0.385, 1.215)$
   (f) None

6. (a) $[1, \infty)$ **(b)** $(-\infty, 1]$
   (c) $(-\infty, \infty)$ **(d)** None
   (e) Local minimum at $(1, 0)$
   (f) None

7. (a) $[0, 1)$ **(b)** $(-1, 0]$
   (c) $(-1, 1)$ **(d)** None
   (e) Local minimum at $(0, 1)$
   (f) None

8. (a) $(-\infty, -2^{-1/3}] \approx (-\infty, -0.794]$
   (b) $[-2^{-1/3}, 1) \approx [-0.794, 1)$ and $(1, \infty)$
   (c) $(-\infty, -2^{1/3}) \approx (-\infty, -1.260)$ and $(1, \infty)$
   (d) $(-1.260, 1)$
   (e) Local maximum at
$$\left(-2^{-1/3}, \frac{2}{3} \cdot 2^{-1/3}\right) \approx (-0.794, 0.529)$$
   (f) $\left(-2^{1/3}, \frac{1}{3} \cdot 2^{1/3}\right) \approx (-1.260, 0.420)$

9. (a) None   **(b)** $[-1, 1]$
   (c) $(-1, 0)$ **(d)** $(0, 1)$
   (e) Local maximum at $(-1, \pi)$;
local minimum at $(1, 0)$
   (f) $\left(0, \frac{\pi}{2}\right)$

10. (a) $[-\sqrt{3}, \sqrt{3}]$
   (b) $(-\infty, -\sqrt{3}]$ and $[\sqrt{3}, \infty)$
   (c) Approximately $(-2.584, -0.706)$
and $(3.290, \infty)$
   (d) Approximately $(-\infty, -2.584)$
and $(-0.706, 3.290)$
   (e) Local maximum at
$$\left(\sqrt{3}, \frac{\sqrt{3} - 1}{4}\right) \approx (1.732, 0.183);$$
local minimum at
$$\left(-\sqrt{3}, \frac{-\sqrt{3} - 1}{4}\right) \approx (-1.732, -0.683)$$
   (f) $\approx (-2.584, -0.573), (-0.706, -0.338),$ and $(3.290, 0.161)$

11. (a) $(0, 2]$ **(b)** $[-2, 0)$
   (c) None   **(d)** $(-2, 0)$ and $(0, 2)$
   (e) Local maxima at $(-2, \ln 2)$ and $(2, \ln 2)$
   (f) None

12. (a) Approximately $[0, 0.176], \left[0.994, \frac{\pi}{2}\right],$
$[2.148, 2.965], \left[3.834, \frac{3\pi}{2}\right],$ and $\left[5.591, 2\pi\right]$
   (b) Approximately $[0.176, 0.994], \left[\frac{\pi}{2}, 2.148\right],$
$[2.965, 3.834],$ and $\left[\frac{3\pi}{2}, 5.591\right]$
   (c) Approximately $(0.542, 1.266), (1.876, 2.600),$
$(3.425, 4.281),$ and $(5.144, 6.000)$
   (d) Approximately $(0, 0.542), (1.266, 1.876),$
$(2.600, 3.425), (4.281, 5.144),$ and $(6.000, 2\pi)$

12. continued

(e) Local maxima at $\approx(0.176, 1.266)$, $\left(\dfrac{\pi}{2}, 0\right)$
and $(2.965, 1.266)$, $\left(\dfrac{3\pi}{2}, 2\right)$, and $(2\pi, 1)$;

local minima at $\approx(0, 1)$, $(0.994, -0.513)$,

$(2.148, -0.513)$, $(3.834, -1.806)$,

and $(5.591, -1.806)$

Note that the local extrema at $x \approx 3.834$,

$x = \dfrac{3\pi}{2}$, and $x \approx 5.591$ are also absolute

extrema.

(f) $\approx(0.542, 0.437)$, $(1.266, -0.267)$,
$(1.876, -0.267)$, $(2.600, 0.437)$,
$(3.425, -0.329)$, $(4.281, 0.120)$,
$(5.144, 0.120)$, and $(6.000, -0.329)$

13. (a) $\left(0, \dfrac{2}{\sqrt{3}}\right]$

(b) $(-\infty, 0]$ and $\left[\dfrac{2}{\sqrt{3}}, \infty\right)$

(c) $(-\infty, 0)$ **(d)** $(0, \infty)$

(e) Local maximum at

$\left(\dfrac{2}{\sqrt{3}}, \dfrac{16}{3\sqrt{3}}\right) \approx (1.155, 3.079)$

(f) None

14. (a) Approximately $[-0.578, 1.692]$

(b) Approximately $(-\infty, -0.578]$ and $[1.692, \infty)$

(c) Approximately $(-\infty, 1.079)$

(d) Approximately $(1.079, \infty)$

(e) Local maximum at $\approx (1.692, 20.517)$;
local minimum at $\approx (-0.578, 0.972)$

(f) $\approx(1.079, 13.601)$

15. (a) $\left[0, \dfrac{8}{9}\right]$ **(b)** $(-\infty, 0]$ and $\left[\dfrac{8}{9}, \infty\right)$

(c) $\left(-\infty, -\dfrac{2}{9}\right)$ **(d)** $\left(-\dfrac{2}{9}, 0\right)$ and $(0, \infty)$

(e) Local maximum at

$\approx (0.889, 1.011)$;

local minimum at $(0, 0)$

(f) $\approx \left(-\dfrac{2}{9}, 0.667\right)$

16. (a) Approximately $(-\infty, 0.215]$

(b) Approximately $[0.215, 2)$ and $(2, \infty)$

(c) Approximately $(2, 3.710)$

(d) $(-\infty, 2)$ and approximately $(3.710, \infty)$

(e) Local maximum at $\approx (0.215, -2.417)$

(f) $\approx(3.710, -3.420)$

17. (a) None **(b)** At $x = -1$

(c) At $x = 0$ and $x = 2$

18. (a) At $x = -1$ **(b)** At $x = 2$

(c) At $x = \dfrac{1}{2}$

19. $f(x) = -\dfrac{1}{4}x^{-4} - e^{-x} + C$

20. $f(x) = \sec x + C$

21. $f(x) = 2\ln x + \dfrac{1}{3}x^3 + x + C$

22. $f(x) = \dfrac{2}{3}x^{3/2} + 2x^{1/2} + C$

23. $f(x) = -\cos x + \sin x + 2$

24. $f(x) = \dfrac{3}{4}x^{4/3} + \dfrac{x^3}{3} + \dfrac{x^2}{2} + x - \dfrac{31}{12}$

25. $s(t) = 4.9t^2 + 5t + 10$

26. $s(t) = 16t^2 + 20t + 5$

27. $L(x) = 2x + \dfrac{\pi}{2} - 1$

28. $L(x) = \sqrt{2}x - \dfrac{\pi\sqrt{2}}{4} + \sqrt{2}$

29. $L(x) = -x + 1$ **30.** $L(x) = 2x + 1$

31. Global minimum value of $\dfrac{1}{2}$ at $x = 2$

32. (a) T **(b)** P

33. (a) $(0, 2]$ **(b)** $[-3, 0)$

(c) Local maxima at $(-3, 1)$ and $(2, 3)$

34. The 24th day

35.

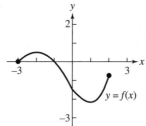

36. (a) Absolute minimum is -2 at $x = 1$;
absolute maximum is 3 at $x = 3$

(b) None

(c)

37. (a) $f(x)$ is continuous on $[0.5, 3]$ and differentiable
on $(0.5, 3)$.

(b) $c \approx 1.579$ **(c)** $y \approx 1.457x - 1.075$

(d) $y \approx 1.457x - 1.579$

38. (a) $v(t) = -3t^2 - 6t + 4$

(b) $a(t) = -6t - 6$

(c) The particle starts at position 3 moving in the
positive direction, but decelerating.
At approximately $t = 0.528$, it reaches
position 4.128 and changes direction,
beginning to move in the negative direction.
After that, it continues to accelerate while
moving in the negative direction.

39. (a) $L(x) = -1$

(b) Using the linearization, $f(0.1) \approx -1$

(c) Greater than the approximation in (b), since $f'(x)$ is actually positive over the interval $(0, 0.1)$ and the estimate is based on the derivative being 0.

40. (a) $dy = (2x - x^2)e^{-x}\, dx$

(b) $dy \approx 0.00368$

41. (a) $y = \dfrac{2701.73}{1 + 17.28e^{-0.36x}}$

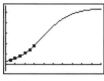

[0, 20] by [−300, 2800]

(b) In 1998. There are approximately 1351 million transactions in that year.

(c) Approximately 2702 million transactions per year

42. $x \approx 0.828361$

43. 1200 m/sec

44. 1162.5 m

45. $r = 25$ ft and $s = 50$ ft

46. 54 square units

47. Base is 6 ft by 6 ft, height $= 3$ ft

48. Base is 4 ft by 4 ft, height $= 2$ ft

49. Height $= 2$, radius $= \sqrt{2}$

50. $r = h = 4$ ft

51. (a) $V(x) = x(15 - 2x)(5 - x)$

(b) $0 < x < 5$

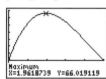

[0, 5] by [−10, 70]

(c) Maximum volume ≈ 66.019 in^3 when $x \approx 1.962$ in.

(d) $V'(x) = 6x^2 - 50x + 75$ which is zero at $x = \dfrac{25 - 5\sqrt{7}}{6} \approx 1.962$.

52. 29.925 square units

53. $x = \dfrac{48}{\sqrt{7}} \approx 18.142$ mi and $y = \dfrac{36}{\sqrt{7}} \approx 13.607$ mi

54. $x = 100$ m and $r = \dfrac{100}{\pi}$ m

55. 276 grade A and 553 grade B tires

56. (a) 0.765 units

(b) When $t = \dfrac{7\pi}{8} \approx 2.749$

(plus multiples of π if they keep going)

57. Dimensions: base is 6 in. by 12 in., height $= 2$ in.; maximum volume $= 144$ in^3

58. $-40\text{m}^2/\text{sec}$

59. 5 m/sec

60. Increasing 1 cm/min

61. $\dfrac{dx}{dt} = 4$ units/second

62. (a) $h = \dfrac{5r}{2}$

(b) $\dfrac{125}{144\pi} \approx 0.276$ ft/min

63. 5 radians/sec

64. Not enough speed. Duck!

65. $dV \approx \dfrac{2\pi ah}{3}\, dr$

66. (a) Within 1%   **(b)** Within 3%

67. (a) Within 4%   **(b)** Within 8%

(c) Within 12%

68. Height $= 14$ feet, estimated error $= \pm\dfrac{2}{45}$ feet

69. $\dfrac{dy}{dx} = 2\sin x \cos x - 3$.

Since $\sin x$ and $\cos x$ are both between 1 and -1,

$2 \sin x \cos x$ is never greater than 2, and

therefore $\dfrac{dy}{dx} \le 2 - 3 = -1$ for all values of x.

Chapter 5
The Definite Integral

5.1 Estimating with Finite Sums (pp. 247–257)

Quick Review 5.1

1. 400 miles

2. 144 miles

3. 100 ft/sec ≈ 68.18 mph

4. 9.46×10^{12} km

5. 28 miles

6. 1200 gallons

7. $-3°$

8. 25,920,000 ft^3

9. 17,500 people

10. 176,400 times

Section 5.1 Exercises

1. (a)

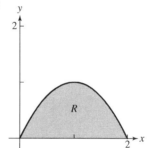

(b)

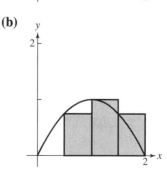

LRAM $= 1.25$

2. (a)

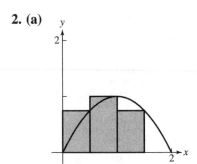

RRAM = 1.25

(b)

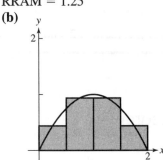

MRAM = 1.375

3.

n	$LRAM_n$	$MRAM_n$	$RRAM_n$
10	1.32	1.34	1.32
50	1.3328	1.3336	1.3328
100	1.3332	1.3334	1.3332
500	1.333328	1.333336	1.333328

4. The area is $\dfrac{4}{3}$.　　　　**5.** 13.5

6. 1.0986　　　　　　　**7.** 0.8821

8. 2　　　　　　　　**9.** ≈ 44.8; ≈ 6.7 L/min

10. (a) 87 in. = 7.25 ft　　**(b)** 87 in. = 7.25 ft

11. (a) 5220 m　　　　**(b)** 4920 m

12. 3665 ft

13. (a) 0.969 mi

　　(b) 0.006 h = 21.6 sec

　　　116 mph

14.

n	MRAM
10	526.21677
20	524.25327
40	523.76240
80	523.63968
160	523.60900

15.

n	error	% error
10	2.61799	0.5
20	0.65450	0.125
40	0.16362	3.12×10^{-2}
80	0.04091	7.8×10^{-3}
160	0.01023	2×10^{-3}

16. (a) $S_8 \approx 146.08406$

　　　Overestimate, because each

　　　rectangle extends beyond the curve.

　　(b) 9%

17. (a) $S_8 \approx 120.95132$

　　　Underestimate

　　(b) 10%

18. (a) 372.27873 m^3　　**(b)** 11%

19. (a) 15,465 ft^3　　　**(b)** 16,515 ft^3

20. 31.41593　　　　　**21.** 39.26991

22. (a) 74.65 ft/sec　　**(b)** 45.28 ft/sec

　　(c) 146.59 ft

23. (a) 240 ft/sec

　　(b) 1520 ft with RRAM and $n = 5$

24. (a) Upper: 758 gal; lower: 543 gal

　　(b) Upper: 2363 gal; lower: 1693 gal

　　(c) Worst case: 31.44 h; best case: 32.37 h

25. (a) Upper: 60.9 tons; lower: 46.8 tons

　　(b) By the end of October

26. The area of the region is the total number of sales,

　　in millions of units, over the 10-year period.

　　The area units are

　　(millions of units/year)years = millions of units.

27. (a) 2　　　　　　**(b)** $2\sqrt{2} \approx 2.828$

　　(c) $8 \sin\left(\dfrac{\pi}{8}\right) \approx 3.061$

　　(d) Each area is less than the area of the circle, π.

　　　As n increases, the polygon area approaches π.

28. False; look at $f(x) = x^2$, $0 \le x \le 1$, $n = 1$.

29. $RRAM_n f = LRAM_n f + f(x_n)\Delta x - f(x_0)\Delta x$

　　Since $f(a) = f(b)$, or $f(x_0) = f(x_n)$, we have

　　$RRAM_n f = LRAM_n f$.

30. (a) $A_T = \dfrac{1}{2} \sin\left(\dfrac{2\pi}{n}\right)$

　　(b) $A_P = \dfrac{n}{2} \sin\left(\dfrac{2\pi}{n}\right)$

　　　$\lim_{n \to \infty} A_P = \pi$

　　(c) $A_T = \dfrac{1}{2}r^2 \sin\left(\dfrac{2\pi}{n}\right)$

　　　$A_P = \dfrac{n}{2}r^2 \sin\left(\dfrac{2\pi}{n}\right)$

　　　$\lim_{n \to \infty} A_P = \pi r^2$

5.2 Definite Integrals
(pp. 258–268)

Quick Review 5.2

1. 55　　　　　　　　**2.** 20

3. 5500　　　　　　　**4.** $\displaystyle\sum_{k=1}^{99} k$

5. $\displaystyle\sum_{k=0}^{25} 2k$　　　　**6.** $\displaystyle\sum_{k=1}^{500} 3k^2$

7. $\displaystyle\sum_{x=1}^{50} (2x^2 + 3x)$ **8.** $\displaystyle\sum_{k=0}^{20} x^k$

9. $\displaystyle\sum_{k=0}^{n} (-1)^k = 0$ if n is odd.

10. $\displaystyle\sum_{k=0}^{n} (-1)^k = 1$ if n is even.

Section 5.2 Exercises

1. $\displaystyle\int_0^2 x^2 \, dx$ **2.** $\displaystyle\int_{-7}^5 (x^2 - 3x) \, dx$

3. $\displaystyle\int_1^4 \frac{1}{x} \, dx$ **4.** $\displaystyle\int_2^3 \frac{1}{1 - x} \, dx$

5. $\displaystyle\int_0^1 \sqrt{4 - x^2} \, dx$ **6.** $\displaystyle\int_{-\pi}^{\pi} \sin^3 x \, dx$

7. 15   **8.** -80

9. -480 **10.** $\dfrac{3\pi}{2}$

11. 2.75   **12.** 4
13. 21   **14.** 2

15. $\dfrac{9\pi}{2}$ **16.** 4π

17. $\dfrac{5}{2}$ **18.** 1

19. 3   **20.** $2 + \dfrac{\pi}{2}$

21. $\dfrac{3\pi^2}{2}$ **22.** 24

23. $\dfrac{1}{2}b^2$ **24.** $2b^2$

25. $b^2 - a^2$ **26.** $\dfrac{3}{2}(b^2 - a^2)$

27. $\dfrac{3}{2}a^2$ **28.** a^2

29. 0   **30.** $\dfrac{13}{4}$

31. $\dfrac{1}{4}$ **32.** $\dfrac{1}{2}$

33. $\dfrac{3}{4}$ **34.** $-\dfrac{1}{4}$

35. $\dfrac{1}{2}$ **36.** 0

37. $-\dfrac{3}{4}$ **38.** $\dfrac{3}{4}$

39. ≈ 0.9905 **40.** ≈ 4.3863

41. $\dfrac{32}{3}$ **42.** ≈ 1.8719

43. (a) 0   (b) 1
44. (a) $-5, -4, -3, -2, -1, 0, 1, 2, 3, 4, 5$
   (b) -88

45. (a) -1 (b) $-\dfrac{7}{2}$

46. (a) 3   (b) $-\dfrac{77}{2}$

47. (a) $f \to +\infty$

   (b) Using right endpoints we have
   $$\int_0^1 \frac{1}{x^2} \, dx = \lim_{n \to \infty} \sum_{k=1}^n \frac{1}{n} \frac{n^2}{k^2}$$
   $$= \lim_{n \to \infty} \sum_{k=1}^n \frac{n}{k^2} = \lim_{n \to \infty} n\left[1 + \frac{1}{2^2} + \cdots + \frac{1}{n^2}\right].$$
   $$n\left(1 + \frac{1}{2^2} + \cdots + \frac{1}{n^2}\right) > n \text{ and } n \to \infty$$
   so $n\left(1 + \frac{1}{2^2} + \cdots + \frac{1}{n^2}\right) \to \infty.$

48. (a) RRAM $= \left(\dfrac{1}{n}\right) \cdot \dfrac{1}{n} + \left(\dfrac{2}{n}\right)^2 \cdot \dfrac{1}{n} + \cdots$
   $$+ \left(\dfrac{n}{n}\right)^2 \cdot \dfrac{1}{n}$$
   $$= \sum_{k=1}^n \left[\left(\dfrac{k}{n}\right)^2 \cdot \dfrac{1}{n}\right]$$

   (b) $\displaystyle\sum_{k=1}^n \left[\left(\frac{k}{n}\right)^2 \cdot \frac{1}{n}\right] = \sum_{k=1}^n \left(\frac{1}{n^3} \cdot k^2\right) = \frac{1}{n^3} \sum_{k=1}^n k^2$

   (c) $\dfrac{1}{n^3} \displaystyle\sum_{k=1}^n k^2 = \dfrac{1}{n^3} \cdot \dfrac{n(n+1)(2n+1)}{6}$
   $$= \frac{n(n+1)(2n+1)}{6n^3}$$

   (d) $\displaystyle\lim_{n \to \infty} \sum_{k=1}^{\infty} \left[\left(\frac{k}{n}\right)^2 \cdot \frac{1}{n}\right] = \lim_{n \to \infty} \frac{n(n+1)(2n+1)}{6n^3}$
   $$= \frac{1}{3}$$

   (e) Because $\displaystyle\int_0^1 x^2 \, dx$ equals the limit of any Riemann sum as $n \to \infty$ over the interval $[0, 1]$.

5.3 Definite Integrals and Antiderivatives (pp. 268–276)

Quick Review 5.3

1. $\sin x$ **2.** $\cos x$
3. $\tan x$ **4.** $\cot x$
5. $\sec x$ **6.** $\ln (x)$
7. x^n **8.** $-\dfrac{2^x \ln 2}{(2^x + 1)^2}$

9. $xe^x + e^x$ **10.** $\dfrac{1}{x^2 + 1}$

Section 5.3 Exercises

1. (a) 0   (b) -8
   (c) -12 (d) 10
   (e) -2 (f) 16

2. (a) 2   **(b)** 9
    (c) −2   **(d)** 1
    (e) −6   **(f)** 1

3. (a) 5   **(b)** $5\sqrt{3}$
    (c) −5   **(d)** −5

4. (a) $-\sqrt{2}$ **(b)** $\sqrt{2}$
    (c) $-\sqrt{2}$ **(d)** 1

5. (a) 4   **(b)** −4

6. (a) 6   **(b)** 6

7. −14   **8.** 10

9. 1   **10.** −2

11. −1   **12.** $-\dfrac{7}{4}$

13. $\dfrac{\pi}{2}$ **14.** $\dfrac{\pi}{3}$

15. $e^2 - 1 \approx 6.389$ **16.** $6 \ln 2 \approx 4.159$

17. $\dfrac{16}{3}$ **18.** 16

19. $\dfrac{19}{3}$ **20.** $\dfrac{8}{3}$

21.

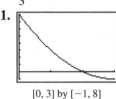

[0, 3] by [−1, 8]

   (a) 6   **(b)** $\dfrac{22}{3}$

22.

[0, 2] by [−5, 3]

   (a) $-\dfrac{2}{3}$ **(b)** 3

23.

[0, 3] by [−3, 2]

   (a) 0   **(b)** $\dfrac{8}{3}$

24.

[0, 5] by [−5, 5]

   (a) $-\dfrac{25}{3}$ **(b)** 13

25. 0, at $x = 1$ **26.** $-\dfrac{3}{2}$, at $x = \sqrt{3}$

27. −2, at $x = \dfrac{1}{\sqrt{3}}$ **28.** 1, at $x = 0, x = 2$

29. $\dfrac{3}{2}$ **30.** $\dfrac{4 - \pi}{4}$

31. 0   **32.** 0

33. $\dfrac{1}{2} \le \displaystyle\int_0^1 \dfrac{1}{1 + x^4}\, dx \le 1$

34. $\dfrac{8}{17} \le \displaystyle\int_0^{0.5} \dfrac{1}{1 + x^4}\, dx \le \dfrac{1}{2}$

$\dfrac{1}{4} \le \displaystyle\int_{0.5}^1 \dfrac{1}{1 + x^4}\, dx \le \dfrac{8}{17}$

$\dfrac{49}{68} \le \displaystyle\int_0^1 \dfrac{1}{1 + x^4}\, dx \le \dfrac{33}{34}$

35. $0 \le \displaystyle\int_0^1 \sin(x^2)\, dx \le \sin(1) < 1$

36. $\displaystyle\int_0^1 \sqrt{8}\, dx \le \int_0^1 \sqrt{x + 8}\, dx \le \int_0^1 \sqrt{9}\, dx$

$2\sqrt{2} \le \displaystyle\int_0^1 \sqrt{x + 8}\, dx \le 3$

37. $0 \le (b - a) \min f(x) \le \displaystyle\int_a^b f(x)\, dx$

38. $\displaystyle\int_a^b f(x)\, dx \le (b - a) \max f(x) \le 0$

39. Yes; $av(f) = \dfrac{1}{b - a} \displaystyle\int_a^b f(x)\, dx$, therefore $\displaystyle\int_a^b f(x)\, dx$

$= av(f)(b - a) = \displaystyle\int_a^b av(f)\, dx.$

40. (a) 300 miles   **(b)** 8 hours
    (c) 37.5 mph

    (d) Average speed is $\dfrac{\text{total distance travelled}}{\text{time}}$ for the

       whole trip.

$$\dfrac{d_1 + d_2}{t_1 + t_2} \ne \dfrac{1}{2}\left(\dfrac{d_1}{t_1} + \dfrac{d_2}{t_2}\right)$$

41. Avg rate $= \dfrac{\text{total amount released}}{\text{total time}}$

$= \dfrac{2000 \text{ m}^3}{100 \text{ min} + 50 \text{ min}} = 13\dfrac{1}{3} \text{ m}^3/\text{min}$

42. $\dfrac{1}{2}$ **43.** $\dfrac{7}{6}$

44. (a) $A = \dfrac{1}{2}(b)(h) = \dfrac{1}{2}bh$

    (b) $\dfrac{h}{2b}x^2 + C$

    (c) $\displaystyle\int_0^b y(x)\, dx = \dfrac{h}{2b}x^2 \Big]_0^b = \dfrac{hb^2}{2b} = \dfrac{1}{2}bh$

45. $k \approx 2.39838$

46. $\displaystyle\int_a^b F'(x)\, dx = \int_a^b G'(x)\, dx \to F(b) - F(a) =$
$G(b) - G(a)$

5.4 Fundamental Theorem of Calculus (pp. 277–288)

Quick Review 5.4

   1. $2x \cos x^2$ **2.** $2 \sin x \cos x$

3. 0

4. 0

5. $2^x \ln 2$

6. $\dfrac{1}{2\sqrt{x}}$

7. $\dfrac{-x \sin x - \cos x}{x^2}$

8. $-\cot t$

9. $\dfrac{y+1}{2y-x}$

10. $\dfrac{1}{3x}$

Section 5.4 Exercises

1. $5 - \ln 6 \approx 3.208$

2. $-\dfrac{26}{3 \ln 3} \approx -7.889$

3. 1

4. $10\sqrt{5} \approx 22.361$

5. $\dfrac{5}{2}$

6. 1

7. 2

8. π

9. $2\sqrt{3}$

10. $2\sqrt{3}$

11. 0

12. 4

13. $\dfrac{8}{3}$

14. 0

15. $\dfrac{5}{2}$

16. 12

17. $\dfrac{1}{2}$

18. 8

19. (a) No, $f(x) = \dfrac{x^2-1}{x+1}$ is discontinuous at $x = -1$.

  (b) $-\dfrac{5}{2}$. $f(x)$ is bounded with only one discontinuity. Split it up at $x = -1$, or use area.

20. (a) No, $f(x) = \dfrac{9-x^2}{3x-9}$ is discontinuous at $x = 3$.

  (b) $-\dfrac{55}{6}$. See 19(b).

21. (a) No, $f(x) = \tan x$ is discontinuous at $x = \dfrac{\pi}{2}$ and $x = \dfrac{3\pi}{2}$.

  (b) No, $\displaystyle\int_0^b \tan x \, dx \to \infty$ as $b \to \dfrac{\pi}{2}^-$.

22. (a) No, $f(x) = \dfrac{x+1}{x^2-1}$ is discontinuous at $x = 1$.

  (b) No, $\displaystyle\int_b^2 \dfrac{x+1}{x^2-1}\, dx \to \infty$ as $b \to 1^+$.

23. (a) No, $f(x) = \dfrac{\sin x}{x}$ is discontinuous at $x = 0$.

  (b) ≈ 2.55. Area is finite. $\dfrac{\sin x}{x}$ is bounded with only one discontinuity.

24. (a) No, $f(x) = \dfrac{1-\cos x}{x^2}$ is discontinuous at $x = 0$.

  (b) ≈ 2.08. See 23(b).

25. $\dfrac{5}{6}$

26. 3

27. π

28. $\sqrt{3} - \dfrac{\pi}{3}$

29. ≈ 3.802

30. ≈ 1.427

31. ≈ 0.914

32. ≈ 8.886

33. $x \approx 0.699$

34. ≈ 0.883

35. $-\dfrac{3}{2}$

36. $\dfrac{\sin 2 \cos 2 - 2}{2} \approx -1.189$

37. $\sqrt{1+x^2}$

38. $-\dfrac{1}{x}$

39. $\dfrac{\sin x}{2\sqrt{x}}$

40. $2\cos(2x)$

41. $3x^2 \cos(2x^3) - 2x \cos(2x^2)$

42. $-\sin x \cos^2 x - \sin^2 x \cos x$

43. (d)

44. (c)

45. (b)

46. (a)

47. $x = a$

48. $f(x) = 2x - 2$

49. $L(x) = 2 + 10x$

50. 1

51. $\displaystyle\int_0^{\pi/k} \sin kx \, dx = \dfrac{2}{k}$

52. (a) $\dfrac{125}{6}$

  (b) $\dfrac{25}{4}$

53. (a) 0

  (b) H is increasing on [0,6] where $H'(x) = f(x) > 0$.

  (c) H is concave up on (9,12) where $H''(x) = f'(x) > 0$.

  (d) $H(12) = \displaystyle\int_0^{12} f(t) \, dt > 0$ because there is more area above the x-axis than below for $y = f(x)$.

  (e) $x = 6$ since $H'(6) = f(6) = 0$ and $H''(6) = f'(6) < 0$.

  (f) $x = 0$ since $H(x) > 0$ on (0, 12].

54. (a) $s'(5) = f(5) = 2$ units/sec

  (b) $s''(5) = f'(5) < 0$

  (c) $s(3) = \displaystyle\int_0^3 f(x)\, dx = \dfrac{1}{2}(9) = \dfrac{9}{2}$ units

  (d) $s'(6) = f(6) = 0$, $s''(6) = f'(6) < 0$ so s has its largest value at $t = 6$ sec.

  (e) $s''(t) = f'(t) = 0$ at $t = 4$ sec and $t = 7$ sec.

  (f) Particle is moving toward on (6, 9) and away on (0, 6) since $s'(6) = f(t) > 0$ on (0, 6) and then $s'(6) = f(t) < 0$ on (6, 9).

  (g) The positive side

55. (a) $s'(3) = f(3) = 0$ (b) $s''(3) = f'(3) > 0$

  (c) $s(3) = \displaystyle\int_0^3 f(x)\, dx = -\dfrac{1}{2}(3)(6) = -9$ units

  (d) $s(t) = 0$ at $t = 6$ sec because $\displaystyle\int_0^6 f(x)\, dx = 0$

  (e) $s''(t) = f'(t) = 0$ at $t = 7$ sec

  (f) $0 < t < 3$: $s < 0$, $s' < 0 \Rightarrow$ away
  $3 < t < 6$: $s < 0$, $s' > 0 \Rightarrow$ toward
  $t > 6$: $s > 0$, $s' > 0 \Rightarrow$ away

  (g) The positive side

56. (a) $f(t)$ is even, so $\displaystyle\int_0^x f(t)\, dt = \displaystyle\int_{-x}^0 f(t)\, dt$, so $-\displaystyle\int_0^x f(t)\, dt = -\displaystyle\int_{-x}^0 f(t)\, dt = \displaystyle\int_0^{-x} f(t)\, dt$.

  (b) 0

  (c) $k\pi, k = \pm 1, \pm 2, \ldots$

56. continued

(d)

[−20, 20] by [−3, 3]

57. (a) $9 (b) $10

58. $4500

59. (a) 300 drums (b) $6.00

60. (a) True, $h'(x) = f(x) \Rightarrow h''(x) = f'(x)$
(b) True, h and h' are both differentiable.
(c) $h'(1) = f(1) = 0$
(d) True, $h''(1) = f'(1) < 0$ and $h'(1) = 0$
(e) False, $h''(1) = f'(1) < 0$
(f) False, $h''(1) = f'(1) \neq 0$
(g) True, $\dfrac{dh}{dx} = f(x) = 0$ at $x = 1$ and $h'(x) = f(x)$
is a decreasing function.

61. Using area, $\displaystyle\int_0^x f(t)\,dt = -\int_{-x}^0 f(t)\,dt = \int_0^{-x} f(t)\,dt$

62. Using area, $\displaystyle\int_0^x f(t)\,dt = \int_{-x}^0 f(t)\,dt = -\int_0^{-x} f(t)\,dt$

63. f odd $\Rightarrow \displaystyle\int_0^x f(t)\,dt$ is even, but $\dfrac{d}{dx}\displaystyle\int_0^x f(t)\,dt = f(x)$
so f is the derivative of an even function. Similarly
for f even.

64. $x \approx 1.0648397$. $\displaystyle\lim_{t\to\infty} \dfrac{\sin t}{t} = 0$. Not enough area
between x-axis and $\dfrac{\sin x}{x}$ for $x > 1.0648397$ to get
$\displaystyle\int_0^x \dfrac{\sin t}{t}\,dt$ back to 1.

or: Si(x) doesn't decrease enough (for
$x > 1.0648397$) to get back to 1.

5.5 Trapezoidal Rule (pp. 289–297)

Quick Review 5.5

1. Concave down 2. Concave up
3. Concave down 4. Concave down
5. Concave up 6. Concave down
7. Concave up 8. Concave up
9. Concave down 10. Concave down

Section 5.5 Exercises

1. (a) 2 (b) Exact
(c) 2

2. (a) 2.75 (b) Over
(c) $\dfrac{8}{3}$

3. (a) 4.25 (b) Over
(c) 4

4. (a) 0.697 (b) Over
(c) $\ln 2 \approx 0.693$

5. (a) 5.146 (b) Under
(c) $\dfrac{16}{3}$

6. (a) 1.896 (b) Under
(c) 2

7. 15,990 ft^3

8. (a) 26,360,000 ft^3 (b) 988

9. 0.9785 mi

10. (a) 12 (b) 12, $|E_S| = 0$
(c) $f^{(4)}(x) = 0$ for $f(x) = x^3 - 2x$, so $M_{f^{(4)}} = 0$.
(d) Simpson's Rule will always give the exact
value for cubic polynomials.

11. The average of the 13 discrete temperatures gives
equal weight to the low values at the end.

12. (b) We are approximating the area under the
temperature graph. Doubling the endpoints
increases the error in the first and last
trapezoids.

13. $S_{50} \approx 3.1379$, $S_{100} \approx 3.14029$

14. $S_{50} \approx 1.08943$, $S_{100} \approx 1.08943$

15. $S_{50} = 1.3706$, $S_{100} = 1.3706$ using $a = 0.0001$ as
lower limit
$S_{50} = 1.37076$, $S_{100} = 1.37076$ using
$a = 0.000000001$ as lower limit

16. $S_{50} \approx 0.82812$, $S_{100} \approx 0.82812$

17. (a) $T_{10} = 1.983523538$, $T_{100} = 1.999835504$
$T_{1000} = 1.999998355$

(b)

n	$|E_T|$
10	$0.016476462 = 1.6476462 \times 10^{-2}$
100	1.64496×10^{-4}
1000	1.645×10^{-6}

(c) $\left|E_{T_{10n}}\right| \approx 10^{-2} \times \left|E_{T_n}\right|$

(d) $\left|E_{T_n}\right| \le \dfrac{\pi^3 M}{12n^2}$, $\left|E_{T_{10n}}\right| \le \dfrac{\pi^3 M}{12(10n)^2}$
$= \dfrac{\pi^3 M}{12n^2} \times 10^{-2}$

18. (a) $S_{10} = 2.000109517$
$S_{100} = 2.000000011$
$S_{1000} = 2$

(b)

n	$|E_S|$
10	1.09517×10^{-4}
100	1.1×10^{-8}
1000	0

18. continued

(c) $\left| E_{S_{10n}} \right| \approx 10^{-4} \times \left| E_{S_n} \right|$

(d) $\left| E_{S_n} \right| \le \dfrac{M(\pi)^5}{180n^4}.\ \left| E_{S_{10n}} \right| \le \dfrac{M(\pi)^5}{180(10n)^4}$
$= \dfrac{M(\pi)^5}{180n^4} \times 10^{-4}$

19. (a) $f''(x) = 2\cos(x^2) - 4x^2 \sin(x^2)$

(b)

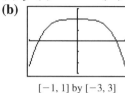

[−1, 1] by [−3, 3]

(c) The graph shows that $-3 \le f''(x) \le 2$ for $-1 \le x \le 1$.

(d) $\left| E_T \right| \le \dfrac{1 - (-1)}{12}(h^2)(3) = \dfrac{h^2}{2}$

(e) $\left| E_T \right| \le \dfrac{h^2}{2} \le \dfrac{0.1^2}{2} < 0.1$

(f) $n \ge 20$

20. (a) $-48x^2 \cos(x^2) + 16x^4 \sin(x^2) - 12\sin(x^2)$

(b)

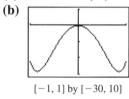

[−1, 1] by [−30, 10]

(c) The graph shows that $-30 \le f^{(4)}(x) \le 0$, for $-1 < x < 1$.

(d) $\left| E_S \right| \le \dfrac{1 - (-1)}{180}(h^4)(30) = \dfrac{h^4}{3}$

(e) $\left| E_S \right| \le \dfrac{h^4}{3} \le \dfrac{0.4^4}{3} < 0.01$

(f) $n \ge 5$

21. 466.67 in^2 **22.** 10.63 ft

23. Each quantity is equal to
$\dfrac{h}{2}(y_0 + 2y_1 + 2y_2 + \cdots + 2y_{n-1} + y_n).$

24. Each quantity is equal to
$\dfrac{h}{3}(y_0 + 4y_1 + 2y_2 + 4y_3 + \cdots + 2y_{2n-2}$
$+ 4y_{2n-1} + y_{2n}).$

Chapter 5 Review Exercises (pp. 298–301)

1.

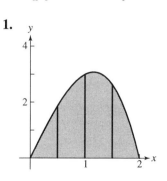

2. 3.75

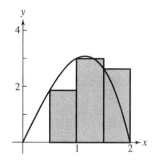

3. 4.125

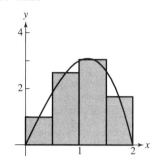

4. 3.75

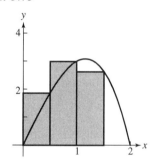

5. 3.75

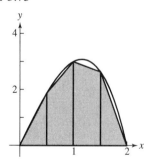

6. 4

7.

n	LRAM$_n$	MRAM$_n$	RRAM$_n$
10	1.78204	1.60321	1.46204
20	1.69262	1.60785	1.53262
30	1.66419	1.60873	1.55752
50	1.64195	1.60918	1.57795
100	1.62557	1.60937	1.59357
1000	1.61104	1.60944	1.60784

8. ln 5

9. (a) True   **(b)** True
(c) False

10. (a) $V = \lim\limits_{n \to \infty} \sum\limits_{i=1}^{n} \pi \sin^2 (m_i) \, \Delta x$

(b) 4.9348

11. (a) 26.5 m
(b)

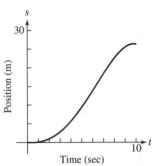

12. (a) $\displaystyle\int_0^{10} x^3 \, dx$ **(b)** $\displaystyle\int_0^{10} x \sin x \, dx$

(c) $\displaystyle\int_0^{10} x(3x - 2)^2 \, dx$ **(d)** $\displaystyle\int_0^{10} (1 + x^2)^{-1} \, dx$

(e) $\displaystyle\int_0^{10} \pi\left(9 - \sin^2 \dfrac{\pi x}{10}\right) dx$

13. 10   **14.** 2
15. 20   **16.** 42
17. $\dfrac{\sqrt{2}}{2}$ **18.** 16
19. 3   **20.** 2
21. 2   **22.** 1
23. $\sqrt{3}$ **24.** 1
25. 8   **26.** 2
27. -1 **28.** 0
29. 2 ln 3   **30.** π
31. 40   **32.** 64π
33. (a) Upper = 4.392 L;   **(b)** 4.2 L
  lower = 4.008 L
34. (a) Lower = 87.15 ft; **(b)** 95.1 ft
  upper = 103.05 ft
35. One possible answer:
  The dx is important because it corresponds to
  actual physical quantity Δx in a Riemann sum.
  Without the Δx, our integral approximations would
  be way off.
36. $\dfrac{16}{3}$

37. $1 \le \sqrt{1 + \sin^2 x} \le \sqrt{2}$

38. (a) $\dfrac{4}{3}$ **(b)** $\dfrac{2}{3}a^{3/2}$

39. $\sqrt{2 + \cos^3 x}$ **40.** $14x\sqrt{2 + \cos^3 (7x^2)}$

41. $\dfrac{-6}{3 + x^4}$ **42.** $\dfrac{2}{4x^2 + 1} - \dfrac{1}{x^2 + 1}$

43. $230

44. $av(I) = 4800$ cases;
  average holding cost = $192 per day
45. $x \approx 1.63052$ or $x \approx -3.09131$

46. (a) True   **(b)** True
(c) True   **(d)** False
(e) True   **(f)** False
(g) True

47. $F(1) - F(0)$ **48.** $y = \displaystyle\int_5^x \dfrac{\sin t}{t} \, dt + 3$

49. Use the fact that $y' = 2x + \dfrac{1}{x}$.

50. (b);
  $\dfrac{dy}{dx} = 2x \to y = x^2 + c. \, y(1) = 4 \to c = 3$
51. (a) ≈ 2.42 gal   **(b)** ≈ 24.83 mpg
52. (a) 6,144 ft
(b) 4,296 ft   **(c)** B
53. (a) $h(y_1 + y_3) + 2(2hy_2) = h(y_1 + 4y_2 + y_3)$

(b) Each expression is equal to
  $\dfrac{1}{3}[h(y_0 + 4y_1 + y_2) + h(y_2 + 4y_3 + y_4)$
  $+ \cdots + h(y_{2n-2} + 4y_{2n-1} + y_{2n}).]$
54. (a) 0   **(b)** -1
(c) $-\pi$ **(d)** $x = 1$
(e) $y = 2x + 2 - \pi$ **(f)** $x = -1, x = 2$
(g) $[-2\pi, 0]$
55. (a) NINT$(e^{-x^2/2}, x, -10, 10) \approx 2.506628275$
  NINT$(e^{-x^2/2}, x, -20, 20) \approx 2.506628275$
(b) The area is $\sqrt{2\pi}$.
56. ≈ 1500 yd^3
57. (a) $(V^2)_{av} = \dfrac{(V_{max})^2}{2}$ **(b)** ≈ 339 volts

  $V_{rms} = \dfrac{V_{max}}{\sqrt{2}}$

Chapter 6
Differential Equations and Mathematical Modeling

6.1 Antiderivatives and Slope Fields
(pp. 303–315)

Quick Review 6.1

1. $106.00   **2.** $106.14
3. $106.17   **4.** $106.18

5. 3 cos 3x   **6.** $\dfrac{5}{2} \sec^2 \dfrac{5}{2}x$

7. $2Ce^{2x}$ **8.** $\dfrac{1}{x+2}$

9.

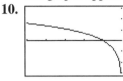

[0.01, 5] by [−3, 3]

The graphs appear to be the same.

10.

[−5, −0.01] by [−3, 3]

The graphs appear to be the same.

Section 6.1 Exercises

1. $\dfrac{x^3}{3} - x^2 + x + C$ **2.** $x^{-3} + C$

3. $\dfrac{x^3}{3} - \dfrac{8}{3}x^{3/2} + C$ **4.** $8x - \csc x + C$

5. $\dfrac{e^{4x}}{4} + C$ **6.** $\ln|x + 3| + C$

7. $\dfrac{x^6}{6} - 3x^2 + 3x + C$ **8.** $\dfrac{x^{-2}}{2} + \dfrac{x^2}{2} - x + C$

9. $2e^{t/2} + \dfrac{5}{t} + C$ **10.** $t^{4/3} + C$

11. $\dfrac{x^4}{4} + \dfrac{1}{2x^2} + C$ **12.** $\dfrac{3}{4}x^{4/3} + \dfrac{3}{2}x^{2/3} + C$

13. $x^{1/3} + C$

14. $-3\cos x + \dfrac{\cos 3x}{3} + C$

15. $\sin\left(\dfrac{\pi}{2}x\right) + C$ **16.** $2\sec t + C$

17. $2\ln|x - 1| + \ln|x| + C$

18. $\ln|x - 2| - \dfrac{\cos 5x}{5} + \dfrac{e^{-2x}}{2} + C$

19. $\tan 5r + C$ **20.** $-\dfrac{\cot 7t}{7} + C$

21. $\dfrac{x}{2} + \dfrac{\sin 2x}{4} + C$ **22.** $\dfrac{x}{2} - \dfrac{\sin 2x}{4} + C$

23. $\tan\theta - \theta + C$ **24.** $-\cot t - t + C$

25. (a) Graph (b)

    (b) The slope is always positive, so (a) and (c) can be ruled out.

26. (a) Graph (b)

    (b) The solution should have positive slope when x is negative, zero slope when x is zero and negative slope when x is positive since slope $= \dfrac{dy}{dx} = -x$. Graphs (a) and (c) don't show this slope pattern.

27. $y = x^2 - x - 2$ **28.** $y = \dfrac{x^2}{2} - \dfrac{1}{x} - \dfrac{1}{2}$

29. $y = \tan x - 2$ **30.** $y = 3x^{1/3} - 2$

31. $y = 3x^3 - 2x^2 + 5x + 10$

32. $y = \sin x - \cos x$

33. $y = -2e^{-t} + 1$ **34.** $y = \ln|x| - 3$

35. $y = -\sin\theta + \theta - 3$

36. $y = -x^3 + x^2 + 4x + 1$

37. $y = \dfrac{1}{2}\ln|t| + \dfrac{5}{4}t^2 - \dfrac{1}{4}$

38. $y = \sin\theta + \cos\theta - \dfrac{\theta^3}{3} - 2\theta - 4$

39. $s = 4.9t^2 + 5t + 10$

40. $s = -\dfrac{1}{\pi}(1 + \cos\pi t)$

41. $s = 16t^2 + 20t$

42. $s = -\cos t - t + 2$

43.

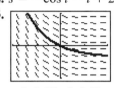

[−2, 2] by [−3, 3]

44.

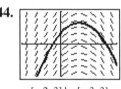

[−2, 3] by [−3, 3]

45–48. The derivative of the right hand side of the equation is equal to the integrand on the left hand side.

49. (a) $y = \dfrac{x^2}{2} + \dfrac{1}{x} + \dfrac{1}{2}, x > 0$

    (b) $y = \dfrac{x^2}{2} + \dfrac{1}{x} + \dfrac{3}{2}, x < 0$

    (c) $y' = \begin{cases} x - \dfrac{1}{x^2}, & x < 0 \\ x - \dfrac{1}{x^2}, & x > 0 \end{cases}$

    (d) $C_1 = \dfrac{3}{2}, C_2 = \dfrac{1}{2}$

    (e) $C_1 = \dfrac{1}{2}, C_2 = -\dfrac{7}{2}$

50. $r(x) = x^3 - 3x^2 + 12x$

51. $c(x) = x^3 - 6x^2 + 15x + 400$

52. (a) $x^2 e^x + C$ **(b)** $x\sin x + C$

    (c) $-x^2 e^x + C$ **(d)** $-x\sin x + C$

    (e) $x^2 e^x + x\sin x + C$

    (f) $x^2 e^x - x\sin x + C$

    (g) $\dfrac{x^2}{2} + x^2 e^x + C$ **(h)** $x\sin x - 4x + C$

53. (a) $s = \dfrac{-kt^2}{2} + 88t$ **(b)** $t = \dfrac{88}{k}$

    (c) $k = 16$ ft/sec^2

54. ≈ 21.5 ft/sec^2 **55.** ≈ 1.240 sec

56. $\dfrac{d^2 s}{dt^2} = a, s(0) = s_0, v(0) = v_0$

57. $h = \left[-\dfrac{125}{48\pi}t + 10^{5/2}\right]^{2/5}$

    $V = \dfrac{4\pi}{75}\left[-\dfrac{125}{48\pi}t + 10^{5/2}\right]^{6/5}$

58. (a) $y = 500e^{0.0475t}$

 (b) $t = \dfrac{\ln 2}{0.0475} \approx 14.6$ yr

59. (a) $y = 1200e^{0.0625t}$

 (b) $t = \dfrac{\ln 3}{0.0625} \approx 17.6$ yr

60. (a) $\displaystyle\int_0^x t^2 \cos t\, dt + C$ **(b)** $\displaystyle\int_0^x t^2 \cos t\, dt + 1$

61. (a) $\displaystyle\int_0^x te^t\, dt + C$ **(b)** $\displaystyle\int_0^x te^t\, dt + 1$

62. (a) $y = x^3 + 1$

 (b) Only one function satisfies the differential equation and the initial conditions.

63.

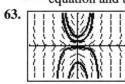

 $[-6, 6]$ by $[-4, 4]$

 The concavity of each solution curve indicates the sign of y''.

64.

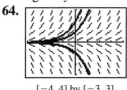

 $[-4, 4]$ by $[-3, 3]$

 The concavity of each solution curve indicates the sign of y''.

65.

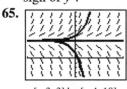

 $[-3, 3]$ by $[-4, 10]$

 The concavity of each solution curve indicates the sign of y''.

66.

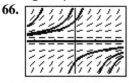

 $[-2.35, 2.35]$ by $[-1.55, 1.55]$

 The concavity of each solution curve indicates the sign of y''.

67. (a) $\dfrac{d}{dx}(\ln x + C) = \dfrac{1}{x}$ for $x > 0$

 (b) $\dfrac{d}{dx}(\ln (-x) + C) = \dfrac{1}{x}$ for $x < 0$

 (c) $\dfrac{d}{dx}\ln |x| = \dfrac{1}{x}$ for all x except 0.

 (d) $\dfrac{dy}{dx} = \dfrac{1}{x}$ for all x except 0.

6.2 Integration by Substitution (pp. 315–323)

Quick Review 6.2

1. $\dfrac{32}{5}$ **2.** $\dfrac{16}{3}$

3. 3^x **4.** 3^x

5. $4(x^3 - 2x^2 + 3)^3(3x^2 - 4x)$

6. $8 \sin (4x - 5) \cos (4x - 5)$

7. $-\tan x$ **8.** $\cot x$

9. $\sec x$ **10.** $-\csc x$

Section 6.2 Exercises

1. $-\dfrac{1}{3} \cos 3x + C$ **2.** $\dfrac{1}{4} \sin (2x^2) + C$

3. $\dfrac{1}{2} \sec 2x + C$ **4.** $(7x - 2)^4 + C$

5. $\dfrac{1}{3} \tan^{-1}\left(\dfrac{x}{3}\right) + C$ **6.** $-6\sqrt{1 - r^3} + C$

7. $\dfrac{2}{3}\left(1 - \cos \dfrac{t}{2}\right)^3 + C$ **8.** $\dfrac{2}{3}(y^4 + 4y^2 + 1)^3 + C$

9. $\dfrac{1}{1 - x} + C$ **10.** $\tan (x + 2) + C$

11. $\dfrac{2}{3}(\tan x)^{3/2} + C$ **12.** $\sec\left(\theta + \dfrac{\pi}{2}\right) + C$

13. $\ln (\ln 6)$ **14.** $\dfrac{2}{3}$

15. $\dfrac{1}{3} \sin (3z + 4) + C$ **16.** $-\dfrac{2}{3}(\cot x)^{3/2} + C$

17. $\dfrac{1}{7}(\ln x)^7 + C$ **18.** $\dfrac{1}{4} \tan^8\left(\dfrac{x}{2}\right) + C$

19. $\dfrac{3}{4} \sin (s^{4/3} - 8) + C$ **20.** $-\dfrac{1}{3} \cot (3x) + C$

21. $\dfrac{1}{2} \sec (2t + 1) + C$ **22.** $\dfrac{-6}{2 + \sin t} + C$

23. 0 **24.** $\ln 9 - \ln 2 \approx 1.504$

25. $\dfrac{1}{2} \ln 5 \approx 0.805$ **26.** 2π

27. $\dfrac{1}{3} \ln |\sec (3x)| + C = -\dfrac{1}{3} \ln |\cos (3x)| + C$

28. $\dfrac{2}{5}\sqrt{5x + 8} + C$

29. $\ln |\sec x + \tan x| + C$

30. $-\ln |\csc x + \cot x| + C$

31. $\dfrac{14}{3}$ **32.** $\dfrac{1}{3}$

33. $-\dfrac{1}{2}$ **34.** 0

35. $\dfrac{10}{3}$ **36.** 0

37. $2\sqrt{3}$ **38.** $\dfrac{3}{4}$

39. $y = Ce^{(1/2)x^2 + 2x} - 5$

40. $y = \left[\tan^{-1}\left(\dfrac{x^2}{4} + C\right)\right]^2$

41. $y = -\ln\left(C - e^{\sin x}\right)$ **42.** $y = \ln (e^x + C)$

43. $y = \dfrac{1}{x^2 + 3}$

44. $y = (\ln x)^4$

45. (a) $\dfrac{d}{dx}\left(\dfrac{2}{3}(x + 1)^{3/2} + C\right) = \sqrt{x + 1}$

(b) Because $\dfrac{dy_1}{dx} = \sqrt{x + 1}$ and $\dfrac{dy_2}{dx} = \sqrt{x + 1}$

(c) $4\dfrac{2}{3}$

(d) $C = y_1 - y_2$

$$= \int_0^x \sqrt{x + 1}\, dx - \int_3^x \sqrt{x + 1}\, dx$$
$$= \int_0^x \sqrt{x + 1}\, dx + \int_x^3 \sqrt{x + 1}\, dx$$
$$= \int_0^3 \sqrt{x + 1}\, dx$$

46. (a) $\dfrac{d}{dx}[F(x) + C]$ should equal $f(x)$.

(b) The slope field should help you visualize the solution curve $y = F(x)$.

(c) The graphs of $y_1 = F(x)$ and $y_2 = \displaystyle\int_0^x f(t)\, dt$ should differ only by a vertical shift, C.

(d) A table of values for $y_1 - y_2$ should show C.

(e) The graph of NDER of $F(x)$ and $f(x)$ should be the same.

(f) a) $\dfrac{d}{dx}\left(\sqrt{x^2 + 1} + C\right) = \dfrac{x}{\sqrt{x^2 + 1}}$

b)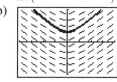

[−4, 4] by [−3, 3]

c)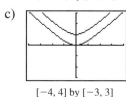

[−4, 4] by [−3, 3]

d)

x	$y_1 - y_2$
0	1
1	1
2	1
3	1
4	1

e)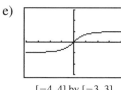

[−4, 4] by [−3, 3]

47. (a) $\dfrac{1}{2}\sqrt{10} - \dfrac{3}{2} \approx 0.081$

(b) $\dfrac{1}{2}\sqrt{10} - \dfrac{3}{2} \approx 0.081$

48. (a) $\dfrac{1}{2}$ (b) $\dfrac{1}{2}$

49. Show $\dfrac{dy}{dx} = \tan x$ and $y(3) = 5$.

50. (a) $F_1(\theta) = -\dfrac{1}{4}\cot^2 2\theta$

(b) $F_2(\theta) = -\dfrac{1}{4}\csc^2 2\theta$

(c) $F_1{}'(\theta) = F_2{}'(\theta) = \csc^2 2\theta \cot 2\theta$

(d) $\dfrac{1}{4}$

51. (a) $\sin^2 x + C$

(b) $-\cos^2 x + C$

(c) $-\dfrac{1}{2}\cos 2x + C$

(d) The derivative of each expression is $2 \sin x \cos x$.

6.3 Integration by Parts
(pp. 323–329)

Quick Review 6.3

1. $2x^3 \cos 2x + 3x^2 \sin 2x$

2. $\dfrac{3e^{2x}}{3x + 1} + 2e^{2x}\ln(3x+1)$

3. $\dfrac{2}{1 + 4x^2}$

4. $\dfrac{1}{\sqrt{1 - (x + 3)^2}}$

5. $x = \dfrac{1}{3}\tan y$

6. $x = \cos y - 1$

7. $\dfrac{2}{\pi}$

8. $y = \dfrac{1}{2}e^{2x} + C$

9. $y = \dfrac{1}{2}x^2 - \cos x + 3$

10. $\dfrac{d}{dx}\left[\dfrac{1}{2}e^x(\sin x - \cos x)\right] = e^x \sin x$

Section 6.3 Exercises

1. $-x \cos x + \sin x + C$

2. $2x \cos x + (x^2 - 2) \sin x + C$

3. $\dfrac{1}{2}y^2 \ln y - \dfrac{1}{4}y^2 + C$

4. $y \tan^{-1} y - \dfrac{1}{2}\ln(1 + y^2) + C$

5. $x \tan x + \ln|\cos x| + C$

6. $\theta \sin^{-1}\theta + \sqrt{1 - \theta^2} + C$

7. $(2 - t^2)\cos t + 2t \sin t + C$

8. $-t \cot t + \ln|\sin t| + C$

9. $\dfrac{1}{4}x^4 \ln x - \dfrac{1}{16}x^4 + C$

10. $(-x^4 - 4x^3 - 12x^2 - 24x - 24)e^{-x} + C$

11. $(x^2 - 7x + 7)e^x + C$

12. $\left(-\dfrac{x^3}{2} - \dfrac{3x^2}{4} - \dfrac{3x}{4} - \dfrac{3}{8}\right)e^{-2x} + C$

13. $\dfrac{1}{2}e^y(\sin y - \cos y) + C$

14. $\dfrac{1}{2}e^{-y}(\sin y - \cos y) + C$

15. $\frac{\pi^2}{8} - \frac{1}{2} \approx 0.734$ **16.** $\frac{3}{4} - \frac{3\pi^2}{16} \approx -1.101$

17. $\frac{1}{13}[e^6(2 \cos 9 + 3 \sin 9) - e^{-4}(2 \cos 6 - 3 \sin 6)]$
   ≈ -18.186

18. $-\frac{e^{-4}}{4}(\cos 4 + \sin 4) + \frac{e^6}{4}(\cos 6 - \sin 6)$
   ≈ 125.03

19. $y = \left(\frac{x^2}{4} - \frac{x}{8} + \frac{1}{32}\right)e^{4x} + C$

20. $y = \frac{1}{3}x^3 \ln x - \frac{1}{9}x^3 + C$

21. $y = \frac{\theta^2}{2}\sec^{-1}\theta - \frac{1}{2}\sqrt{\theta^2 - 1} + C$

22. $y = \theta \sec \theta - \ln|\sec \theta + \tan \theta| + C$

23. (a) π **(b)** 3π
   (c) 4π

24. ≈ 0.726

25. $\frac{1 - e^{-2\pi}}{2\pi} \approx 0.159$

26. (a) $(x - 1)e^x + C$
   (b) $(x^2 - 2x + 2)e^x + C$
   (c) $(x^3 - 3x^2 + 6x - 6)e^x + C$
   (d) $\left[x^n - \frac{d(x^n)}{dx} + \frac{d^2(x^n)}{dx^2} - \cdots + (-1)^n\frac{d^n(x^n)}{dx^n}\right]e^x$
      $+ C$ or
      $[x^n - nx^{n-1} + n(n-1)x^{n-2} - \cdots$
         $+ (-1)^{n-1}(n!)x + (-1)^n(n!)]e^x + C$
   (e) Use mathematical induction or argue based on
      tabular integration.

27. $-2(\sqrt{x} \cos \sqrt{x} - \sin \sqrt{x}) + C$

28. $\frac{2(\sqrt{3x + 9} - 1)e^{\sqrt{3x+9}}}{3} + C$

29. $\frac{(x^6 - 3x^4 + 6x^2 - 6)e^{x^2}}{2} + C$

30. $\frac{r}{2}[\sin(\ln r) - \cos(\ln r)] + C$

31. $u = x^n, dv = \cos x \, dx$

32. $u = x^n, dv = \sin x \, dx$

33. $u = x^n, dv = e^{ax} \, dx$

34. $u = (\ln x)^n, dv = dx$

35. (a) Let $y = f^{-1}(x)$. Then $x = f(y)$,
      so $dx = f'(y) \, dy$. Substitute directly.
   (b) $u = y, dv = f'(y) \, dy$

36. $u = f^{-1}(x), dv = dx$

37. (a) $\int \sin^{-1} x \, dx = x \sin^{-1} x + \cos(\sin^{-1} x) + C$
   (b) $\int \sin^{-1} x \, dx = x \sin^{-1} x + \sqrt{1 - x^2} + C$
   (c) $\cos(\sin^{-1} x) = \sqrt{1 - x^2}$

38. (a) $\int \tan^{-1} x \, dx$
      $= x \tan^{-1} x + \ln|\cos(\tan^{-1} x)| + C$
   (b) $\int \tan^{-1} x \, dx = x \tan^{-1} x - \frac{1}{2}\ln(1 + x^2) + C$
   (c) $\ln|\cos(\tan^{-1} x)| = \ln\left(\frac{1}{\sqrt{1 + x^2}}\right)$
      $= -\frac{1}{2}\ln(1 + x^2)$

39. (a) $\int \cos^{-1} x \, dx = x \cos^{-1} x - \sin(\cos^{-1} x) + C$
   (b) $\int \cos^{-1} x \, dx = x \cos^{-1} x - \sqrt{1 - x^2} + C$
   (c) $\sin(\cos^{-1} x) = \sqrt{1 - x^2}$

40. (a) $\int \log_2 x \, dx = x \log_2 x - \left(\frac{1}{\ln 2}\right)2^{\log_2 x} + C$
   (b) $\int \log_2 x \, dx = x \log_2 x - \left(\frac{1}{\ln 2}\right)x + C$
   (c) $2^{\log_2 x} = x$

6.4 Exponential Growth and Decay
(pp. 330–341)

Quick Review 6.4

1. $a = e^b$ **2.** $c = \ln(d)$

3. $x = e^2 - 3$ **4.** $x = \frac{1}{2}\ln 6$

5. $x = \frac{\ln 2.5}{\ln 0.85} \approx -5.638$

6. $k = \frac{\ln 2}{\ln 3 - \ln 2} \approx 1.710$

7. $t = \frac{\ln 10}{\ln 1.1} \approx 24.159$ **8.** $t = \frac{1}{2}\ln 4 = \ln 2$

9. $y = -1 + e^{2x+3}$ **10.** $y = -2 \pm e^{3t-1}$

Section 6.4 Exercises

Most of the numerical answers in this section are
approximations.

1. $y(t) = 100e^{1.5t}$ **2.** $y(t) = 200e^{-0.5t}$

3. $y(t) = 50e^{(0.2 \ln 2)t}$ **4.** $y(t) = 60e^{-(0.1 \ln 2)t}$

5. 8.06 yr doubling time; \$13,197.14 in 30 yr

6. 4.62% rate; \$8000 in 30 yr

7. \$600 initially; 13.2 yr doubling time

8. 7.2% rate; 9.63 yr doubling time

9. (a) 14.94 yr **(b)** 14.62 yr
   (c) 14.68 yr **(d)** 14.59 yr

10. (a) 8.74 yr   **(b)** 8.43 yr
    (c) 8.49 yr   **(d)** 8.40 yr
11. (a) 2.8×10^{14} bacteria
    (b) The bacteria reproduce fast enough that even if many are destroyed there are enough left to make the person sick.
12. 1250 bacteria   **13.** 0.585 days
14. (a) 138.6 days   **(b)** 599 days
15. $y \approx 2e^{0.4581t}$ **16.** $y \approx 1.1e^{-0.3344t}$
17. $y = y_0 e^{-kt} = y_0 e^{-k(3/k)} = y_0 e^{-3} < 0.05 y_0$
18. 5°F
19. (a) 17.53 minutes longer
    (b) 13.26 minutes
20. (a) 53.45° above room temperature
    (b) 23.79° above room temperature
    (c) 232.5 min or 3.9 hours
21. 6658 years
22. (a) 12,571 B.C.   **(b)** 12,101 B.C.
    (c) 13,070 B.C.
23. (a) 168.5 meters   **(b)** 41.13 seconds
24. (a) 7780 meters   **(b)** 31.65 minutes
25. 585.4 kg   **26.** 16.09 years
27. (a) $p = 1013e^{-0.121h}$ **(b)** 2.383 millibars
    (c) 0.977 km
28. 54.88 grams
29. (a) $V = V_0 e^{-t/40}$ **(b)** 92.1 seconds
30. (a) $A(t) = A_0 e^t$;
       It grows by a factor of e each year.
    (b) $\ln 3 \approx 1.1$ yr
    (c) $(e - 1)$ times your initial amount, or $\approx 172\%$ increase.
31. (b) $\lim\limits_{t\to\infty} s(t) = \dfrac{v_0 m}{k}$
32. (a) $\dfrac{\ln 90}{100} = 0.045$ or 4.5%
    (b) $\dfrac{\ln 131}{100} = 0.049$ or 4.9%
33. $s(t) = 1.32(1 - e^{-0.606t})$

A graph of the model is shown superimposed on a graph of the data.

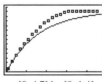

[0, 4.7] by [0, 1.4]

34. (a) $T - T_s = 79.47(0.932^t)$
    (b) $T = 10 + 79.47(0.932^t)$

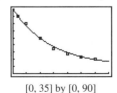

[0, 35] by [0, 90]

    (c) 52.5 seconds   **(d)** 89.47°C
35. (b) $T = T_s$ is a horizontal asymptote.

36. (a) $2y_0 = y_0 e^{rt} \Rightarrow t = \dfrac{\ln 2}{r}$
    (b)

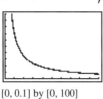

[0, 0.1] by [0, 100]

    (c) $\ln 2 \approx 0.69$, so the doubling time is $\dfrac{0.69}{r}$ which is almost the same as the rules.
    (d) $\dfrac{70}{5} = 14$ years or $\dfrac{72}{5} = 14.4$ years
    (e) $\dfrac{108}{100r}$ (108 has more factors than 110.)
37. (a)

x	$\left(1 + \dfrac{1}{x}\right)^x$
10	2.5937
100	2.7048
1000	2.7169
10,000	2.7181
100,000	2.7183

$e \approx 2.7183$

    (b) $r = 2$

x	$\left(1 + \dfrac{2}{x}\right)^x$
10	6.1917
100	7.2446
1000	7.3743
10,000	7.3876
100,000	7.3889

$e^2 \approx 7.389$

$r = 0.5$

x	$\left(1 + \dfrac{0.5}{x}\right)^x$
10	1.6289
100	1.6467
1000	1.6485
10,000	1.6487
100,000	1.6487

$e^{0.5} \approx 1.6487$

    (c) As we compound more times the increment of time between compounding approaches 0. Continuous compounding is based on an instantaneous rate of change which is a limit of average rates as the increment in time approaches 0.
38. (b) $\sqrt{\dfrac{mg}{k}}$
    (c) 179 ft/sec $\approx$ 122 mi/hr

6.5 Population Growth (pp. 342–349)

Quick Review 6.5

1. All real numbers

2. $\lim_{x \to +\infty} f(x) = 50; \lim_{x \to -\infty} f(x) = 0$

3. $y = 0$ and $y = 50$

4. All real numbers

5.

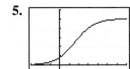

[−30, 70] by [−10, 60]

no zeros

6.

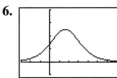

[−30, 70] by [−0.5, 2]

   (a) $(-\infty, \infty)$
   (b) None

7.

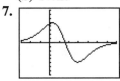

[−30, 70] by [−0.08, 0.08]

   (a) $(-\infty, 10 \ln 5) \approx (-\infty, 16.094)$
   (b) $(10 \ln 5, \infty) \approx (16.094, \infty)$

8. $(10 \ln 5, 25) \approx (16.094, 25)$

9. $A = 3, B = -2$

10. $A = -2, B = 4$

Section 6.5 Exercises

1. (a) $\dfrac{dP}{dt} = 0.025P$

   (b) $P(t) = 75,000e^{0.025t}$

   (c)

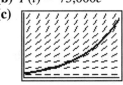

[0, 100] by [0, 1,000,000]

2. (a) $\dfrac{dP}{dt} = 0.019P$

   (b) $P(t) = 110,000e^{0.019t}$

   (c)

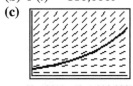

[0, 100] by [0, 1,000,000]

3. (a) $\dfrac{dP}{dt} = 0.00025P(200 - P)$

   (b) $P(t) = \dfrac{200}{1 + 19e^{-0.05t}}$

   (c)

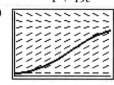

[0, 100] by [0, 250]

4. (a) $\dfrac{dP}{dt} = \dfrac{1}{7500}P(150 - P)$

   (b) $P(t) = \dfrac{150}{1 + 9e^{-0.02t}}$

   (c)

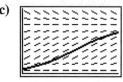

[0, 200] by [0, 200]

5. −30%   **6.** 7.5%

7. $k = 0.04; M = 100$ **8.** $k = 0.04; M = 500$

9. (d)   **10.** (b)

11. (c)   **12.** (a)

13. (a) $k = 0.7; M = 1000$

   (b) $P(0) \approx 8$; Initially there are 8 rabbits.

14. (a) $k = 1; M = 200$

   (b) $P(0) \approx 1$; Initially 1 student has the measles.

15. (a) 0.875%   **(b)** 275,980,017

16. (a) About 10.32 yrs

   (b) About 44.4 yrs

17. (a) $P(t) = \dfrac{150}{1 + 24e^{-0.225t}}$

   (b) About 17.21 weeks; 21.28 weeks

18. (a) $P(t) \approx \dfrac{250}{1 + 7.9286e^{-0.1t}}$

   (b) 83 yrs to reach $249.5 \approx 250$

19. (a) $y = y_0 e^{-0.00001t}$

   (b) $\approx$10,536 yrs

   (c) $\approx$81.9%

20. $\approx$13.8 yrs

21. (a) $x = 11,000e^{0.1t} - 10,000$

   (b) $\approx$ 23 yrs

22. (a) $p(x) = 20.09e^{1-0.01x}$

   (b) $p(10) \approx \$49.41$ $p(90) \approx \$22.20$

   (c) $r'(x) = 20.09e^{1-0.01x}(1 - 0.01x)$, so $r'(x) > 0$ for $x < 100$ and $r'(x) < 0$ for $x > 100$.

23. (a) $y = \dfrac{18.70}{1 + 1.075e^{-0.0422x}}$

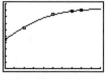

[0, 100] by [0, 20]

   (b) 18.7 million

   (c) $x \approx 1.7$ (year 1912); population $\approx$ 9.35 million

24. (a) $y = \dfrac{24.76}{1 + 7.195e^{-0.0513x}}$

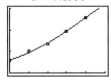

[0, 50] by [0, 15]

(b) 24.76 million

(c) $x \approx 38.44$ (year 1988);
population ≈ 12.38 million

25. Separate variables and rewrite $\dfrac{M}{P(M - P)}$ as

$\dfrac{1}{P} + \dfrac{1}{M - P}$ in order to integrate.

26. (a) $y = \dfrac{16.90}{1 + 5.132e^{-0.0666x}}$

(b) 16.9 million

27. $y = e^{\sin x} - 1$

28. $y = 3 + 2e^{-2x}$

29. $y = \sqrt{x^2 + 4}$

30. $y = e^{(2/3)x^{(3/2)}}$

31. (a) $\dfrac{dP}{dt}$ has the same sign as $(M - P)(P - m)$.

(b) $P(t) = \dfrac{1200Ae^{11kt/12} + 100}{1 + Ae^{11kt/12}}$

(c) $P(t) = \dfrac{300(8e^{11kt/12} + 3)}{9 + 2e^{11kt/12}}$

(d)

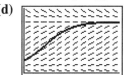

[0, 75] by [0, 1500]

(e) $P(t) = \dfrac{AMe^{(M-m)kt/M} + m}{1 + Ae^{(M-m)kt/M}}$ where

$A = \dfrac{P(0) - m}{M - P(0)}$

32. (a) Use the Fundamental Theorem of Calculus.

(b) $p(9) \approx 109.65$. This is the price of $100 item

after 9 years during which the inflation rate is

$\dfrac{0.04}{1 + t}$ per year.

(c) $143.33

(d) $168.54

33. (a) $P(t) = \dfrac{P_0}{1 - kP_0t}$

(b) Vertical asymptote at $t = \dfrac{1}{kP_0}$

6.6 Numerical Methods (pp. 350–356)

Quick Review 6.6

1. 9

2. $L(x) = 9x - 16$

3. 2

4. $L(x) = 2x - \dfrac{\pi}{2} + 1$

5. 0.4875

6. $y = 0.4875x + 0.9$

7. (a) 0.001762

(b) 0.061%

8. (a) 0.006976

(b) 0.236%

9. (a) 0.042361

(b) 1.351%

10. (a) 0.047321

(b) 1.783%

Section 6.6 Exercises

1. $f'(x) = 1 - 2e^{-x} = x - f(x)$ and $f(0) = 1$.

2. $f'(x) = 1 + e^{-x} = x - f(x)$ and $f(0) = -2$.

3. $f'(x) = \dfrac{1}{5}(2e^{2x} - 2\cos x + \sin x) = 2f(x) + \sin x$
and $f(0) = 0$.

4. $f'(x) = e^x - 2e^{2x} = f(x) - e^{2x} + 1$
and $f(0) = -1$.

5. $y = 2e^x - 1$

6. $y = -e^{(-x^2/2)+2} + 1$

7. $y = 2e^{x^2+2x}$

8. $y = -\dfrac{1}{x^2 + x + 1}$

9.

x	y (Euler)	y (exact)	Error
0	0	0	0
0.1	0	0.0053	0.0053
0.2	0.0100	0.0229	0.0129
0.3	0.0318	0.0551	0.0233
0.4	0.0678	0.1051	0.0374
0.5	0.1203	0.1764	0.0561
0.6	0.1923	0.2731	0.0808
0.7	0.2872	0.4004	0.1132
0.8	0.4090	0.5643	0.1553
0.9	0.5626	0.7723	0.2097
1.0	0.7534	1.0332	0.2797

10.

x	y (Euler)	y (exact)	Error
0	-2	-2	0
0.1	-1.8000	-1.8048	0.0048
0.2	-1.6100	-1.6187	0.0087
0.3	-1.4290	-1.4408	0.0118
0.4	-1.2561	-1.2703	0.0142
0.5	-1.0905	-1.1065	0.0160
0.6	-0.9314	-0.9488	0.0174
0.7	-0.7783	-0.7966	0.0183
0.8	-0.6305	-0.6493	0.0189
0.9	-0.4874	-0.5066	0.0191
1.0	-0.3487	-0.3679	0.0192

11.

x	$y\left(\begin{array}{c}\text{improved}\\\text{Euler}\end{array}\right)$	y (exact)	Error
-2	2	2	0
-1.9	1.6560	1.6539	0.0021
-1.8	1.3983	1.3954	0.0030
-1.7	1.2042	1.2010	0.0032
-1.6	1.0578	1.0546	0.0032
-1.5	0.9478	0.9447	0.0031
-1.4	0.8663	0.8634	0.0029
-1.3	0.8077	0.8050	0.0027
-1.2	0.7683	0.7658	0.0025
-1.1	0.7456	0.7415	0.0024
-1.0	0.7381	0.7358	0.0023
-0.9	0.7455	0.7432	0.0023
-0.8	0.7682	0.7658	0.0024
-0.7	0.8075	0.8050	0.0024
-0.6	0.8659	0.8634	0.0025
-0.5	0.9473	0.9447	0.0026
-0.4	1.0572	1.0546	0.0026
-0.3	1.2036	1.2010	0.0026
-0.2	1.3976	1.3954	0.0022
-0.1	1.6553	1.6540	0.0014
0	1.9996	2	0.0004

12.

x	$y\left(\begin{array}{c}\text{improved}\\\text{Euler}\end{array}\right)$	y (exact)	Error
-2	0	0	0
-1.9	-0.2140	-0.2153	0.0013
-1.8	-0.4593	-0.4623	0.0029
-1.7	-0.7371	-0.7419	0.0049
-1.6	-1.0473	-1.0544	0.0071
-1.5	-1.3892	-1.3989	0.0097
-1.4	-1.7607	-1.7732	0.0125
-1.3	-2.1585	-2.1740	0.0155
-1.2	-2.5780	-2.5966	0.0186
-1.1	-3.0131	-3.0350	0.0219
-1.0	-3.4565	-3.4817	0.0252
-0.9	-3.9000	-3.9283	0.0284
-0.8	-4.3341	-4.3656	0.0315
-0.7	-4.7491	-4.7834	0.0344
-0.6	-5.1348	-5.1719	0.0370
-0.5	-5.4815	-5.5208	0.0394
-0.4	-5.7796	-5.8210	0.0413
-0.3	-6.0210	-6.0639	0.0430
-0.2	-6.1986	-6.2427	0.0441
-0.1	-6.3073	-6.3522	0.0449
0	-6.3438	-6.3891	0.0452

13.

x	y (Euler)	$y\left(\dfrac{\text{improved}}{\text{Euler}}\right)$	y (exact)	Error (Euler)	Error $\left(\dfrac{\text{improved}}{\text{Euler}}\right)$
0	1	1	1	0	0
0.1	0.9000	0.9100	0.9097	0.0097	0.0003
0.2	0.8200	0.8381	0.8375	0.0175	0.0006
0.3	0.7580	0.7824	0.7816	0.0236	0.0008
0.4	0.7122	0.7416	0.7406	0.0284	0.0010
0.5	0.6810	0.7142	0.7131	0.0321	0.0011
0.6	0.6629	0.6988	0.6976	0.0347	0.0012
0.7	0.6566	0.6944	0.6932	0.0366	0.0012
0.8	0.6609	0.7000	0.6987	0.0377	0.0013
0.9	0.6748	0.7145	0.7131	0.0383	0.0013
1.0	0.6974	0.7371	0.7358	0.0384	0.0013
1.1	0.7276	0.7671	0.7657	0.0381	0.0013
1.2	0.7649	0.8037	0.8024	0.0375	0.0013
1.3	0.8084	0.8463	0.8451	0.0367	0.0013
1.4	0.8575	0.8944	0.8932	0.0357	0.0012
1.5	0.9118	0.9475	0.9463	0.0345	0.0012
1.6	0.9706	1.0050	1.0038	0.0332	0.0012
1.7	1.0335	1.0665	1.0654	0.0318	0.0011
1.8	1.1002	1.1317	1.1306	0.0304	0.0011
1.9	1.1702	1.2002	1.1991	0.0290	0.0010
2.0	1.2432	1.2716	1.2707	0.0275	0.0010

14.

x	y (Euler)	$y\left(\dfrac{\text{improved}}{\text{Euler}}\right)$	y (exact)	error (Euler)	Error $\left(\dfrac{\text{improved}}{\text{Euler}}\right)$
0	-1	-1	-1	0	0
0.1	-1.1000	-1.1161	-1.1162	0.0162	0.0002
0.2	-1.2321	-1.2700	-1.2704	0.0383	0.0004
0.3	-1.4045	-1.4715	-1.4723	0.0677	0.0007
0.4	-1.6272	-1.7325	-1.7337	0.1065	0.0012
0.5	-1.9125	-2.0678	-2.0696	0.1571	0.0018
0.6	-2.2756	-2.4954	-2.4980	0.2224	0.0026
0.7	-2.7351	-3.0378	-3.0414	0.3063	0.0037
0.8	-3.3142	-3.7224	-3.7275	0.4133	0.0050
0.9	-4.0409	-4.5832	-4.5900	0.5492	0.0068
1.0	-4.9499	-5.6616	-5.6708	0.7209	0.0092
1.1	-6.0838	-7.0087	-7.0208	0.9370	0.0121
1.2	-7.4947	-8.6872	-8.7031	1.2084	0.0159
1.3	-9.2465	-10.7738	-10.7944	1.5480	0.0206
1.4	-11.4175	-13.3628	-13.3894	1.9719	0.0267
1.5	-14.1037	-16.5696	-16.6038	2.5001	0.0342
1.6	-17.4227	-20.5358	-20.5795	3.1568	0.0437
1.7	-21.5182	-25.4345	-25.4902	3.9720	0.0556
1.8	-26.5664	-31.4781	-31.5486	4.9822	0.0705
1.9	-32.7829	-38.9262	-39.0153	6.2324	0.0891
2.0	-40.4313	-48.0970	-48.2091	7.7778	0.1121

15. (a) $y = \dfrac{-1}{x^2 - 2x + 2}$, $y(3) = -0.2$

   (b) -0.1851, error ≈ 0.0149

   (c) -0.1929, error ≈ 0.0071

   (d) -0.1965, error ≈ 0.0035

16. (a) $y = 2e^x + 1$, $y(1) \approx 6.4366$

   (b) 5.9766, error ≈ 0.4599

   (c) 6.1875, error ≈ 0.2491

   (d) 6.3066, error ≈ 0.1300

17. (a) -0.2024, error ≈ 0.0024

   (b) -0.2005, error ≈ 0.0005

   (c) -0.2001, error ≈ 0.0001

   (d) As the step size decreases, the accuracy of the method increases and so the error decreases.

18. (a) 6.4054, error ≈ 0.0311

   (b) 6.4282, error ≈ 0.0084

   (c) 6.4344, error ≈ 0.0022

   (d) As the step size decreases, the accuracy of the method increases and the error decreases.

19.

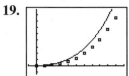

$[-0.1, 1.1]$ by $[-0.13, 0.88]$

20.

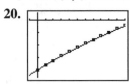

$[-0.1, 1.1]$ by $[-2.3, 0.3]$

21.

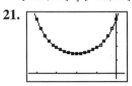

$[-2.2, 0.2]$ by $[-0.2, 2.2]$

22.

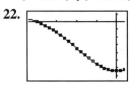

$[-2.2, 0.2]$ by $[-7.3, 1.1]$

23.

x	y (Euler)	y (exact)	Error
0	1	1.0	0
-0.1	0.9000	0.9097	0.0097
-0.2	0.8200	0.8375	0.0175
-0.3	0.7580	0.7816	0.0236
-0.4	0.7122	0.7406	0.0284
-0.5	0.6810	0.7131	0.0321
-0.6	0.6629	0.6976	0.0347
-0.7	0.6566	0.6932	0.0366
-0.8	0.6609	0.6987	0.0377
-0.9	0.6748	0.7131	0.0383
-1.0	0.6974	0.7358	0.0384

24.

x	$y\left(\begin{array}{c}\text{Improved}\\\text{Euler}\end{array}\right)$	y (exact)	Error
0	1	1.0	0
-0.1	0.9100	0.9097	0.0003
-0.2	0.8381	0.8375	0.0006
-0.3	0.7824	0.7816	0.0008
-0.4	0.7416	0.7406	0.0010
-0.5	0.7142	0.7131	0.0011
-0.6	0.6988	0.6976	0.0012
-0.7	0.6944	0.6932	0.0012
-0.8	0.7000	0.6987	0.0013
-0.9	0.7145	0.7131	0.0013
-1.0	0.7371	0.7358	0.0013

25. (a)

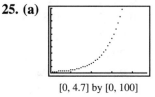

$[0, 4.7]$ by $[0, 100]$

   (b)

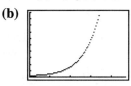

$[0, 4.7]$ by $[0, 100]$

26. (a)

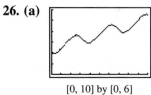

$[0, 10]$ by $[0, 6]$

   (b)

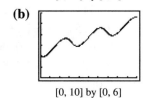

$[0, 10]$ by $[0, 6]$

27. (a)

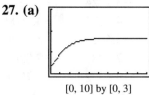

$[0, 10]$ by $[0, 3]$

   (b)

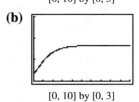

$[0, 10]$ by $[0, 3]$

28. (a)

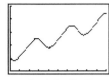

[0, 10] by [0, 5]

(b)

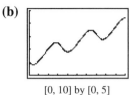

[0, 10] by [0, 5]

29. 2.6533, e **30.** ≈ 19.8845, e^3

31.

x	y (Runge-Kutta)	y (exact)	error
0	1	1	0
0.1	1.2103	1.2103	0.0000002
0.2	1.4428	1.4428	0.0000004
0.3	1.6997	1.6997	0.0000006
0.4	1.9836	1.9836	0.0000009
0.5	2.2974	2.2974	0.0000013
0.6	2.6442	2.6442	0.0000017
0.7	3.0275	3.0275	0.0000022
0.8	3.4511	3.4511	0.0000027
0.9	3.9192	3.9192	0.0000034
1.0	4.4366	4.4366	0.0000042

32. (a)

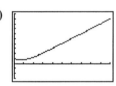

[0, 10] by [−3, 10]

(b)

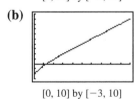

[0, 10] by [−3, 10]

Chapter 6 Review Exercises (pp. 358–361)

1. $\sqrt{3}$ **2.** 2
3. 8   **4.** 0
5. 2   **6.** $\dfrac{147}{8}$
7. $e - 1$ **8.** $\dfrac{2}{3}$
9. $-\ln|2 - \sin x| + C$ **10.** $\dfrac{1}{2}(3x + 4)^{2/3} + C$
11. $\dfrac{1}{2}\ln(t^2 + 5) + C$ **12.** $-\sec\dfrac{1}{\theta} + C$
13. $-\ln|\cos(\ln y)| + C$
14. $\ln|\sec(e^x) + \tan(e^x)| + C$

15. $\ln|\ln x| + C$ **16.** $\dfrac{-2}{\sqrt{t}} + C$
17. $x^3 \sin x + 3x^2 \cos x - 6x \sin x - 6 \cos x + C$
18. $\dfrac{x^5 \ln x}{5} - \dfrac{x^5}{25} + C$
19. $\left(\dfrac{3 \sin x}{10} - \dfrac{\cos x}{10}\right)e^{3x} + C$
20. $\left(-\dfrac{x^2}{3} - \dfrac{2x}{9} - \dfrac{2}{27}\right)e^{-3x} + C$
21. $y = \dfrac{x^3}{6} + \dfrac{x^2}{2} + x + 1$
22. $y = \dfrac{x^3}{3} + 2x - \dfrac{1}{x} - \dfrac{1}{3}$
23. $y = \ln(t + 4) + 2$
24. $y = -\dfrac{1}{2}\csc 2\theta + \dfrac{3}{2}$
25. $y = \dfrac{x^3}{3} + \ln x - x + \dfrac{2}{3}$
26. $r = \sin t - \dfrac{t^2}{2} - 2t - 1$
27. $y = 4e^x - 2$
28. $y = 2e^{x^2+x} - 1$
29. $-1 + \sqrt{x} + C$ or $\sqrt{x} + C$
30. $\dfrac{x^2}{2} + 1 - \sqrt{x} + C$ or $\dfrac{x^2}{2} - \sqrt{x} + C$
31. $-2\sqrt{x} - x + C$
32. $2 - 3x + C$ or $-3x + C$
33. (b)
34. (d)
35. **iv**, since the given graph looks like $y = x^2$, which satisfies $\dfrac{dy}{dx} = 2x$ and $y(1) = 1$.
36. Yes, $y = x$ is a solution.
37. (a) $v = 2t + 3t^2 + 4$
    (b) 6 m
38.

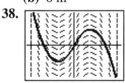

[−10, 10] by [−10, 10]

39.

x	y
0	0
0.1	0.1000
0.2	0.2095
0.3	0.3285
0.4	0.4568
0.5	0.5946
0.6	0.7418
0.7	0.8986
0.8	1.0649
0.9	1.2411
1.0	1.4273
1.1	1.6241
1.2	1.8319
1.3	2.0513
1.4	2.2832
1.5	2.5285
1.6	2.7884
1.7	3.0643
1.8	3.3579
1.9	3.6709
2.0	4.0057

40.

x	y
-3	1
-2.9	0.6680
-2.8	0.2599
-2.7	-0.2294
-2.6	-0.8011
-2.5	-1.4509
-2.4	-2.1687
-2.3	-2.9374
-2.2	-3.7333
-2.1	-4.5268
-2.0	-5.2840
-1.9	-5.9686
-1.8	-6.5456
-1.7	-6.9831
-1.6	-7.2562
-1.5	-7.3488
-1.4	-7.2553
-1.3	-6.9813
-1.2	-6.5430
-1.1	-5.9655
-1.0	-5.2805

41. 0.9063 **42.** 4.4974

43. (a)

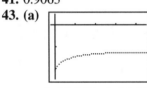

$[-0.2, 4.5]$ by $[-2.5, 0.5]$

(b)

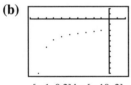

$[-1, 0.2]$ by $[-10, 2]$

44. (a)

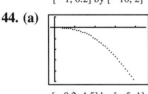

$[-0.2, 4.5]$ by $[-5, 1]$

(b)

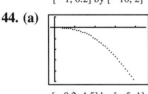

$[-4.5, 0.2]$ by $[-1, 5]$

45. (a) $k \approx 0.262059$
(b) About 3.81593 years
46. About 92 minutes **47.** $-3°C$
48. About 41.2 years
49. About 18,935 years old
50. About 5.3%
51. About 59.8 ft

52. (a) $y = c + (y_0 - c)e^{-(kA/V)t}$
(b) c
53. (a) $k = 1$; carrying capacity $= 150$
(b) ≈ 2; Initially there were 2 infected students.
(c) About 6 days
54. Use the Fundamental Theorem of Calculus to obtain $y' = \sin(x^2) + 3x^2 + 1$. Then differentiate again and also verify the initial conditions.
55. $P = \dfrac{800}{1 + 15e^{-0.002t}}$

56. Method 1—Compare graph of $y_1 = x^2 \ln x$ with $y_2 = \text{NDER}\left(\dfrac{x^3 \ln x}{3} - \dfrac{x^3}{9}\right)$.

Method 2—Compare graph of $y_1 = \text{NINT}(x^2 \ln x)$ with $y_2 = \dfrac{x^3 \ln x}{3} - \dfrac{x^3}{9}$.

57. (a) About 11.3 years
(b) About 11 years

58. (a) $\dfrac{d}{dx}\displaystyle\int_0^x u(t)\,dt = u(x)$

$\dfrac{d}{dx}\displaystyle\int_3^x u(t)\,dt = u(x)$

(b) $C = \displaystyle\int_0^3 u(t)\,dt$

59. (a) $y = \dfrac{56.0716}{1 + 5.894e^{-0.0205x}}$

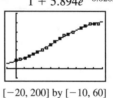

$[-20, 200]$ by $[-10, 60]$

(b) ≈ 56.0716 million

(c) ≈ 1887, ≈ 28.0 million
60. (a) $T = 79.961(0.9273)^t$

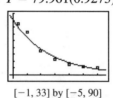

$[-1, 33]$ by $[-5, 90]$

(b) About 9.2 sec
(c) About 79.96°C
61. $s = 0.97(1 - e^{-0.8866t})$

A graph of the model is shown superimposed on a graph of the data.

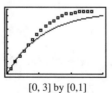

$[0, 3]$ by $[0,1]$

Chapter 7
Applications of Definite Integrals

7.1 Integral as Net Change
(pp. 363–374)

Quick Review 7.1

1. Changes sign at $-\dfrac{\pi}{2}, 0, \dfrac{\pi}{2}$

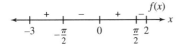

2. Changes sign at 1, 2

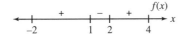

3. Always positive

4. Changes sign at $-\dfrac{1}{2}$

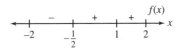

5. Changes sign at $\dfrac{\pi}{4}, \dfrac{3\pi}{4}, \dfrac{5\pi}{4}$

6. Always positive
7. Changes sign at 0

8. Changes sign at $-2, -\sqrt{2}, \sqrt{2}, 2$

9. Changes sign at $0.9633 + k\pi$
$\qquad\qquad\qquad 2.1783 + k\pi$
where k is an integer

10. Changes sign at $\dfrac{1}{3\pi}, \dfrac{1}{2\pi}$

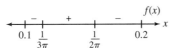

Section 7.1 Exercises

1. (a) Right: $0 \le t < \dfrac{\pi}{2}, \dfrac{3\pi}{2} < t \le 2\pi$
     Left: $\dfrac{\pi}{2} < t < \dfrac{3\pi}{2}$
     Stopped: $t = \dfrac{\pi}{2}, \dfrac{3\pi}{2}$
  (b) 0   **(c)** 20

2. (a) Right: $0 < t < \dfrac{\pi}{3}$
     Left: $\dfrac{\pi}{3} < t \le \dfrac{\pi}{2}$
     Stopped: $t = 0, \dfrac{\pi}{3}$
  (b) 2   **(c)** 6

3. (a) Right: $0 \le t < 5$
     Left: $5 < t \le 10$
     Stopped: $t = 5$
  (b) 0   **(c)** 245

4. (a) Right: $0 \le t < 1$
     Left: $1 < t < 2$
     Stopped: $t = 1, 2$
  (b) 4   **(c)** 6

5. (a) Right: $0 < t < \dfrac{\pi}{2}, \dfrac{3\pi}{2} < t < 2\pi$
     Left: $\dfrac{\pi}{2} < t < \pi, \pi < t < \dfrac{3\pi}{2}$
     Stopped: $t = 0, \dfrac{\pi}{2}, \pi, \dfrac{3\pi}{2}, 2\pi$
  (b) 0   **(c)** $\dfrac{20}{3}$

6. (a) Right: $0 \le t < 4$
     Left: never
     Stopped: $t = 4$
  (b) $\dfrac{16}{3}$ **(c)** $\dfrac{16}{3}$

7. (a) Right: $0 \le t < \dfrac{\pi}{2}, \dfrac{3\pi}{2} < t \le 2\pi$
     Left: $\dfrac{\pi}{2} < t < \dfrac{3\pi}{2}$
     Stopped: $t = \dfrac{\pi}{2}, \dfrac{3\pi}{2}$
  (b) 0   **(c)** $2e - \dfrac{2}{e} \approx 4.7$

8. (a) Right: $0 < t \le 3$
     Left: never
     Stopped: $t = 0$
  (b) $\dfrac{\ln 10}{2} \approx 1.15$ **(c)** $\dfrac{\ln 10}{2} \approx 1.15$

9. (a) 63 mph   **(b)** 344.52 feet
10. (a) ≈ -1.44952 meters
    (b) ≈ 1.91411 meters
11. (a) -6 ft/sec   **(b)** 5.625 sec
   (c) 0   **(d)** 253.125 feet
12. -23 cm   **13.** 33 cm
14. a: 11
   b: 16
   c: -8

15. $t = a$ **16.** $t = c$
17. (a) 6   **(b)** 4 meters
18. (a) 2   **(b)** 4 meters
19. (a) 5   **(b)** 7 meters
20. (a) -2.5 **(b)** 19.5 meters
21. ≈ 332.965 billion barrels
22. 93.6 kilowatt-hours
23. (a) 2 miles
  (b) $2\pi r\Delta r$
  (c) Population = Population density $\times$ Area
  (d) $\approx 83,776$
24. (a) $2\pi r\Delta r$
  (b) $8(10 - r^2)\dfrac{\text{in.}}{\text{sec}} \cdot (2\pi r)\Delta r \text{ in}^2 = \text{flow in } \dfrac{\text{in}^3}{\text{sec}}$
  (c) $396\pi \dfrac{\text{in}^3}{\text{sec}}$ or $\approx 1244.07 \dfrac{\text{in}^3}{\text{sec}}$
25. One possible answer:
  Plot the speeds vs. time. Connect the points and
  find the area under the line graph. The definite
  integral also gives the area under the curve.
26. (a) 797.5 thousand
  (b) $B(x) = 1.6x^2 + 2.3x + 5.0$
  (c) ≈ 904.02 thousand
  (d) The answer in (a) corresponds to the area of
  left hand rectangles. These rectangles lie under
  the curve $B(x)$. The answer in (c) corresponds
  to the area under the curve. This area is greater
  than the area of the rectangles.
27. (a) ≈ 798.97 thousand
  (b) The answer in (a) corresponds to the area of
  midpoint rectangles. Part of each rectangle is
  above the curve and part is below.
28. 1156.5
29. (a) 18 N   **(b)** 81 N $\cdot$ cm
30. (a) 1250 inch-pounds
  (b) 3750 inch-pounds
31. 0.04875
32. 40 thousandths or 0.040
33. (a, b) Take $dm = \delta \, dA$ as m_k and letting $dA \to 0$,
  $k \to \infty$ in the center of mass equations.
34. $\bar{x} = 0, \bar{y} = \dfrac{12}{5}$ **35.** $\bar{x} = \dfrac{4}{3}, \bar{y} = 0$

7.2 Areas in the Plane (pp. 374–382)

Quick Review 7.2

1. 2   **2.** $\dfrac{1}{2}(e^2 - 1) \approx 3.195$
3. 2   **4.** 4
5. $\dfrac{9\pi}{2}$ **6.** $(6, 12); (-1, 5)$
7. $(0, 1)$ **8.** $(0, 0); (\pi, 0)$
9. $(-1, -1); (0, 0); (1, 1)$
10. $(-0.9286, -0.8008); (0, 0); (0.9286, 0.8008)$

Section 7.2 Exercises

1. $\dfrac{\pi}{2}$ **2.** $\dfrac{4\pi}{3}$
3. $\dfrac{1}{12}$ **4.** $\dfrac{4}{3}$
5. $\dfrac{128}{15}$ **6.** $\dfrac{22}{15}$
7. $\dfrac{5}{6}$ **8.** $\dfrac{5}{6}$
9. 16   **10.** $8\dfrac{1}{6}$
11. $10\dfrac{2}{3}$ **12.** $10\dfrac{2}{3}$
13. 4   **14.** 8
15. $\dfrac{2}{3}a^3$
16. $1\dfrac{2}{3}$ (3 points of intersection)
17. $21\dfrac{1}{3}$ **18.** $4\dfrac{1}{2}$
19. $30\dfrac{3}{8}$ **20.** 4
21. $\dfrac{8}{3}$ **22.** $6\dfrac{14}{15}$
23. 8   **24.** 4
25. $6\sqrt{3}$ **26.** $\dfrac{4}{3} - \dfrac{4}{\pi} \approx 0.0601$
27. $\dfrac{4 - \pi}{\pi} \approx 0.273$ **28.** $\dfrac{\pi}{2}$
29. $4 - \pi \approx 0.858$ **30.** 2
31. $\dfrac{1}{2}$ **32.** 1
33. $\sqrt{2} - 1 \approx 0.414$ **34.** $\dfrac{32}{3}$
35. (a) $(-\sqrt{c}, c); (\sqrt{c}, c)$

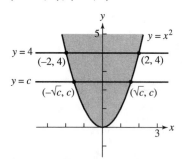

  (b) $\displaystyle\int_0^c \sqrt{y} \, dy = \int_c^4 \sqrt{y} \, dy \Rightarrow c = 2^{4/3}$
  (c) $\displaystyle\int_0^{\sqrt{c}} (c - x^2) \, dx$
    $= (4 - c)\sqrt{c} + \displaystyle\int_{\sqrt{c}}^2 (4 - x^2) \, dx \Rightarrow c = 2^{4/3}$
36. $\dfrac{11}{3}$ **37.** $\dfrac{3}{4}$
38. 4   **39.** Neither; both are zero
40. Sometimes; If $f(x) \geq g(x)$ on (a, b), then true.
41. $\ln 4 - \dfrac{1}{2} \approx 0.886$ **42.** ≈ 0.4303

43. $k \approx 1.8269$

44. (a) $y = \pm b \sqrt{1 - \dfrac{x^2}{a^2}}$

   (b) $2 \displaystyle\int_{-a}^{a} b \sqrt{1 - \dfrac{x^2}{a^2}} \, dx$

   (c) Answers may vary.

   (d, e) $ab\pi$

45. Since $f(x) - g(x)$ is the same for each region where $f(x)$ and $g(x)$ represent the upper and lower edges, area $= \displaystyle\int_{a}^{b} [f(x) - g(x)] \, dx$ will be the same for each.

46. $m - \ln(m) - 1$

7.3 Volumes
(pp. 383–394)

Quick Review 7.3

1. x^2

2. $\dfrac{x^2}{2}$

3. $\dfrac{\pi x^2}{2}$

4. $\dfrac{\pi x^2}{8}$

5. $\dfrac{\sqrt{3}}{4} x^2$

6. $\dfrac{x^2}{2}$

7. $\dfrac{x^2}{4}$

8. $\dfrac{\sqrt{15}}{4} x^2$

9. $6x^2$

10. $\dfrac{3\sqrt{3}}{2} x^2$

Section 7.3 Exercises

1. (a) $\pi(1 - x^2)$ **(b)** $4(1 - x^2)$

   (c) $2(1 - x^2)$ **(d)** $\sqrt{3}(1 - x^2)$

2. (a) πx **(b)** $4x$

   (c) $2x$ **(d)** $\sqrt{3} x$

3. 16

4. $\dfrac{16}{15} \pi$

5. $\dfrac{16}{3}$

6. $\dfrac{8}{3}$

7. (a) $2\sqrt{3}$ **(b)** 8

8. (a) $\pi\sqrt{3} - \dfrac{\pi^2}{6}$ **(b)** $4\sqrt{3} - \dfrac{2}{3}\pi$

9. 8π

10. $\dfrac{8}{3}$

11. (a) $s^2 h$ **(b)** $s^2 h$

12. The volumes are equal by Cavalieri's Theorem.

13. $\dfrac{2}{3}\pi$

14. 6π

15. $4 - \pi$

16. $\dfrac{\pi^2}{16}$

17. $\dfrac{32\pi}{5}$

18. $\dfrac{128\pi}{7}$

19. 36π

20. $\dfrac{\pi}{30}$

21. $\dfrac{2}{3}\pi$

22. π

23. $\dfrac{117\pi}{5}$

24. $\dfrac{108\pi}{5}$

25. $\pi^2 - 2\pi$

26. 8π

27. 2.301

28. $\pi(3\pi - 8)$

29. 2π

30. 4π

31. $\dfrac{4}{3}\pi$

32. $\dfrac{2}{3}\pi$

33. 8π

34. $\dfrac{2\pi}{15}$

35. (a) 8π **(b)** $\dfrac{32\pi}{5}$

   (c) $\dfrac{8\pi}{3}$ **(d)** $\dfrac{224\pi}{15}$

36. (a) $\dfrac{2}{3}\pi$ **(b)** $\dfrac{8\pi}{3}$

37. (a) $\dfrac{16\pi}{15}$ **(b)** $\dfrac{56\pi}{15}$

   (c) $\dfrac{64\pi}{15}$

38. (a) $\dfrac{\pi}{3} bh^2$ **(b)** $\dfrac{\pi}{3} b^2 h$

39. 8π

40. $\dfrac{5\pi}{6}$

41. $\dfrac{128\pi}{5}$

42. $\dfrac{7\pi}{15}$

43. (a) $\dfrac{6\pi}{5}$ **(b)** $\dfrac{4\pi}{5}$

   (c) 2π **(d)** 2π

44. (a) $\dfrac{8\pi}{3}$ **(b)** $\dfrac{8\pi}{5}$

   (c) 8π **(d)** 4π

45. (a) $\dfrac{512\pi}{21}$ **(b)** $\dfrac{832\pi}{21}$

46. (a) $\dfrac{\pi}{6}$ **(b)** $\dfrac{\pi}{6}$

47. (a) $\dfrac{11\pi}{48}$ **(b)** $\dfrac{11\pi}{48}$

48. (b) 4π

49. (a) $\dfrac{36\pi}{5}$ cm^3 **(b)** 192.3 g

50. (a) $\dfrac{2}{\pi}, \dfrac{\pi^2 - 8}{2}$ **(b)** 0

   (c) $V = \dfrac{\pi(2c^2\pi - 8c + \pi)}{2}$

   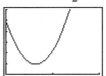

   [0, 2] by [0, 6]

   Volume $\to \infty$

51. (a) 2.3, 1.6, 1.5, 2.1, 3.2, 4.8, 7.0, 9.3, 10.7, 10.7, 9.3, 6.4, 3.2

   (b) $\dfrac{1}{4\pi} \displaystyle\int_{0}^{6} C(y)^2 \, dy$

   (c) ≈ 34.7 in^3

52. (a) 25π **(b)** $\dfrac{3}{8\pi}$

53. (a) $\dfrac{32\pi}{3}$

    (b) The answer is independent of r.

54. Partition the appropriate interval on the axis of
revolution and measure the radius $r(x)$ of the
shadow region at these points. Then use an
approximation such as the trapezoidal rule to
estimate the integral $\displaystyle\int_a^b \pi r^2(x)\,dx$.

55. 5

56. For a tiny horizontal slice,

    slant height $= \Delta s = \sqrt{(\Delta x)^2 + (\Delta y)^2}$

    $= \sqrt{1 + (g'(y))^2}\,\Delta y$. So the surface area is

    approximated by the Riemann sum

    $\displaystyle\sum_{k=1}^{n} 2\pi\, g(y_k)\sqrt{1 + (g'(y))^2}\,\Delta y$. The limit of that is

    the integral.

57. ≈ 13.614 **58.** ≈ 0.638

59. ≈ 16.110 **60.** ≈ 2.999

61. ≈ 53.226 **62.** ≈ 44.877

63. ≈ 6.283 **64.** ≈ 51.313

65. Hemisphere cross sectional area:

    $\pi(\sqrt{R^2 - h^2})^2 = A_1$

    Right circular cylinder with cone removed cross
sectional area: $\pi R^2 - \pi h^2 = A_2$

    Since $A_1 = A_2$, the two volumes are equal by
Cavalieri's theorem. Thus,

    volume of hemisphere

        $=$ volume of cylinder $-$ volume of cone

        $= \pi R^3 - \dfrac{1}{3}\pi R^3 = \dfrac{2}{3}\pi R^3.$

66. $2a^2 b\pi^2$

67. (a) $\dfrac{\pi h^2(3a - h)}{3}$

    (b) $\dfrac{1}{120\pi}$ m/sec

68. (a) A cross section has radius $r = \sqrt{a^2 - x^2}$ and

        area $A(x) = \pi r^2 = \pi(a^2 - x^2)$.

        $V = \displaystyle\int_{-a}^{a} \pi(a^2 - x^2) = \dfrac{4}{3}\pi a^3$

    (b) A cross section has radius $x = r\left(1 - \dfrac{y}{h}\right)$ and

        area $A(y) = \pi x^2 = \pi r^2\left(1 - \dfrac{2y}{h} + \dfrac{y^2}{h^2}\right)$.

        $V = \displaystyle\int_0^h \pi r^2\left(1 - \dfrac{2y}{h} + \dfrac{y^2}{h^2}\right) dy = \dfrac{1}{3}\pi r^2 h$

7.4 Lengths of Curves
(pp. 395–401)

Quick Review 7.4

1. $x + 1$ **2.** $\dfrac{2 - x}{2}$

3. $\sec x$ **4.** $\dfrac{x^2 + 4}{4x}$

5. $\sqrt{2}\cos x$ **6.** 4

7. 0   **8.** -3

9. 2   **10.** $k\pi$, k any integer

Section 7.4 Exercises

1. (a) $\displaystyle\int_{-1}^{2} \sqrt{1 + 4x^2}\,dx$

    (b)

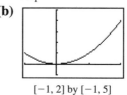

        $[-1, 2]$ by $[-1, 5]$

    (c) ≈ 6.126

2. (a) $\displaystyle\int_{-\pi/3}^{0} \sqrt{1 + \sec^4 x}\,dx$

    (b)

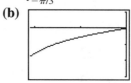

        $\left[-\dfrac{\pi}{3}, 0\right]$ by $[-3, 1]$

    (c) ≈ 2.057

3. (a) $\displaystyle\int_0^{\pi} \sqrt{1 + \cos^2 y}\,dy$

    (b)

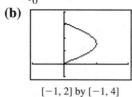

        $[-1, 2]$ by $[-1, 4]$

    (c) ≈ 3.820

4. (a) $\displaystyle\int_{-1/2}^{1/2} \sqrt{1 + \dfrac{y^2}{1 - y^2}}\,dy$

    (b)

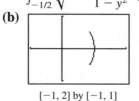

        $[-1, 2]$ by $[-1, 1]$

    (c) ≈ 1.047

5. (a) $\int_{-1}^{7} \sqrt{1 + \dfrac{1}{2x + 2}}\, dx$

(b)

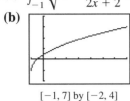

[−1, 7] by [−2, 4]

(c) ≈9.294

6. (a) $\int_{0}^{\pi} \sqrt{1 + x^2 \sin^2 x}\, dx$

(b)

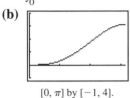

[0, π] by [−1, 4].

(c) ≈4.698

7. (a) $\int_{0}^{\pi/6} \sqrt{1 + \tan^2 x}\, dx$

(b)

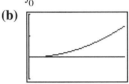

$\left[0, \dfrac{\pi}{6}\right]$ by [−0.1, 0.2]

(c) ≈0.549

8. (a) $\int_{-\pi/3}^{\pi/4} \sec y\, dy$

(b)

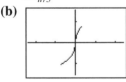

[−2.4, 2.4] by $\left[-\dfrac{\pi}{2}, \dfrac{\pi}{2}\right]$

(c) ≈2.198

9. (a) $\int_{-\pi/3}^{\pi/3} \sqrt{1 + \sec^2 x \tan^2 x}\, dx$

(b)

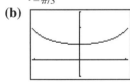

$\left[-\dfrac{\pi}{3}, \dfrac{\pi}{3}\right]$ by [−1, 3]

(c) ≈3.139

10. (a) $\int_{-3}^{3} \sqrt{1 + \left(\dfrac{e^x - e^{-x}}{2}\right)^2}\, dx$

(b)

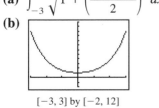

[−3, 3] by [−2, 12]

(c) ≈20.036

11. 12

12. $\dfrac{80\sqrt{10} - 8}{27}$

13. $\dfrac{53}{6}$

14. $\dfrac{123}{32}$

15. $\dfrac{17}{12}$

16. $\dfrac{53}{6}$

17. 2

18. $\dfrac{7\sqrt{3}}{3}$

19. (a) $y = \sqrt{x}$

 (b) Only one. We know the derivative of the function and the value of the function at one value of x.

20. (a) $y = \dfrac{1}{1 - x}$

 (b) Only one. We know the derivative of the function and the value of the function at one value of x.

21. 1

22. 6

23. ≈21.07 inches

24. \$38,422

25. ≈(−19.909, 8.410)

26. ≈3.6142

27. ≈2.1089

28. ≈13.132

29. ≈1.623

30. ≈16.647

31. Because the limit of the sum $\sum \Delta x_k$ as the norm of the partition goes to zero will always be the length $(b - a)$ of the interval (a, b).

32. No. Consider the curve $y = \dfrac{1}{3} \sin\left(\dfrac{1}{x}\right) + 0.5$ for $0 < x < 1$.

33. (a) The fin is the hypotenuse of a right triangle with leg lengths Δx_k and

$$\left.\dfrac{df}{dx}\right|_{x = x_{k-1}} \Delta x_k = f'(x_{k-1})\, \Delta x_k.$$

 (b) $\displaystyle\lim_{n\to\infty} \sum_{k=1}^{n} \sqrt{(\Delta x_k)^2 + (f'(x_{k-1})\, \Delta x_k)^2}$

$$= \lim_{n\to\infty} \sum_{k=1}^{n} \Delta x_k \sqrt{1 + (f'(x_{k-1}))^2}$$

$$= \int_{a}^{b} \sqrt{1 + (f'(x))^2}\, dx$$

34. Yes. Any curve of the form $y = \pm x + c$, c a constant.

7.5 Applications from Science and Statistics (pp. 401–411)

Quick Review 7.5

1. a. $1 - \dfrac{1}{e}$ **b.** ≈0.632

2. a. $e - 1$ **b.** ≈1.718

3. a. $\dfrac{\sqrt{2}}{2}$ **b.** ≈0.707

4. 15

5. a. $\dfrac{1}{3} \ln\left(\dfrac{9}{2}\right)$ **b.** ≈0.501

6. $\int_0^7 2\pi(x+2)\sin x\,dx$ **7.** $\int_0^7 (1-x^2)(2\pi x)\,dx$

8. $\int_0^7 \pi\cos^2 x\,dx$ **9.** $\int_0^7 \pi\left(\frac{y}{2}\right)^2(10-y)\,dy$

10. $\int_0^7 \frac{\sqrt{3}}{4}\sin^2 x\,dx$

Section 7.5 Exercises

1. ≈ 4.4670 J   **2.** ≈ 3.8473 J
3. 9 J   **4.** ≈ 19.5804 J
5. 4900 J   **6.** 5880 J
7. 1944 ft-lb
8. (a) 200 lb/in.   (b) 400 in.-lb
    (c) 8 in.
9. (a) 7238 lb/in.
    (b) ≈ 905 in.-lb and ≈ 2714 in.-lb
10. (a) 300 lb   (b) 18.75 in.-lb
11. 780 J
12. (b) $-37,968.75$ in.-lb
13. (b) 1123.2 lb   **14.** (b) 7987.2 lb
15. (b) 3705 lb   **16.** (b) ≈ 1506.1 lb
17. (a) 1,497,600 ft-lb   (b) ≈ 100 min
    (d) 1,494,240 ft-lb, ≈ 100 min
    1,500,000 ft-lb, 100 min
18. $\approx 7,238,229$ ft-lb
19. Through valve: $\approx 84,687.3$ ft-lb
    Over the rim: $\approx 98,801.8$ ft-lb
    Through a hose attached to a valve in the bottom is
    faster, because it takes more time to do more work.
20. ≈ 91.3244 in.-oz
21. $\approx 53,482.5$ ft-lb   **22.** $\approx 34,582.65$ ft-lb
23. $\approx 967,611$ ft-lb, yes   **24.** ≈ 31 hr
25. (a) ≈ 209.73 lb
    (b) ≈ 838.93 lb; the fluid force doubles
26. ≈ 4.2 lb
27. (a) 0.5 (50%)   (b) ≈ 0.24 (24%)
    (c) ≈ 0.0036 (0.36%)
    (d) 0 if we assume a continuous distribution;
       ≈ 0.071; 7.1% between 59.5 in. and 60.5 in.
28. (a) ≈ 0.34 (34%)   (b) 6.5
29. Integration is a good approximation to the area.
30. The proportion of lightbulbs that last between 100
    and 800 hours.
31. 5.1446×10^{10} J
32. (a) 1.15×10^{-28} J
    (b) $\approx 7.6667 \times 10^{-29}$ J

33. $F = m\dfrac{dv}{dt} = mv\dfrac{dv}{dx}$, so $W = \displaystyle\int_{x_1}^{x_2} F(x)\,dx$

$= \displaystyle\int_{x_1}^{x_2} mv\dfrac{dv}{dx}\,dx = \int_{v_1}^{v_2} mv\,dv = \frac{1}{2}mv_2{}^2 - \frac{1}{2}mv_1{}^2$

34. 50 ft-lb   **35.** ≈ 85.1 ft-lb
36. 122.5 ft-lb   **37.** ≈ 64.6 ft-lb
38. ≈ 109.7 ft-lb   **39.** ≈ 110.6 ft-lb
40. 4.5 ft

Chapter 7 Review Exercises (pp. 413–415)

1. ≈ 10.417 ft   **2.** ≈ 31.361 gal
3. ≈ 1464 **4.** 14 g
5. 14,400   **6.** 1
7. $\dfrac{9}{2}$ **8.** $\dfrac{1}{6}$
9. 18   **10.** 30.375
11. ≈ 0.0155 **12.** 4
13. ≈ 8.9023 **14.** ≈ 2.1043
15. $2\sqrt{3} - \dfrac{2}{3}\pi \approx 1.370$ **16.** $2\sqrt{3} + \dfrac{4}{3}\pi \approx 7.653$
17. ≈ 1.2956 **18.** ≈ 5.7312
19. 4π **20.** 2π
21. (a) $\dfrac{32\pi}{3}$ (b) $\dfrac{128\pi}{15}$
    (c) $\dfrac{64\pi}{5}$ (d) $\dfrac{32\pi}{3}$
22. (a) 4π (b) πk^2
    (c) $\dfrac{1}{\pi}$
23. $88\pi \approx 276$ in^3 **24.** $\dfrac{\pi^2}{4}$
25. $\pi(2 - \ln 3)$
26. $\dfrac{28\pi}{3}$ ft$^3 \approx 29.3215$ ft^3
27. ≈ 19.4942 **28.** ≈ 5.2454
29. 2.296 sec   **30.** (a) is true
31. 39
32. (a) 4000 J   (b) 640 J
    (c) 4640 J
33. 22,800,000 ft-lb   **34.** 12 J, ≈ 213.3 J
35. No, the work going uphill is positive, but the work
    going downhill is negative.
36. ≈ 113.097 in.-lb   **37.** ≈ 426.67 lbs
38. base ≈ 6.6385 lb, front and back: 5.7726 lb,
    sides ≈ 9.4835 lb
39. ≈ 14.4
40. ≈ 0.2051 (20.5%)
41. Answers will vary.
42. (a) ≈ 0.6827 (68.27%)
    (b) ≈ 0.9545 (95.45%)
    (c) ≈ 0.9973 (99.73%)
43. The probability that the variable has some value in
    the range of all possible values is 1.
44. π **45.** 3π
46. $2\pi^2$ **47.** $\dfrac{16\pi}{3}$
48. ≈ 9.7717
49. (a) $y = 5 - \dfrac{5}{4}x^2$ (b) ≈ 335.1032 in^3
50. $f(x) = \dfrac{x^2 - 2\ln x + 3}{4}$
51. ≈ 3.84 **52.** ≈ 5.02

Chapter 8
L'Hôpital's Rule, Improper Integrals, and Partial Fractions

8.1 L'Hôpital's Rule
(pp. 417–425)

Quick Review 8.1

1. 1.1052
2. 2.7183
3. 1
4. ∞
5. 2
6. 2
7. 3
8. 1
9. $y = \dfrac{\sin h}{h}$
10. $y = (1 + h)^{1/h}$

Section 8.1 Exercises

1. $\dfrac{1}{4}$
2. 5
3. 1
4. $\dfrac{5}{7}$
5. $\dfrac{3}{11}$
6. $\dfrac{1}{2}$
7. e^2
8. 0
9. (a)

x	10	10^2	10^3	10^4	10^5
$f(x)$	1.1513	0.2303	0.0354	0.0046	0.00058

Estimated limit = 0

(b) Note $\ln x^5 = 5 \ln x$.

$$\lim_{x \to \infty} \frac{5 \ln x}{x} = \lim_{x \to \infty} \frac{5/x}{1} = \frac{0}{1} = 0$$

10. (a)

x	10^0	10^{-1}	10^{-2}	10^{-3}	10^{-4}
$f(x)$	0.1585	0.1666	0.1667	0.1667	0.1667

Estimated limit $= \dfrac{1}{6}$

(b) $\displaystyle\lim_{x \to 0^+} \frac{x - \sin x}{x^3} = \lim_{x \to 0^+} \frac{1 - \cos x}{3x^2}$
$= \displaystyle\lim_{x \to 0^+} \frac{\sin x}{6x} = \lim_{x \to 0^+} \frac{\cos x}{6} = \frac{1}{6}$

11. $\dfrac{3}{4}$
12. 0
13. 1
14. $-\dfrac{2}{3}$
15. 0
16. $\dfrac{1}{4}$
17. -1
18. $\dfrac{1}{\pi + 1}$
19. $\ln 2$
20. $\dfrac{\ln 3}{\ln 2}$
21. 1
22. 1
23. 0
24. 1

25. 1
26. $\ln 2$
27. 0
28. ∞
29. e^2
30. 1
31. 0
32. $\dfrac{7}{11}$
33. 1
34. $e^{1/2}$
35. 1
36. 1
37. e
38. e
39. 1
40. 1
41. e^{-1}
42. $\ln 2$

43. (a) L'Hôpital's Rule does not help because applying l'Hôpital's Rule to this quotient essentially "inverts" the problem by interchanging the numerator and denominator. It is still essentially the same problem and one is no closer to a solution. Applying l'Hôpital's Rule a second time returns to the original problem.

  (b, c) 3

44. (a) L'Hôpital's Rule does not help because applying l'Hôpital's Rule to this quotient essentially "inverts" the problem by interchanging the numerator and denominator. It is still essentially the same problem and one is no closer to a solution. Applying l'Hôpital's Rule a second time returns to the original problem.

  (b, c) 1

45. Possible answers:
  (a) $f(x) = 7(x - 3), g(x) = x - 3$
  (b) $f(x) = (x - 3)^2, g(x) = x - 3$
  (c) $f(x) = x - 3, g(x) = (x - 3)^3$

46. Possible answers:
  (a) $f(x) = 3x + 1, g(x) = x$
  (b) $f(x) = x + 1, g(x) = x^2$
  (c) $f(x) = x^2, g(x) = x + 1$

47. $c = \dfrac{27}{10}$, because this is the limit of $f(x)$ as x approaches 0.

48. The limit of $f(x)$ as $x \to 0$ is 1. Therefore, f has a removable discontinuity at $x = 0$, and the definition of f should be extended by defining $f(0) = 1$.

49. (a) $\ln\left(1 + \dfrac{r}{k}\right)^{kt} = kt \ln\left(1 + \dfrac{r}{k}\right)$. And, as $k \to \infty$,

$$\lim_{k \to \infty} kt \ln\left(1 + \frac{r}{k}\right) = \lim_{k \to \infty} \frac{t \ln\left(1 + \dfrac{r}{k}\right)}{\dfrac{1}{k}}$$

$$= \lim_{k \to \infty} \frac{t\left(\dfrac{-r}{k^2}\right)\left(1 + \dfrac{r}{k}\right)^{-1}}{\dfrac{-1}{k^2}}.$$

$$= \lim_{k \to \infty} \frac{rt}{1 + \dfrac{r}{k}} = rt.$$

Hence, $\displaystyle\lim_{k \to \infty} A_0\left(1 + \frac{r}{k}\right)^{kt} = A_0 e^{rt}.$

49. continued

(b) Part (a) shows that as the number of compoundings per year increases toward infinity, the limit of interest compounded k times per year is interest compounded continuously.

50. (a) For $x \neq 0$, $\dfrac{f'(x)}{g'(x)} = \dfrac{1}{1} = 1$ and

$\dfrac{f(x)}{g(x)} = \dfrac{x+2}{x+1} \to 2$ as $x \to 0$.

(b) This does not contradict l'Hôpital's Rule since $\lim\limits_{x \to 0} f(x) = 2$ and $\lim\limits_{x \to 0} g(x) = 1$.

51. (a) 1

(b) $\dfrac{\pi}{2}$

(c) π

52. (a) 0

(b) L'Hôpital's Rule cannot be applied to $\dfrac{\sin x}{1 + 2x}$ because the denominator has limit 1.

53. (a) $(-\infty, -1) \cup (0, \infty)$

(b) ∞

(c) e

54. (a) Because the difference in the numerator is so small compared to the values being subtracted, any calculator or computer with limited precision will give the incorrect result that $1 - \cos x^6$ is 0 for even moderately small values of x. For example, at $x = 0.1$, $\cos x^6 \approx 0.9999999999995$ (13 places), so on a 10-place calculator, $\cos x^6 = 1$ and $1 - \cos x^6 = 0$.

(b) Same as (a)

(c) $\dfrac{1}{2}$

(d) The graph and/or table on a grapher show the value of the function to be 0 for x-values moderately close to 0, but the limit is 1/2. The calculator is giving unreliable information because there is significant round-off error in computing values of this function on a limited precision device.

55. (a) $c = \dfrac{1}{3}$

(b) $c = \dfrac{\pi}{4}$

56. (a) $\ln f(x)^{g(x)} = g(x) \ln f(x)$.

$\lim\limits_{x \to c} (g(x) \ln f(x)) = \left(\lim\limits_{x \to c} g(x) \right) \left(\lim\limits_{x \to c} \ln f(x) \right)$
$= (\infty)(-\infty) = -\infty$

Therefore, $\lim\limits_{x \to c} f(x)^{g(x)} = 0$.

(b) $\lim\limits_{x \to c} (g(x) \ln f(x)) = (-\infty)(-\infty) = \infty$

Therefore, $\lim\limits_{x \to c} f(x)^{g(x)} = \infty$.

8.2 Relative Rates of Growth (pp. 425–433)

Quick Review 8.2

1. 0

2. ∞

3. ∞

4. 0

5. $-3x^4$

6. $2x^2$

7. $\lim\limits_{x \to \infty} \dfrac{f(x)}{g(x)} = \lim\limits_{x \to \infty} \left(1 + \dfrac{\ln x}{x} \right) = 1 + 0 = 1$

8. $\lim\limits_{x \to \infty} \dfrac{f(x)}{g(x)} = \lim\limits_{x \to \infty} \sqrt{1 + \dfrac{5}{4x}} = 1$

9. (a) Local minimum at $(0, 1)$
Local maximum at $\approx (2, 1.541)$

(b) $[0, 2]$

(c) $(-\infty, 0]$ and $[2, \infty)$

10. f doesn't have an absolute maximum value. The values are always less than 2 and the values get arbitrarily close to 2 near $x = 0$, but the function is undefined at $x = 0$.

Section 8.2 Exercises

1. Slower   **2.** Slower

3. Faster   **4.** Slower

5. Same rate   **6.** Slower

7. Slower   **8.** Faster

9. Slower   **10.** Same rate

11. Same rate   **12.** Faster

13. Slower   **14.** Same rate

15. Slower   **16.** Faster

17. Same rate   **18.** Same rate

19. Slower   **20.** Slower

21. Faster   **22.** Same rate

23. $e^{x/2}$, e^x, $(\ln x)^x$, x^x

24. $(\ln 2)^x$, x^2, 2^x, e^x

25. $\lim\limits_{x \to \infty} \dfrac{f_2(x)}{f_1(x)} = \sqrt{10}$ and $\lim\limits_{x \to \infty} \dfrac{f_3(x)}{f_1(x)} = 1$, so f_2 and f_3 also grow at the same rate.

26. $\lim\limits_{x \to \infty} \dfrac{f_2(x)}{f_1(x)} = 1$ and $\lim\limits_{x \to \infty} \dfrac{f_3(x)}{f_1(x)} = 1$, so f_2 and f_3 also grow at the same rate.

27. $\lim\limits_{x \to \infty} \dfrac{f_2(x)}{f_1(x)} = 1$ and $\lim\limits_{x \to \infty} \dfrac{f_3(x)}{f_1(x)} = 1$, so f_2 and f_3 also grow at the same rate.

28. $\lim\limits_{x \to \infty} \dfrac{f_2(x)}{f_1(x)} = 1$ and $\lim\limits_{x \to \infty} \dfrac{f_3(x)}{f_1(x)} = 2$, so f_2 and f_3 also grow at the same rate.

29. (a) False   **(b)** False

(c) True   (d) True

(e) True   (f) True

(g) False   (h) True

30. (a) True   **(b)** True
   (c) False   **(d)** True
   (e) True   **(f)** True
   (g) True   **(h)** False

31. $g = o(f)$ **32.** $f = o(g)$

33. f and g grow at the same rate.

34. f and g grow at the same rate.

35. (a) The nth derivative of x^n is $n!$, which is a constant. Therefore n applications of l'Hôpital's Rule give

$$\lim_{x\to\infty} \frac{e^x}{x^n} = \cdots = \lim_{x\to\infty} \frac{e^x}{n!} = \infty.$$

   (b) In this case, n applications of l'Hôpital's Rule give $\lim_{x\to\infty} \dfrac{a^x}{x^n} = \cdots = \lim_{x\to\infty} \dfrac{a^x(\ln a)^n}{n!} = \infty$

36. (a) $\lim_{x\to\infty} \dfrac{e^x}{a_n x^n + \cdots + a_0} = \lim_{x\to\infty} \dfrac{e^x}{a_n n!} = \infty$

   (b) $\lim_{x\to\infty} \dfrac{a^x}{a_n x^n + \cdots + a_0} = \lim_{x\to\infty} \dfrac{(\ln a)^n a^x}{a_n n!} = \infty$

37. (a) $\lim_{x\to\infty} \dfrac{\ln x}{x^{1/n}} = \lim_{x\to\infty} \dfrac{\frac{1}{x}}{x^{(1/n)-1}} = \lim_{x\to\infty} \dfrac{n}{x^{1/n}} = 0$

   (b) $\lim_{x\to\infty} \dfrac{\ln x}{x^a} = \lim_{x\to\infty} \dfrac{\frac{1}{x}}{ax^{a-1}} = \lim_{x\to\infty} \dfrac{1}{ax^a} = 0$

38. Let $p(x)$ be any nonconstant polynomial. Then $p'(x)$ is either a nonzero constant or a polynomial of degree at least one. Therefore,

$$\lim_{x\to\infty} \frac{\ln x}{p(x)} = \lim_{x\to\infty} \frac{\frac{1}{x}}{p'(x)} = \lim_{x\to\infty} \frac{1}{xp'(x)} = 0$$

   and $\ln$ grows slower than $p(x)$.

39. The one which is $O(n \log_2 n)$ is likely the most efficient, because of the three given functions, it grows the most slowly as $n \to \infty$.

40. (a) 1,000,000
   (b) 20

41. This is the case because if $\lim_{x\to\infty} \dfrac{f(x)}{g(x)} = L$ where L is a nonzero finite real number, then for sufficiently large x, it must be the case that $\dfrac{f(x)}{g(x)} < L + 1 \le M$, for some integer M. Similarly for $g = O(f)$.

42. (a) The limit will be the ratio of the leading coefficients of the polynomials.
   (b) The limit will be the same as in (a).

43. (a) x^5 grows faster than x^2.
   (b) They grow at the same rate.
   (c) $m > n$
   (d) $m = n$
   (e) $m > n$ (or, degree of g > degree of f)
   (f) $m = n$ (or, degree of g = degree of f)

44. (a) $f = o(g)$ as $x \to a$ if $\lim_{x\to a} \dfrac{f(x)}{g(x)} = 0$.
   Suppose that f and g are both positive in some open interval containing a. Then $f = O(g)$ as $x \to a$ if there is a positive integer M for which $\dfrac{f(x)}{g(x)} \le M$ for x sufficiently close to a.

   (b) $\dfrac{|E_s|}{h^4} \le (b-a)\dfrac{M}{180} \le \text{int}\left[(b-a)\dfrac{M}{180}\right] + 1$, for all values of h, where M is a bound for the absolute value of $f^{(4)}$.

   (c) $\dfrac{|E_T|}{h^2} \le (b-a)\dfrac{M}{12} \le \text{int}\left[(b-a)\dfrac{M}{12}\right] + 1$, for all values of h, where M is a bound for the absolute value of f''.

45. (a) and **(b)** both follow from the fact that if f and g are negative, then

$$\lim_{x\to\infty} \frac{|f(x)|}{|g(x)|} = \lim_{x\to\infty} \frac{-f(x)}{-g(x)} = \lim_{x\to\infty} \frac{f(x)}{g(x)}$$

46. (a) and **(b)** both follow from the fact that

$$\lim_{x\to-\infty} \frac{f(x)}{g(x)} = \lim_{x\to\infty} \frac{f(-x)}{g(-x)}$$

8.3 Improper Integrals (pp. 433–444)

Quick Review 8.3

1. $\ln 2$ **2.** 0

3. $\dfrac{1}{2}\tan^{-1}\dfrac{x}{2} + C$ **4.** $-\dfrac{1}{3}x^{-3} + C$

5. $(-3, 3)$ **6.** $(1, \infty)$

7. Because $-1 \le \cos x \le 1$ for all x

8. Because $\sqrt{x^2 - 1} < \sqrt{x^2} = x$ for $x > 1$

9. $\lim_{x\to\infty} \dfrac{4e^x - 5}{3e^x + 7} = \dfrac{4}{3}$ **10.** $\lim_{x\to\infty} \dfrac{\sqrt{2x-1}}{\sqrt{x+3}} = \sqrt{2}$

Section 8.3 Exercises

1. (a) Because of an infinite limit of integration
   (b) Converges
   (c) $\dfrac{\pi}{2}$

2. (a) Because the integrand has an infinite discontinuity at $x = 0$
   (b) Converges
   (c) 2

3. (a) Because the integrand has an infinite discontinuity at $x = 0$
   (b) Converges
   (c) $-\dfrac{9}{2}$

4. (a) Because of two infinite limits of integration
   (b) Converges
   (c) 0
5. (a) Because the integrand has an infinite discontinuity at $x = 0$
   (b) Diverges
   (c) No value
6. (a) Because the integrand has an infinite discontinuity at $x = 0$
   (b) Diverges
   (c) No value
7. 1000

8. 6
9. 4

10. 1000
11. $\dfrac{\pi}{2}$

12. $\dfrac{3\pi}{4}$
13. $\ln 3$

14. $3 \ln 2$
15. $\sqrt{3}$

16. $\dfrac{\pi}{2} + 2$
17. π

18. $\dfrac{\pi}{2}$
19. $\dfrac{\pi}{3}$

20. $\ln 2$
21. $2\pi^2$

22. 6
23. -1

24. 1
25. 2

26. $-\dfrac{1}{4}$

27. Diverges

28. Converges
29. Converges

30. Converges
31. Converges

32. Diverges
33. Converges

34. Diverges
35. Diverges

36. Converges
37. Converges

38. Diverges
39. Converges

40. Diverges
41. Diverges

42. Converges
43. Converges

44. Converges
45. Converges

46. Diverges
47. 1

48. ∞
49. (a) The integral in Example 1 gives the area of the region.
   (b) ∞
   (c) π
   (d) Gabriel's horn has finite volume so it could only hold a finite amount of paint, but it has infinite surface area so it would require an infinite amount of paint to cover itself.

50. (a) Increasing on $(-\infty, 0]$; decreasing on $[0, \infty)$; local maximum at $\left(0, \dfrac{1}{\sqrt{2\pi}}\right)$
   (b) $n = 1$: integral ≈ 0.683
      $n = 2$: integral ≈ 0.954
      $n = 3$: integral ≈ 0.997
   (c) We can make $\displaystyle\int_{-b}^{b} f(x)\, dx$ as close to 1 as we want by choosing $b > 1$ large enough. Also we can make $\displaystyle\int_{b}^{\infty} f(x)\, dx$ and $\displaystyle\int_{-\infty}^{-b} f(x)\, dx$ as small as we want by choosing b large enough.

51. (a) For $x \ge 6$, $x^2 \ge 6x$, and therefore, $e^{-x^2} \le e^{-6x}$. The inequality for the integrals follows. The value of the second integral is $\dfrac{e^{-36}}{6}$, which is less than 4×10^{-17}.
   (b) The error in the estimate is the integral over the interval $[6, \infty)$, and we have shown that it is bounded by 4×10^{-17} in part (a).
   (c) 0.13940279264 (This agrees with Figure 8.16.)
   (d) $\displaystyle\int_{0}^{\infty} e^{-x^2}\, dx = \int_{0}^{3} e^{-x^2}\, dx + \int_{3}^{\infty} e^{-x^2}\, dx$. The error in the approximation is
   $$\int_{3}^{\infty} e^{-x^2}\, dx \le \int_{3}^{\infty} e^{-3x}\, dx < 0.000042.$$

52. (a) Since f is an even function, the substitution $u = -x$ gives $\displaystyle\int_{-\infty}^{0} f(x)\, dx = \int_{0}^{\infty} f(u)\, du$.
   (b) Since f is an odd function, the substitution $u = -x$ gives $\displaystyle\int_{-\infty}^{0} f(x)\, dx = -\int_{0}^{\infty} f(u)\, du$.

53. (a) It is divergent because as $x \to \infty$,
   $$\lim_{x \to \infty} \ln(x^2 + 1) = \infty.$$
   (b) *Both* the integral over $[0, \infty)$ and the integral over $(-\infty, 0]$ must converge in order for the integral over $(-\infty, \infty)$ to converge.
   (c) Since this is an odd function, the integral over any interval of the form $[-b, b]$ equals 0. Therefore the limit as $b \to \infty$ is 0.
   (d) Because the determination of convergence is not made using the method in part (c). In order for the integral to converge, there must be finite areas in both directions (toward ∞ and toward $-\infty$). In this case, there are infinite areas in both directions, but when one computes the integral over an interval $[-b, b]$, there is cancellation which gives 0 as the result.

54. 6

55. From the properties of integrals, for any $b > a$,
$$\int_{a}^{b} f(x) \le \int_{a}^{b} g(x)\, dx.$$
If the infinite integral of g converges, then taking the limit in the above inequality as $b \to \infty$ shows that the infinite integral of f is bounded above by the infinite integral of g. Therefore, the infinite integral of f must be finite and it converges.
If the infinite integral of f diverges, it must grow to infinity. So taking the limit in the above inequality as $b \to \infty$ shows that the infinite integral of g must also diverge to infinity.

56. (a) $n = 0$: integral $= 1$
      $n = 1$: integral $= 1$
      $n = 2$: integral $= 2$

(b) Integration by parts gives

$$\int x^n e^{-x}\, dx = -x^n e^{-x} + n\int x^{n-1} e^{-x}\, dx + C.$$

Since the term $(-x^n e^{-x})$ has value 0 at $x = 0$ and has limit equal to 0 as $x \to \infty$, when the above equation is evaluated "from 0 to infinity", it gives $f(n + 1) = n f(n)$.

(c) This follows from the formula

$$f(n + 1) = n f(n)$$ by an induction argument.

In fact, it follows that $\displaystyle\int_0^\infty x^n e^{-x}\, dx = n!$.

57. (a) Although the values oscillate a bit, they appear to be approaching a limit of approximately 1.57.

(b) Yes, it converges.

58. (a) $\displaystyle\int_{-\infty}^1 \frac{dx}{1+x^2} = \frac{3\pi}{4}, \int_1^\infty \frac{dx}{1+x^2} = \frac{\pi}{4}$

$$\int_{-\infty}^\infty \frac{dx}{1+x^2} = \frac{3\pi}{4} + \frac{\pi}{4} = \pi$$

(b) $\displaystyle\int_{-\infty}^c f(x)\, dx = \int_{-\infty}^0 f(x)\, dx + \int_0^c f(x)\, dx$

$$\int_c^\infty f(x)\, dx = \int_c^0 f(x)\, dx + \int_0^\infty f(x)\, dx$$

Thus,

$$\int_{-\infty}^c f(x)\, dx + \int_c^\infty f(x)\, dx$$
$$= \int_{-\infty}^0 f(x)\, dx + \int_0^c f(x)\, dx + \int_c^0 f(x)\, dx$$
$$+ \int_0^\infty f(x)\, dx$$
$$= \int_{-\infty}^0 f(x)\, dx + \int_0^\infty f(x)\, dx,$$

because

$$\int_0^c f(x)\, dx + \int_c^0 f(x)\, dx = 0.$$

8.4 Partial Fractions and Integral Tables (pp. 444–453)

Quick Review 8.4

1. $A = -2, B = 1$
2. $A = -1, B = 2, C = 3$
3. $2x + 1 + \dfrac{x-3}{x^2 - 3x - 4}$
4. $2 + \dfrac{3x-4}{x^2 + 4x + 5}$
5. $(x-3)(x^2+1)$
6. $(y-2)(y+2)(y-1)(y+1)$
7. $-\dfrac{x+13}{x^2 + x - 6}$
8. $\dfrac{-x^2 + 12x - 15}{(x+5)(x^2 - 4x + 5)}$

9. $-\dfrac{2t^3 + 5t^2 + 5t + 9}{(t^2+2)(t^2+1)}$
10. $\dfrac{2x^2 - 7x + 6}{(x-1)^3}$

Section 8.4 Exercises

1. $\dfrac{2}{x-1} + \dfrac{3}{x-2}$
2. $\dfrac{2}{x-1} + \dfrac{4}{(x-1)^2}$
3. $\dfrac{2}{t-1} - \dfrac{2}{t} - \dfrac{1}{t^2}$
4. $\dfrac{2}{5(s+2)} + \dfrac{4}{15(s-3)} - \dfrac{2}{3s}$
5. $1 - \dfrac{12}{x-2} + \dfrac{17}{x-3}$
6. $y + \dfrac{-4y+1}{y^2+4}$
7. $\dfrac{1}{2}\ln|x+1| - \dfrac{1}{2}\ln|x-1| + C$
8. $\dfrac{1}{2}\ln|x| - \dfrac{1}{2}\ln|x+2| + C$
9. $\dfrac{1}{4}\ln|y+1| + \dfrac{3}{4}\ln|y-3| + C$
10. $4\ln|y| - 3\ln|y+1| + C$
11. $\dfrac{1}{6}\ln|t+2| + \dfrac{1}{3}\ln|t-1| - \dfrac{1}{2}\ln|t| + C$
12. $\dfrac{1}{16}\ln|t+2| + \dfrac{5}{16}\ln|t-2| - \dfrac{3}{8}\ln|t| + C$
13. $\dfrac{s^2}{2} - 2\ln(s^2+4) + C$
14. $\dfrac{s^3}{3} - s + \ln(s^2+1) + \tan^{-1} s + C$
15. $5x - \dfrac{5}{2}\ln(x^2+x+1) - \dfrac{5}{\sqrt{3}}\tan^{-1}\left(\dfrac{2x+1}{\sqrt{3}}\right) + C$
16. $\dfrac{1}{4}\ln|x-1| + \dfrac{3}{4}\ln|x+1| + \dfrac{1}{2(x+1)} + C$
17. $\dfrac{1}{4}\ln|x+1| - \dfrac{1}{4(x+1)} - \dfrac{1}{4}\ln|x-1| - \dfrac{1}{4(x-1)}$
$+ C$
18. $\dfrac{5}{7}\ln|x-1| + \dfrac{2}{7}\ln|x+6| + C$
19. $2\tan^{-1}(r-1) + C$
20. $3\tan^{-1}(r-2) + C$
21. $\ln|x^2+x+1| - \ln|x-1| + C$
22. $3\ln|x+1| - \ln(x^2-x+1) + C$
23. $\dfrac{1}{x^2+4} + \dfrac{3}{2}\tan^{-1}\dfrac{x}{2} + C$
24. $2\tan^{-1} x + \dfrac{1}{2}\ln(x^2+1) + \dfrac{1}{2(x^2+1)} + C$
25. $1 - \ln 2$
26. $2 - \tan^{-1} 2$
27. $\ln|y-1| - \ln|y| = e^x - 1 - \ln 2$
28. $y = \dfrac{1}{\cos\theta + 1} - 1$
29. $y = \ln|x-2| - \ln|x-1| + \ln 2$

30. $\ln |s + 1| = \ln |t| - \ln |t + 2| + \ln 6$

or $|s + 1| = 6 \left| \dfrac{t}{t + 2} \right|$

31. (a) Use $5 + 4x - x^2 = 9 - (x - 2)^2$, substitute
$u = x - 2$, then use Formula 18 with $x = u$
and $a = 3$.

The integral is $\dfrac{1}{6} \ln \left| \dfrac{x + 1}{x - 5} \right| + C$.

(b) Rewrite as $\dfrac{1}{2a} \left(\ln |x + a| - \ln |x - a| \right)$.
Differentiating gives $\dfrac{1}{2a} \left(\dfrac{1}{x + a} - \dfrac{1}{x - a} \right)$ which
equals $\dfrac{1}{a^2 - x^2}$.

32. (a) Use $x^2 - 2x + 2 = (x - 1)^2 + 1$, substitute
$u = x - 1$, then use Formula 17 with $x = u$
and $a = 1$.

The integral is
$\dfrac{x - 1}{2(x^2 - 2x + 2)} + \dfrac{1}{2} \tan^{-1}(x - 1) + C$.

(b) The derivative is
$$\dfrac{1}{2a^2} \left[\dfrac{(1)(a^2 + x^2) - (x)(2x)}{(a^2 + x^2)^2} \right] + \dfrac{1}{2a^3} \left[\dfrac{1/a}{1 + \left(\frac{x}{a} \right)^2} \right]$$

which equals $\dfrac{1}{(a^2 + x^2)^2}$.

33. $6\pi \ln 5$

34. $\dfrac{4\pi \ln 2}{3}$

35. $\ln \left| \sqrt{9 + y^2} + y \right| + C$

36. $\dfrac{25}{2} \sin^{-1} \left(\dfrac{t}{5} \right) + \dfrac{t\sqrt{25 - t^2}}{2} + C$

37. $\dfrac{1}{2} \ln \left| 2x + \sqrt{4x^2 - 49} \right| + C$

38. $-\dfrac{\sqrt{x^2 + 1}}{x} + C$

39. $-\dfrac{x^2 \sqrt{1 - x^2}}{3} - \dfrac{2}{3} \sqrt{1 - x^2} + C$

40. $\sec^{-1} x + \dfrac{\sqrt{x^2 - 1}}{x^2} + C$

41. $\sqrt{16 - z^2} - 4 \ln \left| \dfrac{4}{z} + \dfrac{\sqrt{16 - z^2}}{z} \right| + C$

42. $\dfrac{-2\sqrt{4 - w^2}}{w} + C$

43. $y = \ln \left| \dfrac{x}{3} + \dfrac{\sqrt{x^2 - 9}}{3} \right|$

44. $y = \dfrac{x}{\sqrt{x^2 + 1}} + 1$

45. $\dfrac{3\pi}{4} \approx 2.356$

46. $\pi \left(\dfrac{\pi}{2} + 1 \right) \approx 8.076$

47. (a) $x(t) = \dfrac{1000e^{4t}}{e^{4t} + 499}$ or

$x(t) = \dfrac{1000}{1 + 499e^{-4t}}$

(b) After $t = \dfrac{\ln 499}{4} \approx 1.553$ days

(c) Since $\dfrac{dx}{dt} = kx(1000 - x)$, $\dfrac{dx}{dt}$ will have its
maximum value where $x(1000 - x)$ is greatest,
which is at $x = 500$.

48. $\ln 3 - \dfrac{1}{2}$

49. (a) This can be seen geometrically in the figure.

(b) Using part (a), substitute $z = \dfrac{\sin x}{1 + \cos x}$ and
then obtain a trigonometric identity.

Or, use the trigonometric identity
$\dfrac{1 - \tan^2 \theta}{1 + \tan^2 \theta} = \cos 2\theta$ with $\theta = \dfrac{x}{2}$.

(c) Using part (a), substitute $z = \dfrac{\sin x}{1 + \cos x}$ and
then obtain a trigonometric identity.

Or, use the trigonometric identity
$\dfrac{2 \tan \theta}{1 + \tan^2 \theta} = \sin 2\theta$ with $\theta = \dfrac{x}{2}$.

(d) $dz = \left(\sec^2 \dfrac{x}{2} \right) \dfrac{1}{2} dx$

$\quad = \left(1 + \tan^2 \dfrac{x}{2} \right) \dfrac{1}{2} dx$

$\quad = \left(1 + z^2 \right) \dfrac{1}{2} dx$, then solve for dx.

50. $-\dfrac{2}{1 + \tan \frac{x}{2}} + C$

51. $-\dfrac{1}{\tan \frac{x}{2}} + C$

52. $\dfrac{2}{1 - \tan \frac{\theta}{2}} + C$

53. $\ln \left| 1 + \tan \dfrac{t}{2} \right| + C$

■ Chapter 8 Review Exercises
(pp. 454–455)

1. The limit doesn't exist.   **2.** $\dfrac{3}{5}$

3. 2   **4.** $\dfrac{1}{e}$

5. 1   **6.** e^3

7. 0   **8.** -1

9. $-\dfrac{1}{2}$ **10.** 1

11. 1   **12.** ∞

13. ∞ **14.** 0

15. Same rate, because $\lim\limits_{x\to\infty} \dfrac{f(x)}{g(x)} = \dfrac{1}{5}$

16. Same rate, because $\lim\limits_{x\to\infty} \dfrac{f(x)}{g(x)} = \dfrac{\ln 3}{\ln 2}$

17. Same rate, because $\lim\limits_{x\to\infty} \dfrac{f(x)}{g(x)} = 1$

18. Faster, because $\lim\limits_{x\to\infty} \dfrac{f(x)}{g(x)} = \infty$

19. Faster, because $\lim\limits_{x\to\infty} \dfrac{f(x)}{g(x)} = \infty$

20. Same rate, because $\lim\limits_{x\to\infty} \dfrac{f(x)}{g(x)} = 1$

21. Slower, because $\lim\limits_{x\to\infty} \dfrac{f(x)}{g(x)} = 0$

22. Slower, because $\lim\limits_{x\to\infty} \dfrac{f(x)}{g(x)} = 0$

23. Same rate, because $\lim\limits_{x\to\infty} \dfrac{f(x)}{g(x)} = \dfrac{1}{2}$

24. Slower, because $\lim\limits_{x\to\infty} \dfrac{f(x)}{g(x)} = 0$

25. Same rate, because $\lim\limits_{x\to\infty} \dfrac{f(x)}{g(x)} = 1$

26. Faster, because $\lim\limits_{x\to\infty} \dfrac{f(x)}{g(x)} = \infty$

27. (a) $\lim\limits_{x\to 0} f(x) = \ln 2$
    (b) Define $f(0) = \ln 2$

28. (a) $\lim\limits_{x\to 0^+} f(x) = 0$
    (b) Define $f(0) = 0$

29. True, $\lim\limits_{x\to\infty} \dfrac{\frac{1}{x^2} + \frac{1}{x^4}}{\frac{1}{x^2}} = 1$

30. False, $\lim\limits_{x\to\infty} \dfrac{\frac{1}{x^2} + \frac{1}{x^4}}{\frac{1}{x^4}} = \infty$

31. False, $\lim\limits_{x\to\infty} \dfrac{x}{x + \ln x} = 1$

32. True, $\lim\limits_{x\to\infty} \dfrac{\ln (\ln x)}{\ln x} = 0$

33. True, $\lim\limits_{x\to\infty} \dfrac{\tan^{-1} x}{1} = \dfrac{\pi}{2}$

34. True, $\lim\limits_{x\to\infty} \dfrac{\frac{1}{x^4}}{\frac{1}{x^2} + \frac{1}{x^4}} = 0$

35. True, $\lim\limits_{x\to\infty} \dfrac{\frac{1}{x^4}}{\frac{1}{x^2} + \frac{1}{x^4}} = 0$

36. True, $\lim\limits_{x\to\infty} \dfrac{\ln x}{x + 1} = 0$

37. True, $\lim\limits_{x\to\infty} \dfrac{\ln 2x}{\ln x} = 1$

38. True, $\lim\limits_{x\to\infty} \dfrac{\sec^{-1} x}{1} = \dfrac{\pi}{2}$

39. $\dfrac{\pi}{2}$

40. -1

41. 6

42. 0

43. $\ln 3$

44. $\ln \dfrac{3}{4} + 1$

45. 2

46. $-\dfrac{1}{9}$

47. Diverges

48. π

49. Diverges, by the limit comparison test, comparing with $\dfrac{1}{\theta}$ or directly from the antiderivative.

50. Converges; directly from the antiderivative, value $\dfrac{1}{2}$.

51. Diverges; by the direct comparison test with $\dfrac{1}{z}$ or directly from the antiderivative.

52. Converges; by the direct comparison test with e^{-t}.

53. Converges; by the direct comparison test with e^{-x} on $[0, \infty)$ and with e^x on $(-\infty, 0]$ or directly from the antiderivative, value $\dfrac{\pi}{2}$.

54. Diverges; the problem is near $x = 0$. Compare with $\dfrac{1}{4x^2}$ there. For $0 < x \le 1$, $1 + e^x < 4$ and $\dfrac{1}{x^2(1 + e^x)} \ge \dfrac{1}{4x^2}$.

55. $9 \ln |x - 4| - 7 \ln |x - 3| + C$

56. $\ln |x| - \ln |x + 2| + \dfrac{2}{x} - \dfrac{2}{x^2} + C$

57. $4 \ln |t| - \dfrac{1}{2} \ln (t^2 + 1) + 4 \tan^{-1} t + C$

58. $\dfrac{1}{2} \tan^{-1} t - \dfrac{1}{2\sqrt{3}} \tan^{-1} \dfrac{t}{\sqrt{3}} + C$

59. $x + \ln |x - 1| - \ln |x| + C$

60. $\dfrac{x^2}{2} + \dfrac{3}{2} \ln |x + 1| - \dfrac{9}{2} \ln |x + 3| + C$

61. $y = \dfrac{500}{1 + 24e^{-x}}$

62. $y = \tan \left(\ln |x + 1| + \tan^{-1} \dfrac{\pi}{4} \right)$

63. $\ln \left| \sqrt{1 + 9y^2} + 3y \right| + C$

64. $\dfrac{1}{6} \sin^{-1} 3t + \dfrac{1}{2} t \sqrt{1 - 9t^2} + C$

65. $\ln (5x + \sqrt{25x^2 - 9}) + C$

66. $\dfrac{4x}{\sqrt{1 - x^2}} - 4 \sin^{-1} x + C$

67. 2π

68. 1

69. (a) $x = a - \dfrac{1}{kt + \frac{1}{a}}$

    (b) $x = \dfrac{ab(e^{akt} - e^{bkt})}{ae^{akt} - be^{bkt}}$

Chapter 9
Infinite Series

9.1 Power Series
(pp. 457–468)

Quick Review 9.1

1. $\dfrac{4}{3}, 1, \dfrac{4}{5}, \dfrac{2}{3}, \dfrac{1}{8}$

2. $-1, \dfrac{1}{2}, -\dfrac{1}{3}, \dfrac{1}{4}, \dfrac{1}{30}$

3. (a) 3   (b) 39,366

   (c) $a_n = 2(3^{n-1})$

4. (a) $-\dfrac{1}{2}$ (b) $-\dfrac{1}{64}$

   (c) $a_n = 8\left(-\dfrac{1}{2}\right)^{n-1} = 8(-0.5)^{n-1}$

5. (a)

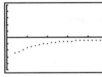

[0, 25] by [−0.5, 0.5]

  (b) 0

6. (a)

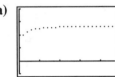

[0, 23.5] by [−1, 4]

  (b) e

7. (a)

[0, 23.5] by [−2, 2]

  (b) The limit does not exist.

8. (a)

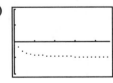

[0, 23.5] by [−2, 2]

  (b) −1

9. (a)

[0, 23,5] by [−1, 3]

  (b) 2

10. (a)

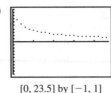

[0, 23.5] by [−1, 1]

  (b) 0

Section 9.1 Exercises

1. (a) $* = n^2$ (b) $* = (n+1)^2$
  (c) $* = 3$

2. (a) $\left(\dfrac{1}{3}\right)^n$ (b) $\dfrac{(-1)^{n-1}}{n}$

  (c) $\dfrac{5}{10^n}$

3. Different   4. Same

5. Same   6. Different

7. Converges; sum = 3   8. Diverges

9. Converges; sum = $\dfrac{15}{4}$ 10. Diverges

11. Diverges   12. Converges; sum = $\dfrac{30}{11}$

13. Converges; sum = $2 - \sqrt{2}$

14. Diverges

15. Converges; sum = $\dfrac{e}{\pi - e}$

16. Converges; sum = 1

17. Interval: $-\dfrac{1}{2} < x < \dfrac{1}{2}$; function: $f(x) = \dfrac{1}{1 - 2x}$

18. Interval: $-2 < x < 0$; function: $f(x) = \dfrac{1}{x + 2}$

19. Interval: $1 < x < 5$; function: $f(x) = \dfrac{2}{x - 1}$

20. Interval: $-1 < x < 3$; function: $f(x) = \dfrac{6}{3 - x}$

21. Converges for all values of x except odd integer multiples of $\dfrac{\pi}{2}$; function: $f(x) = \dfrac{1}{1 - \sin x}$

22. Converges for $-\dfrac{\pi}{4} + k\pi < x < \dfrac{\pi}{4} + k\pi$, k any integer; function: $f(x) = \dfrac{1}{1 - \tan x}$

23. (a) The partial sums tend toward infinity.
  (b) The partial sums are alternately 1 and 0.
  (c) The partial sums alternate between positive and negative while their magnitude increases toward infinity.

24. This is a geometric series with $r = \dfrac{e^{\pi}}{\pi^e}$, which is greater than one.

25. $x = \dfrac{19}{20}$

26. One possible answer:
For any real number $a \neq 0$, use

$$\frac{a}{2} + \frac{a}{4} + \frac{a}{8} + \frac{a}{16} + \frac{a}{32} + \cdots.$$

To get 0, use $1 - \dfrac{1}{2} - \dfrac{1}{4} - \dfrac{1}{8} - \dfrac{1}{16} - \dfrac{1}{32} - \cdots.$

27. Assuming the series begins at $n = 1$:

(a) $\displaystyle\sum_{n=1}^{\infty} 2\left(\frac{3}{5}\right)^{n-1}$ (b) $\displaystyle\sum_{n=1}^{\infty} \frac{13}{2}\left(-\frac{3}{10}\right)^{n-1}$

28. Let $a = \dfrac{21}{100}$ and $r = \dfrac{1}{100}$, giving

$(0.21) + (0.21)(0.01) + (0.21)(0.01)^2$

$\quad + (0.21)(0.01)^3 + \cdots$

The sum is $\dfrac{7}{33}$.

29. Let $a = \dfrac{234}{1000}$ and $r = \dfrac{1}{1000}$, giving

$(0.234) + (0.234)(0.001) + (0.234)(0.001)^2$

$\quad + (0.234)(0.001)^3 + \cdots$

The sum is $\dfrac{26}{111}$.

30. $\dfrac{7}{9}$ **31.** $\dfrac{d}{9}$

32. $\dfrac{1}{15}$ **33.** $\dfrac{157}{111}$

34. $\dfrac{41,333}{33,300}$ **35.** $\dfrac{22}{7}$

36. 16 meters **37.** ≈ 7.113 seconds

38. 8 m^2 **39.** $\dfrac{\pi}{2}$

40. (a) $S - rS = a - ar^n$

(b) Just factor and divide by $1 - r$.

41. For $r \neq 1$, the result follows from:

If $|r| < 1$, $r^n \to 0$ as $n \to \infty$, and

if $|r| > 1$ or $r = -1$, r^n has no finite limit as $n \to \infty$.

When $r = 1$, the nth partial sum is na, which goes to $\pm\infty$.

42. Series: $1 - 3x + 9x^2 - \cdots + (-3x)^n + \cdots$

Interval: $-\dfrac{1}{3} < x < \dfrac{1}{3}$

43. Series: $x + 2x^2 + 4x^3 + \cdots + 2^{n-1}x^n + \cdots$

Interval: $-\dfrac{1}{2} < x < \dfrac{1}{2}$

44. Series: $3 + 3x^3 + 3x^6 + \cdots + 3x^{3n} + \cdots$

Interval: $-1 < x < 1$

45. Series: $1 - (x - 4) + (x - 4)^2 - (x - 4)^3 + \cdots$

$\quad + (-1)^n(x - 4)^n + \cdots$

Interval: $3 < x < 5$

46. Series: $\dfrac{1}{4} - \dfrac{1}{4}(x - 1) + \dfrac{1}{4}(x - 1)^2 - \dfrac{1}{4}(x - 1)^3$

$\quad + \cdots + \dfrac{1}{4}(-1)^n(x - 1)^n + \cdots$

Interval: $0 < x < 2$

47. One possible series:

$1 + (x - 1) + (x - 1)^2 + \cdots + (x - 1)^n + \cdots$

Interval: $0 < x < 2$

48. $b = \ln\left(\dfrac{8}{9}\right)$

49. (a) 2

(b) $t > -\dfrac{1}{2}$

(c) $t > 9$

50. (a) First 4 terms: $4 - 4t^2 + 4t^4 - 4t^6$

General term: $(-1)^n(4t^{2n})$

(b) First 4 terms: $4x - \dfrac{4}{3}x^3 + \dfrac{4}{5}x^5 - \dfrac{4}{7}x^7$

General term: $(-1)^n\left(\dfrac{4}{2n + 1}\right)x^{2n+1}$

(c) $-1 < t < 1$

(d) $x = \pm 1$

51. $x - \dfrac{(x - 1)^2}{2} + \dfrac{(x - 1)^3}{3} - \cdots$

$\quad + \dfrac{(-1)^{n-1}(x - 1)^n}{n} + \cdots$

52. Series: $2 + 6x + 12x^2 + (n + 2)(n + 1)x^n + \cdots$

Interval: $-1 < x < 1$

53. (a) No, because if you differentiate it again, you would have the original series for f, but by Theorem 1, that would have to converge for $-2 < x < 2$, which contradicts the assumption that the original series converges only for $-1 < x < 1$.

(b) No, because if you integrate it again, you would have the original series for f, but by Theorem 2, that would have to converge for $-2 < x < 2$, which contradicts the assumption that the original series converges only for $-1 < x < 1$.

54. Let $L = \lim_{n \to \infty} a_n$. Then by definition of convergence, for $\dfrac{\epsilon}{2}$ there corresponds an N such that for all m and n,

$n, m > N \Rightarrow |a_m - L| < \dfrac{\epsilon}{2}$ and $|a_n - L| < \dfrac{\epsilon}{2}$.

Now,

$|a_m - a_n| = |a_m - L + L - a_n|$

$\quad \leq |a_m - L| + |a_n - L| < \dfrac{\epsilon}{2} + \dfrac{\epsilon}{2} = \epsilon$

whenever $m > N$ and $n > N$.

55. Given an $\epsilon > 0$, by definition of convergence there corresponds an N such that for all $n < N$,

$|L_1 - a_n| < \epsilon$ and $|L_2 - a_n| < \epsilon$.

Now $|L_2 - L_1| =$

$|L_2 - a_n + a_n - L_1| \leq |L_2 - a_n| + |a_n - L_1|$

$< \epsilon + \epsilon = 2\epsilon.$

$|L_2 - L_1| < 2\epsilon$ says that the difference between two fixed values is smaller than any positive number 2ϵ. The only nonnegative number smaller than every positive number is 0, so $|L_2 - L_1| = 0$ or $L_1 = L_2$.

56. Consider the two subsequences $a_{k(n)}$ and $a_{i(n)}$, where $\lim\limits_{n\to\infty} a_{k(n)} = L_1$, $\lim\limits_{n\to\infty} a_{i(n)} = L_2$, and $L_1 \neq L_2$. Given an $\epsilon > 0$ there corresponds an N_1 such that for $k(n) > N_1$, $|a_{k(n)} - L_1| < \epsilon$, and an N_2 such that for $i(n) > N_2$, $|a_{i(n)} - L_2| < \epsilon$. Assume a_n converges. Let $N = \max\{N_1, N_2\}$. Then for $n > N$, we have that $|a_n - L_1| < \epsilon$ and $|a_n - L_2| < \epsilon$ for infintely many n. This implies that $\lim\limits_{n\to\infty} a_n = L_1$ and $\lim\limits_{n\to\infty} a_n = L_2$ where $L_1 \neq L_2$. Since the limit of a sequence is unique (by Exercise 55), a_n does not converge and hence diverges.

57. (a) $\lim\limits_{n\to\infty} \dfrac{3n+1}{n+1} = 3$

(b) The line $y = 3$ is a horizontal asymptote of the graph of the function $f(x) = \dfrac{3x+1}{x+1}$, which means $\lim\limits_{x\to\infty} f(x) = 3$. Because $f(n) = a_n$ for all positive integers n, it follows that $\lim\limits_{n\to\infty} a_n$ must also be 3.

9.2 Taylor Series (pp. 469–479)

Quick Review 9.2

1. $2^n e^{2x}$

2. $(-1)^n n!(x-1)^{-(n+1)}$

3. $3^x (\ln 3)^n$

4. $(-1)^{n-1}(n-1)!x^{-n}$

5. $n!$

6. $\dfrac{x^{n-1}}{(n-1)!}$

7. $\dfrac{2^n(x-a)^{n-1}}{(n-1)!}$

8. $\dfrac{(-1)^n x^{2n}}{(2n)!}$

9. $\dfrac{(x+a)^{2n-1}}{(2n-1)!}$

10. $-\dfrac{(1-x)^{n-1}}{(n-1)!}$

Section 9.2 Exercises

1. $2x - \dfrac{4x^3}{3} + \dfrac{4x^5}{15} - \cdots + (-1)^n \dfrac{(2x)^{2n+1}}{(2n+1)!} + \cdots$
converges for all real x

2. $-x - \dfrac{x^2}{2} - \dfrac{x^3}{3} - \cdots - \dfrac{x^n}{n} - \cdots$
converges for $-1 \leq x < 1$

3. $x^2 - \dfrac{x^6}{3} + \dfrac{x^{10}}{5} - \cdots + (-1)^n \dfrac{x^{4n+2}}{2n+1} + \cdots$
converges for $-1 \leq x \leq 1$

4. $7x + 7x^2 + \dfrac{7x^3}{2!} + \cdots + \dfrac{7x^{n+1}}{n!} + \cdots$
converges for all real x

5. $(\cos 2) - (\sin 2)x - \dfrac{(\cos 2)\, x^2}{2} + \cdots$
$+ \dfrac{(-1)^A B x^n}{n!} + \cdots$, where $A = \mathrm{int}\left(\dfrac{n+1}{2}\right)$, and B
is $\cos 2$ if n is even and $\sin 2$ if n is odd. Or, the general term may be written as
$\left[\dfrac{1}{n!}\cos\left(2 + \dfrac{n\pi}{2}\right)\right]x^n$. The series converges for all real x.

6. $x^2 - \dfrac{x^4}{2} + \dfrac{x^6}{24} - \cdots + (-1)^n \dfrac{x^{2n+2}}{(2n)!} + \cdots$
converges for all real x

7. $x + x^4 + x^7 + \cdots + x^{3n+1} + \cdots$
converges for $-1 < x < 1$

8. $1 - 2x + 2x^2 - \cdots + (-1)^n \dfrac{2^n x^n}{n!} + \cdots$
converges for all real x

9. $P_0(x) = \dfrac{1}{2}$

$P_1(x) = \dfrac{1}{2} - \dfrac{x-2}{4}$

$P_2(x) = \dfrac{1}{2} - \dfrac{x-2}{4} + \dfrac{(x-2)^2}{8}$

$P_3(x) = \dfrac{1}{2} - \dfrac{x-2}{4} + \dfrac{(x-2)^2}{8} - \dfrac{(x-2)^3}{16}$

10. $P_0(x) = \dfrac{\sqrt{2}}{2}$

$P_1(x) = \dfrac{\sqrt{2}}{2} + \left(\dfrac{\sqrt{2}}{2}\right)\left(x - \dfrac{\pi}{4}\right)$

$P_2(x) = \dfrac{\sqrt{2}}{2} + \left(\dfrac{\sqrt{2}}{2}\right)\left(x - \dfrac{\pi}{4}\right) - \left(\dfrac{\sqrt{2}}{4}\right)\left(x - \dfrac{\pi}{4}\right)^2$

$P_3(x) = \dfrac{\sqrt{2}}{2} + \left(\dfrac{\sqrt{2}}{2}\right)\left(x - \dfrac{\pi}{4}\right) - \left(\dfrac{\sqrt{2}}{4}\right)\left(x - \dfrac{\pi}{4}\right)^2$
$\quad - \left(\dfrac{\sqrt{2}}{12}\right)\left(x - \dfrac{\pi}{4}\right)^3$

11. $P_0(x) = \dfrac{\sqrt{2}}{2}$

$P_1(x) = \dfrac{\sqrt{2}}{2} - \left(\dfrac{\sqrt{2}}{2}\right)\left(x - \dfrac{\pi}{4}\right)$

$P_2(x) = \dfrac{\sqrt{2}}{2} - \left(\dfrac{\sqrt{2}}{2}\right)\left(x - \dfrac{\pi}{4}\right) - \left(\dfrac{\sqrt{2}}{4}\right)\left(x - \dfrac{\pi}{4}\right)^2$

$P_3(x) = \dfrac{\sqrt{2}}{2} - \left(\dfrac{\sqrt{2}}{2}\right)\left(x - \dfrac{\pi}{4}\right) - \left(\dfrac{\sqrt{2}}{4}\right)\left(x - \dfrac{\pi}{4}\right)^2$
$\quad + \left(\dfrac{\sqrt{2}}{12}\right)\left(x - \dfrac{\pi}{4}\right)^3$

12. $P_0(x) = 2$

$$P_1(x) = 2 + \frac{x-4}{4}$$

$$P_2(x) = 2 + \frac{x-4}{4} - \frac{(x-4)^2}{64}$$

$$P_3(x) = 2 + \frac{x-4}{4} - \frac{(x-4)^2}{64} + \frac{(x-4)^3}{512}$$

13. (a) $4 - 2x + x^3$

(b) $3 + (x-1) + 3(x-1)^2 + (x-1)^3$

14. (a) $-8 + 3x + x^2 + 2x^3$

(b) $-2 + 11(x-1) + 7(x-1)^2 + 2(x-1)^3$

15. (a) 0

(b) $1 + 4(x-1) + 6(x-1)^2 + 4(x-1)^3$

16. (a) $P_3(x) = 4 + 5x - 4x^2 + x^3$

$f(0.2) \approx P_3(0.2) = 4.848$

(b) For f', $P_2(x) = 5 - 8x + 3x^2$

$f'(0.2) \approx P_2(0.2) = 3.52$

17. (a) $P_3(x) = 4 - (x-1) + \frac{3}{2}(x-1)^2 + \frac{1}{3}(x-1)^3$

$f(1.2) \approx P_3(1.2) \approx 3.863$

(b) For f', $P_2(x) = -1 + 3(x-1) + (x-1)^2$

$f'(1.2) \approx P_2(1.2) = -0.36$

18. (a) $f'(0) = \frac{1}{2}, f^{(10)}(0) = \frac{1}{11}$

(b) $x + \frac{x^2}{2!} + \frac{x^3}{3!} + \frac{x^4}{4!} + \cdots + \frac{x^{n+1}}{(n+1)!} + \cdots$

(c) $e^x - 1$

19. (a) $1 + \frac{x}{2} + \frac{x^2}{8} + \cdots + \frac{x^n}{2^n \cdot n!} + \cdots$

(b) $1 + \frac{x}{2!} + \frac{x^2}{3!} + \cdots + \frac{x^n}{(n+1)!} + \cdots$

(c) $g'(1) = 1$ and from the series,

$$g'(1) = \frac{1}{2!} + \frac{2}{3!} + \frac{3}{4!} + \cdots + \frac{n}{(n+1)!} + \cdots$$

$$= \sum_{n=1}^{\infty} \frac{n}{(n+1)!}$$

20. (a) $2 + 2t^2 + 2t^4 + 2t^6 + \cdots + 2t^{2n} + \cdots$

(b) $2x + \frac{2x^3}{3} + \frac{2x^5}{5} + \frac{2x^7}{7} + \cdots + \frac{2x^{2n+1}}{2n+1} + \cdots$

21. (a) $1 + \frac{x}{2} - \frac{x^2}{8} + \frac{x^3}{16}$

(b) $1 + \frac{x^2}{2} - \frac{x^4}{8} + \frac{x^6}{16}$

(c) $5 + x + \frac{x^3}{6} - \frac{x^5}{40}$

22. (a) $1 + 3x + \frac{9x^2}{2} + \frac{9x^3}{2} + \cdots + \frac{3^n x^n}{n!} + \cdots$

(b) $f(x) = e^{3x}$ **(c)** $3e^3$

23. 27 terms (or, up to and including the 52nd degree term)

24. One possible answer: Because the end behavior of a polynomial must be unbounded and $\sin x$ is not unbounded.

Another: Because $\sin x$ has an infinite number of local extrema, but a polynomial can only have a finite number.

25. (1) $\sin x$ is odd and $\cos x$ is even

(2) $\sin 0 = 0$ and $\cos 0 = 1$

26. $\frac{81}{40}$ **27.** $\frac{1}{24}$

28. The linearization is the first order Taylor polynomial.

29. (a)

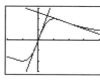

$[-2, 4]$ by $[-3, 3]$

(b) $f''(a)$ must be 0 because of the inflection point, so the second degree term in the Taylor series of f at $x = a$ is zero.

30. When $x = 1$: $\frac{\pi}{4}$

When $x = -1$: $-\frac{\pi}{4}$

31. (a) $1 - \frac{x^2}{3!} + \frac{x^4}{5!} - \cdots + \frac{(-1)^n x^{2n}}{(2n+1)!} + \cdots$

(b) Because f is undefined at $x = 0$.

(c) $k = 1$

32. $\frac{x}{(x-1)^2}$

33. (a) Differentiate 3 times.

(b) Differentiate k times and let $x = 0$.

(c) $\frac{m(m-1)(m-2)\cdots(m-k+1)}{k!}$

(d) $f(0) = 1, f'(0) = m$, and we're done by part (c).

34. Because $f(x) = (1 + x)^m$ is a polynomial of degree m.

9.3 Taylor's Theorem (pp. 480–487)

Quick Review 9.3

1. 2   **2.** 7

3. 1   **4.** $\frac{1}{2}$

5. 7   **6.** Yes

7. No   **8.** Yes

9. Yes   **10.** No

Section 9.3 Exercises

1. $1 - 2x + 2x^2 - \frac{4}{3}x^3 + \frac{2}{3}x^4; f(0.2) \approx 0.6704$

2. $1 - \frac{\pi^2}{8}x^2 + \frac{\pi^4}{384}x^4; f(0.2) \approx 0.9511$

3. $-5x + \frac{5}{6}x^3; f(0.2) \approx -0.9933$

4. $x^2 - \frac{x^4}{2}; f(0.2) \approx 0.0392$

5. $1 + 2x + 3x^2 + 4x^3 + 5x^4; f(0.2) \approx 1.56$

6. $x + x^2 + \dfrac{x^3}{2!} + \dfrac{x^4}{3!} + \cdots + \dfrac{x^{n+1}}{n!} + \cdots$

7. $\dfrac{x^5}{5!} - \dfrac{x^7}{7!} + \dfrac{x^9}{9!} - \cdots + (-1)^n \dfrac{x^{2n+5}}{(2n+5)!} + \cdots$

8. $1 - x^2 + \dfrac{x^4}{3} - \cdots + (-1)^n \dfrac{2^{2n-1}x^{2n}}{(2n)!} + \cdots$

9. $x^2 - \dfrac{x^4}{3} + \dfrac{2x^6}{45} - \cdots + (-1)^n \dfrac{2^{2n+1}x^{2n+2}}{(2n+2)!} + \cdots$

10. $x^2 + 2x^3 + 4x^4 + \cdots + 2^n x^{n+2} + \cdots$

11. Using the theorem, $-0.56 < x < 0.56$
Graphically, $-0.57 < x < 0.57$

12. $|\text{Error}| < 0.0026$ (approximately)
$1 - \dfrac{x^2}{2}$ is too small.

13. $|\text{Error}| < 1.67 \times 10^{-10}$

$x < \sin x$ for negative values of x.

14. $\approx 1.27 \times 10^{-5}$

15. $|\text{Error}| < 1.842 \times 10^{-4}$

16. $\sinh x = x + \dfrac{x^3}{3!} + \dfrac{x^5}{5!} + \cdots + \dfrac{x^{2n+1}}{(2n+1)!} + \cdots$

$\cosh x = 1 + \dfrac{x^2}{2!} + \dfrac{x^4}{4!} + \cdots + \dfrac{x^{2n}}{(2n)!} + \cdots$

17. All of the derivatives of $\cosh x$ are either $\cosh x$ or $\sinh x$. For any real x, $\cosh x$ and $\sinh x$ are both bounded by $e^{|x|}$. So for any real x, let $M = e^{|x|}$ and $r = 1$ in the Remainder Estimation Theorem. It follows that the series converges to $\cosh x$ for all real values of x.

18. $\dfrac{f(b) - f(a)}{b - a} = f'(c)$ can be rewritten as
$f(b) = f(a) + f'(c)(b - a)$. But $f(a)$ is the zeroth order Taylor polynomial for f at $x = a$, and letting $b = x$, $f'(c)(b - a)$ is the remainder from Taylor's Theorem.

19. (a) 0

(b) $-\dfrac{x^2}{2}$

(c) The graphs of the linear and quadratic approximations fit the graph of the function near $x = 0$.

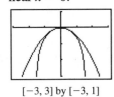

$[-3, 3]$ by $[-3, 1]$

20. (a) $1 + x$

(b) $1 + x + \dfrac{x^2}{2}$

(c) The graphs of the linear and quadratic approximations fit the graph of the function near $x = 0$.

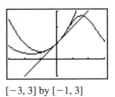

$[-3, 3]$ by $[-1, 3]$

21. (a) 1

(b) $1 + \dfrac{x^2}{2}$

(c) The graphs of the linear and quadratic approximations fit the graph of the function near $x = 0$.

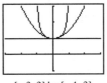

$[-3, 3]$ by $[-1, 3]$

22. (a) 1

(b) $1 + \dfrac{x^2}{2}$

(c) The graphs of the linear and quadratic approximations fit the graph of the function near $x = 0$.

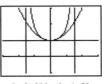

$[-3, 3]$ by $[-1, 3]$

23. (a) x

(b) x

(c) The graphs of the linear and quadratic approximations fit the graph of the function near $x = 0$.

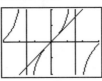

$[-3, 3]$ by $[-2, 2]$

24. $P_2(x) = 1 + kx + \dfrac{k(k-1)x^2}{2}$.
Error is less than $\dfrac{1}{100}$ for $0 \leq x < 0.01^{1/3} \approx 0.215$.

25. $|\text{Error}| < 4.61 \times 10^{-6}$, by Remainder Estimation Theorem (actual maximum error is $\approx 4.251 \times 10^{-6}$)

26. $P_3(x) = 1 + x + x^2 + x^3$.
$|\text{Error}| < 1.70 \times 10^{-4}$, by Remainder Estimation Theorem (actual maximum error is $\approx 1.11 \times 10^{-4}$)

27. (a) No

(b) Yes. $2 + x - \dfrac{x^3}{3} + \dfrac{x^5}{10} - \cdots$

$\qquad + \dfrac{(-1)^{n+1}x^{2n-1}}{[(2n-1)(n-1)!]} + \cdots$

(c) For all real values of x. This is assured by Theorem 2 of Section 9.1, because the series for e^{-x^2} converges for all real values of x.

28. (a) $-x - \dfrac{x^2}{2} - \dfrac{x^3}{3} - \dfrac{x^4}{4} - \cdots - \dfrac{x^n}{n} - \cdots$

(b) $2x + \dfrac{2x^3}{3} + \dfrac{2x^5}{5} + \cdots + \dfrac{2x^{2n+1}}{2n+1} + \cdots$

29. (a) $\tan x$ **(b)** $\sec x$

30. (a) $x^2 - \dfrac{x^4}{3} + \dfrac{2x^6}{45} - \dfrac{x^8}{315} + \dfrac{2x^{10}}{14{,}175} - \cdots$

(b) $2x - \dfrac{4x^3}{3} + \dfrac{4x^5}{15} - \dfrac{8x^7}{315} + \cdots$

(c) part (b) $= 2x - \dfrac{(2x)^3}{3!} + \dfrac{(2x)^5}{5!} - \dfrac{(2x)^7}{7!} + \cdots$

$\qquad\qquad = \sin 2x$

31. (a) It works.

(b) Let $P = \pi + x$ where x is the error in the original estimate. Then

$P + \sin P = (\pi + x) + \sin(\pi + x)$

$\qquad\qquad = \pi + x - \sin x$

But by the Remainder Theorem, $\left|x - \sin x\right| < \dfrac{|x|^3}{6}$. Therefore, the difference between the new estimate $P + \sin P$ and π is less than $\dfrac{|x|^3}{6}$.

32. (a) $\dfrac{1}{2}(e^{i\theta} + e^{-i\theta})$

$= \dfrac{(\cos\theta + i\sin\theta) + (\cos(-\theta) + i\sin(-\theta))}{2}$

$= \dfrac{(\cos\theta + i\sin\theta) + (\cos\theta - i\sin\theta)}{2}$

$= \dfrac{2\cos\theta}{2} = \cos\theta$

(b) $\dfrac{e^{i\theta} - e^{-i\theta}}{2i}$

$= \dfrac{(\cos\theta + i\sin\theta) - (\cos(-\theta) + i\sin(-\theta))}{2i}$

$= \dfrac{(\cos\theta + i\sin\theta) - (\cos\theta - i\sin\theta)}{2i}$

$= \dfrac{2i\sin\theta}{2i} = \sin\theta$

33. The derivative is

$(ae^{ax})(\cos bx + i\sin bx)$

$\quad + (e^{ax})(-b\sin bx + ib\cos bx)$

$= a[e^{ax}(\cos bx + i\sin bx)]$

$\quad + ib[e^{ax}(\cos bx + i\sin bx)]$

$= (a + ib)e^{(a+ib)x}.$

34. (a) The derivative of the right-hand side is

$\dfrac{a - bi}{a^2 + b^2}(a + bi)e^{(a+bi)x}$

$= \dfrac{a^2 - (bi)^2}{a^2 + b^2}e^{(a+bi)x}$

$= \dfrac{a^2 + b^2}{a^2 + b^2}e^{(a+bi)x} = e^{(a+bi)x},$

which confirms the antiderivative formula.

(b) $\displaystyle\int e^{ax}\cos bx\,dx + i\int e^{ax}\sin bx\,dx$

$= \displaystyle\int e^{(a+bi)x}\,dx$

$= \dfrac{a - bi}{a^2 + b^2}e^{(a+bi)x}$

$= \dfrac{a - bi}{a^2 + b^2}e^{ax}(\cos bx + i\sin bx)$

$= \left(\dfrac{e^{ax}}{a^2 + b^2}\right)(a\cos bx + b\sin bx - bi\cos bx$

$\qquad\qquad + ai\sin bx)$

$= \left(\dfrac{e^{ax}}{a^2 + b^2}\right)[(a\cos bx + b\sin bx)$

$\qquad\qquad + i(a\sin bx - b\cos bx)]$

Separating the real and imaginary parts gives

$\displaystyle\int e^{ax}\cos bx\,dx = \dfrac{e^{ax}}{a^2 + b^2}(a\cos bx + b\sin bx)$

and

$\displaystyle\int e^{ax}\sin bx\,dx = \dfrac{e^{ax}}{a^2 + b^2}(a\sin bx - b\cos bx)$

9.4 Radius of Convergence (pp. 487–496)

Quick Review 9.4

1. $|x|$

2. $|x - 3|$

3. 0

4. $\dfrac{x^2}{16}$

5. $\dfrac{|2x + 1|}{2}$

6. $a_n = n^2,\ b_n = 5n,\ N = 6$

7. $a_n = 5^n,\ b_n = n^5,\ N = 6$

8. $a_n = \sqrt{n},\ b_n = \ln n,\ N = 1$

9. $a_n = \dfrac{1}{10^n},\ b^n = \dfrac{1}{n!},\ N = 25$

10. $a_n = \dfrac{1}{n^2},\ b_n = n^{-3},\ N = 2$

Section 9.4 Exercises

1. Diverges (nth-Term Test)
2. Diverges (nth-Term Test, Ratio Test)
3. Converges (Ratio Test)
4. Converges (geometric series)
5. Converges (Ratio Test, Direct Comparison Test)
6. Diverges (nth-Term Test)
7. Converges (Ratio Test)
8. Converges (Ratio Test)
9. Converges (Ratio Test)
10. Diverges (nth-Term Test)
11. Converges (geometric series)
12. Diverges (nth-Term Test, Ratio Test)
13. Diverges (nth-Term Test, Ratio Test)
14. Converges (Ratio Test)
15. Converges (Ratio Test)
16. Converges (Ratio Test)
17. One possible answer:

   $\sum \dfrac{1}{n}$ diverges (see Exploration 1 in this section)
   even though $\lim\limits_{n\to\infty} \dfrac{1}{n} = 0$.

18. One possible answer:
   $a_n = 2^{-n}$ and $b_n = 3^{-n}$

19. 1
20. 1
21. $\dfrac{1}{4}$
22. $\dfrac{1}{3}$
23. 10
24. 1
25. 3
26. ∞
27. 5
28. 4
29. 3
30. 0
31. $\dfrac{1}{2}$
32. $\dfrac{1}{4}$
33. 1
34. $\sqrt{2}$

35. Interval: $-1 < x < 3$

   Sum: $-\dfrac{4}{x^2 - 2x - 3}$

36. Interval: $-4 < x < 2$

   Sum: $-\dfrac{9}{x^2 + 2x - 8}$

37. Interval: $0 < x < 16$

   Sum: $\dfrac{2}{4 - \sqrt{x}}$

38. Interval: $\dfrac{1}{e} < x < e$

   Sum: $\dfrac{1}{1 - \ln x}$

39. Interval: $-2 < x < 2$

   Sum: $\dfrac{3}{4 - x^2}$

40. Interval: $-\infty < x < \infty$

   Sum: $\dfrac{2}{2 - \sin x}$

41. Almost, but the Ratio Test won't determine whether there is convergence or divergence at the endpoints of the interval.

42. **(a)** For $k \le N$, it's obvious that

   $$a_1 + \cdots + a_k$$
   $$\le a_1 + \cdots + a_N + \sum_{n=N+1}^{\infty} c_n$$

   For all $k > N$,

   $$a_1 + \cdots + a_k$$
   $$= a_1 + \cdots + a_N + a_{N+1} + \cdots + a_k$$
   $$\le a_1 + \cdots + a_N + c_{N+1} + \cdots + c_k$$
   $$\le a_1 + \cdots + a_N + \sum_{n=N+1}^{\infty} c_n.$$

   (b) Since all of the a_n are nonnegative, the partial sums of the series form a nondecreasing sequence of real numbers. Part (a) shows that the sequence is bounded above, so it must converge to a limit.

43. **(a)** For $k \le N$, it's obvious that

   $$d_1 + \cdots + d_k$$
   $$\le d_1 + \cdots + d_N + \sum_{n=N+1}^{\infty} a_n$$

   For all $k > N$,

   $$d_1 + \cdots + d_k$$
   $$= d_1 + \cdots + d_N + d_{N+1} + \cdots + d_k$$
   $$\le d_1 + \cdots + d_N + a_{N+1} + \cdots + a_k$$
   $$\le d_1 + \cdots + d_N + \sum_{n=N+1}^{\infty} a_n.$$

   (b) If $\sum a_n$ converged, that would imply that $\sum d_n$ was also convergent.

44. Answers will vary.
45. 1
46. 3
47. 5
48. 1
49. 1
50. $-\dfrac{1}{\ln 2}$
51. $-\dfrac{\pi}{4}$
52. The sum is 6.

9.5 Testing Convergence at Endpoints (pp. 496–508)

Quick Review 9.5

1. Converges, $p > 1$

2. Diverges, limit comparison test with integral of $\dfrac{1}{x}$

3. Diverges, comparison test with integral of $\dfrac{1}{x}$

4. Converges, comparison test with integral of $\dfrac{2}{x^2}$

5. Diverges, limit comparison test with integral of $\dfrac{1}{\sqrt{x}}$

6. Yes

7. Yes

8. No

9. No

10. No

Section 9.5 Exercises

1. Diverges

2. Diverges

3. Diverges

4. Diverges

5. Diverges

6. Converges

7. Diverges

8. Converges

9. Converges

10. Converges

11. Diverges

12. Converges

13. Diverges

14. Converges

15. Diverges

16. Diverges

17. Converges absolutely

18. Converges conditionally

19. Converges absolutely

20. Converges conditionally

21. Diverges

22. Converges absolutely

23. Converges conditionally

24. Converges absolutely

25. Converges conditionally

26. Converges conditionally

27. (a) $(-1, 1)$ **(b)** $(-1, 1)$
  (c) None

28. (a) $(-6, -4)$ **(b)** $(-6, -4)$
  (c) None

29. (a) $\left(-\frac{1}{2}, 0\right)$ **(b)** $\left(-\frac{1}{2}, 0\right)$
  (c) None

30. (a) $\left[\frac{1}{3}, 1\right)$ **(b)** $\left(\frac{1}{3}, 1\right)$
  (c) At $x = \frac{1}{3}$

31. (a) $(-8, 12)$ **(b)** $(-8, 12)$
  (c) None

32. (a) $(-1, 1)$ **(b)** $(-1, 1)$
  (c) None

33. (a) $[-3, 3]$ **(b)** $[-3, 3]$
  (c) None

34. (a) All real numbers **(b)** All real numbers
  (c) None

35. (a) $(-8, 2)$ **(b)** $(-8, 2)$
  (c) None

36. (a) $[-4, 4)$ **(b)** $(-4, 4)$
  (c) At $x = -4$

37. (a) $(-3, 3)$ **(b)** $(-3, 3)$
  (c) None

38. (a) Only at $x = 4$ **(b)** At $x = 4$
  (c) None

39. (a) $\left(\frac{1}{2}, \frac{3}{2}\right)$ **(b)** $\left(\frac{1}{2}, \frac{3}{2}\right)$
  (c) None

40. (a) $\left[1, \frac{3}{2}\right]$ **(b)** $\left[1, \frac{3}{2}\right]$
  (c) None

41. (a) $[-\pi - 1, -\pi + 1)$
  (b) $(-\pi - 1, -\pi + 1)$
  (c) At $x = -\pi - 1$

42. (a) $\left(\frac{1}{e}, e\right)$ **(b)** $\left(\frac{1}{e}, e\right)$
  (c) None

43. $40.554 < \text{sum} < 41.555$

44. Comparing areas in the figures, we have

for all $n \geq 1$, $\displaystyle\int_1^{n+1} f(x)\, dx < a_1 + \cdots$
$$+ a_n < a_1 + \int_1^n f(x)\, dx$$

If the integral diverges, it must go to infinity, and the first inequality forces the partial sums of the series to go to infinity as well, so the series is divergent.
If the integral converges, then the second inequality puts an upper bound on the partial sums of the series, and since they are a nondecreasing sequence, they must converge to a finite sum for the series.

45.

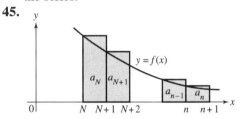

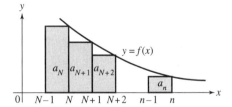

Comparing areas in the figures, we have for all

$$n \geq N, \int_N^{n+1} f(x)\, dx < a_N + \cdots + a_n < a_N$$
$$+ \int_N^n f(x)\, dx.$$

If the integral diverges, it must go to infinity, and the first inequality forces the partial sums of the series to go to infinity as well, so the series is divergent.
If the integral converges, then the second inequality puts an upper bound on the partial sums of the series, and since they are a nondecreasing sequence, they must converge to a finite sum for the series.

46. (a) Diverges by Limit Comparison Test with $\dfrac{1}{k^{1/2}}$

  (b) Diverges by the nth-Term Test

  (c) Converges absolutely by Direct Comparison Test with $\dfrac{1}{k^2}$

  (d) Diverges by the Integral Test

47. Possible answer: $\sum \dfrac{1}{n \ln n}$

This series diverges by the Integral Test, but its partial sums are roughly $\ln(\ln n)$, so they are much smaller than the partial sums for the harmonic series, which are about $\ln n$.

48. (a) $a_k = (-1)^{k+1}\left(\dfrac{2}{k}\right)$

(b) Converges by the Alternating Series Test.

(c) The first few partial sums are:

$$S_1 = 2,\ S_2 = 1,\ S_3 = \frac{5}{3},\ S_4 = \frac{7}{6},\ S_5 = \frac{47}{30},$$
$$S_6 = \frac{37}{30},\ S_7 = \frac{319}{210},\ S_8 = \frac{533}{420},\ S_9 = \frac{1879}{1260}.$$

For an alternating series, the sum is between any two adjacent partial sums, so

$$1 < S_8 \le \text{sum} \le S_9 < \frac{3}{2}.$$

49. (a) Diverges

(b) $S = \displaystyle\sum_{n=1}^{\infty} \dfrac{3n}{3n^3 + n} = \sum_{n=1}^{\infty} \dfrac{3}{3n^2 + 1}$ which converges.

50. (a) $x - \dfrac{x^2}{2} + \dfrac{x^3}{3} - \cdots + \dfrac{(-1)^{n+1}x^n}{n} + \cdots$

(b) $-1 < x \le 1$

(c) Error bound $= \dfrac{\left(\frac{1}{2}\right)^6}{6} < 0.002605$

(d) $\dfrac{1}{2} \ln(1 + x^2)$

51. Convergent for $-\dfrac{1}{2} \le x < \dfrac{1}{2}$.

Use the Ratio Test, Direct Comparison Test, and Alternating Series Test.

52. (a) By Direct Comparison Test with $\dfrac{1}{n^p}$

(b) Divergent by the Integral Test

(c) Use Direct Comparison Test with $\dfrac{1}{n \ln n}$ from part (b).

53. Use the Alternating Series Test.
54. Use the Alternating Series Test.
55. (a) It fails to satisfy $u_n \ge u_{n+1}$ for all $n \ge N$.

(b) The sum is $-\dfrac{1}{2}$.

56. Answers will vary.
57. (a) Converges   (b) Converges
(c) Converges
58. (a) $(-3, 5)$ (b) $[-1, 5)$
(c) $\left(-\dfrac{1}{2}, \dfrac{1}{2}\right)$ (d) $\left(\dfrac{1}{e}, e\right)$

■ Chapter 9 Review Exercises (pp. 509–511)

1. (a) ∞ (b) All real numbers
(c) All real numbers   (d) None
2. (a) 3 (b) $[-7, -1)$
(c) $(-7, -1)$ (d) At $x = -7$
3. (a) $\dfrac{3}{2}$ (b) $\left(-\dfrac{1}{2}, \dfrac{5}{2}\right)$
(c) $\left(-\dfrac{1}{2}, \dfrac{5}{2}\right)$ (d) None
4. (a) ∞ (b) All real numbers
(c) All real numbers   (d) None
5. (a) $\dfrac{1}{3}$ (b) $\left[0, \dfrac{2}{3}\right]$
(c) $\left[0, \dfrac{2}{3}\right]$ (d) None
6. (a) 1 (b) $(-1, 1)$
(c) $(-1, 1)$ (d) None
7. (a) 1 (b) $\left(-\dfrac{3}{2}, \dfrac{1}{2}\right)$
(c) $\left(-\dfrac{3}{2}, \dfrac{1}{2}\right)$ (d) None
8. (a) ∞ (b) All real numbers
(c) All real numbers   (d) None
9. (a) 1 (b) $[-1, 1)$
(c) $(-1, 1)$ (d) At $x = -1$
10. (a) $\dfrac{1}{e}$ (b) $\left[-\dfrac{1}{e}, \dfrac{1}{e}\right]$
(c) $\left[-\dfrac{1}{e}, \dfrac{1}{e}\right]$ (d) None
11. (a) $\sqrt{3}$ (b) $(-\sqrt{3}, \sqrt{3})$
(c) $(-\sqrt{3}, \sqrt{3})$ (d) None
12. (a) 1 (b) $[0, 2]$
(c) $(0, 2)$ (d) At $x = 0$ and $x = 2$
13. (a) 0 (b) $x = 0$ only
(c) $x = 0$ (d) None
14. (a) $\dfrac{1}{10}$ (b) $\left[-\dfrac{1}{10}, \dfrac{1}{10}\right)$
(c) $\left(-\dfrac{1}{10}, \dfrac{1}{10}\right)$ (d) At $x = -\dfrac{1}{10}$
15. (a) 0 (b) $x = 0$ only
(c) $x = 0$ (d) None
16. (a) $\sqrt{3}$ (b) $(-\sqrt{3}, \sqrt{3})$
(c) $(-\sqrt{3}, \sqrt{3})$ (d) None
17. $f(x) = \dfrac{1}{1 + x}$ evaluated at $x = \dfrac{1}{4}$. Sum $= \dfrac{4}{5}$.
18. $f(x) = \ln(1 + x)$ evaluated at $x = \dfrac{2}{3}$.
Sum $= \ln\left(\dfrac{5}{3}\right)$.
19. $f(x) = \sin x$ evaluated at $x = \pi$. Sum $= 0$.
20. $f(x) = \cos x$ evaluated at $x = \dfrac{\pi}{3}$. Sum $= \dfrac{1}{2}$.
21. $f(x) = e^x$ evaluated at $x = \ln 2$. Sum $= 2$.
22. $f(x) = \tan^{-1} x$ evaluated at $x = \dfrac{1}{\sqrt{3}}$. Sum $= \dfrac{\pi}{6}$.
23. $1 + 6x + 36x^2 + \cdots + (6x)^n + \cdots$

24. $1 - x^3 + x^6 - \cdots + (-1)^n x^{3n} + \cdots$

25. $1 - 2x^2 + x^9$

26. $4x + 4x^2 + 4x^3 + \cdots + 4x^{n+1} + \cdots$

27. $\pi x - \dfrac{(\pi x)^3}{3!} + \dfrac{(\pi x)^5}{5!} - \cdots + (-1)^n \dfrac{(\pi x)^{2n+1}}{(2n+1)!} + \cdots$

28. $-\dfrac{2x}{3} + \dfrac{4x^3}{81} - \dfrac{4x^5}{3645} + \cdots$

$\qquad + \dfrac{(-1)^{n+1}}{(2n+1)!}\left(\dfrac{2x}{3}\right)^{2n+1} + \cdots$

29. $-\dfrac{x^3}{3!} + \dfrac{x^5}{5!} - \dfrac{x^7}{7!} + \cdots + (-1)^n \dfrac{x^{2n+1}}{(2n+1)!} + \cdots$

30. $1 + \dfrac{x^2}{2!} + \dfrac{x^4}{4!} + \cdots + \dfrac{x^{2n}}{(2n)!} + \cdots$

31. $1 - \dfrac{5x}{2!} + \dfrac{(5x)^2}{4!} - \cdots + (-1)^n \dfrac{(5x)^n}{(2n)!} + \cdots$

32. $1 + \dfrac{\pi x}{2} + \dfrac{\pi^2 x^2}{8} + \cdots + \dfrac{1}{n!}\left(\dfrac{\pi x}{2}\right)^n + \cdots$

33. $x - x^3 + \dfrac{x^5}{2!} - \dfrac{x^7}{3!} + \cdots + (-1)^n \dfrac{x^{2n+1}}{n!} + \cdots$

34. $3x - \dfrac{(3x)^3}{3} + \dfrac{(3x)^5}{5} - \cdots + (-1)^n \dfrac{(3x)^{2n+1}}{2n+1} + \cdots$

35. $-2x - 2x^2 - \dfrac{8x^3}{3} - \cdots - \dfrac{(2x)^n}{n} - \cdots$

36. $-x^2 - \dfrac{x^3}{2} - \dfrac{x^4}{3} - \cdots - \dfrac{x^{n+1}}{n} - \cdots$

37. $1 + (x-2) + (x-2)^2 + (x-2)^3$
$\qquad + \cdots (x-2)^n + \cdots$

38. $2 + 7(x+1) - 5(x+1)^2 + (x+1)^3$

(Finite. General term for $n \geq 4 = 0$)

39. $\dfrac{1}{3} - \dfrac{x-3}{9} + \dfrac{(x-3)^2}{27} - \dfrac{(x-3)^3}{81} + \cdots$

$\qquad + (-1)^n \dfrac{(x-3)^n}{3^{n+1}} + \cdots$

40. $-(x-\pi) + \dfrac{(x-\pi)^3}{3!} - \dfrac{(x-\pi)^5}{5!} + \dfrac{(x-\pi)^7}{7!} - \cdots$

$\qquad + (-1)^{n+1} \dfrac{(x-\pi)^{2n+1}}{(2n+1)!} + \cdots$

41. Diverges. It is -5 times the harmonic series.

42. Converges conditionally. Alternating Series Test and $p = \dfrac{1}{2}$.

43. Converges absolutely. Direct Comparison Test with $\dfrac{1}{n^2}$.

44. Converges absolutely. Ratio Test

45. Converges conditionally. Alternating Series Test and Direct Comparison Test with $\dfrac{1}{n}$.

46. Converges absolutely. Integral Test

47. Converges absolutely. Ratio Test

48. Converges absolutely. nth-Root Test or Ratio Test

49. Diverges. nth-Term Test for Divergence

50. Converges absolutely. Direct Comparison Test with $\dfrac{1}{n^{3/2}}$.

51. Converges absolutely. Limit Comparison Test with $\dfrac{1}{n^2}$.

52. Diverges. nth-Term Test for Divergence

53. $\dfrac{1}{6}$

54. -1

55. (a) $P_3(x) = 1 + 4(x-3) + 3(x-3)^2 + 2(x-3)^3$
$\qquad f(3.2) \approx P_3(3.2) = 1.936$

(b) For f': $P_2(x) = 4 + 6(x-3) + 6(x-3)^2$
$\qquad f'(2.7) \approx P_2(2.7) = 2.74$

(c) It underestimates the values, since the graph of f is concave up near $x = 3$.

56. (a) $f(4) = 7$ and $f'''(4) = -12$

(b) For f': $P_2(x) = -3 + 10(x-4) - 6(x-4)^2$
$\qquad f'(4.3) \approx P_2(4.3) = -0.54$

(c) $7(x-4) - \dfrac{3}{2}(x-4)^2 + \dfrac{5}{3}(x-4)^3 - \dfrac{1}{2}(x-4)^4$

(d) No. One would need the entire Taylor series for $f(x)$, and it would have to converge to $f(x)$ at $x = 3$.

57. (a) $\dfrac{5x}{2} - \dfrac{5x^3}{48} + \dfrac{x^5}{768} - \cdots$

$\qquad + (-1)^n \dfrac{5}{(2n+1)!}\left(\dfrac{x}{2}\right)^{2n+1} + \cdots$

(b) All real numbers. Use the Ratio Test.

(c) Note that the absolute value of $f^{(n)}(x)$ is bounded by $\dfrac{5}{2^n}$ for all x and all $n = 1, 2, 3, \cdots$
So if $-2 < x < 2$, the truncation error using P_n is bounded by $\dfrac{5}{2^{n+1}} \cdot \dfrac{2^{n+1}}{(n+1)!} = \dfrac{5}{(n+1)!}$.
To make this less than 0.1 requires $n \geq 4$.
So, two nonzero terms (up through degree 4) are needed.

58. (a) $1 + 2x + 4x^2 + 8x^3 + \cdots + (2x)^n + \cdots$

(b) $\left(-\dfrac{1}{2}, \dfrac{1}{2}\right)$. The series for $\dfrac{1}{1-t}$ is known to converge for $-1 < t < 1$, so by substituting $t = 2x$, we find the resulting series converges for $-1 < 2x < 1$.

58. continued

(c) Possible answer:

$f\left(-\dfrac{1}{4}\right) = \dfrac{2}{3}$, so one percent is approximately 0.0067. It takes 7 terms (up through degree 6). This can be found by trial and error.

59. (a) $\dfrac{1}{e}$ **(b)** $-\dfrac{5}{18} \approx -0.278$

(c) By the Alternating Series Estimation Theorem, the error is bounded by the size of the next term, which is $\dfrac{32}{243}$, or about 0.132.

60. (a) $1 - (x-3) + (x-3)^2 - (x-3)^3 + \cdots$
$+ (-1)^n (x-3)^n + \cdots$

(b) $(x-3) - \dfrac{(x-3)^2}{2} + \dfrac{(x-3)^3}{3} - \dfrac{(x-3)^4}{4}$
$+ \cdots + (-1)^n \dfrac{(x-3)^{n+1}}{n+1} + \cdots$

(c) Evaluate at $x = 3.5$. This is an alternating series. By the Alternating Series Estimation Theorem, since the size of the third term is $\dfrac{1}{24} < 0.05$, the first two terms will suffice. The estimate for $\ln\left(\dfrac{3}{2}\right)$ is 0.375.

61. (a) $1 - 2x^2 + 2x^4 - \dfrac{4x^6}{3} + \cdots + (-1)^n \dfrac{2^n x^{2n}}{n!} + \cdots$

(b) All real numbers. Use the Ratio Test.

(c) This is an alternating series. The difference will be bounded by the magnitude of the fifth term, which is $\dfrac{(2x^2)^4}{4!} = \dfrac{2x^8}{3}$.
Since $-0.6 \le x \le 0.6$, this term is less than $\dfrac{2(0.6)^8}{3}$ which is less than 0.02.

62. (a) $x^2 - x^3 + x^4 - x^5 + \cdots + (-1)^n x^{n+2} + \cdots$

(b) No. The partial sums form the sequence 1, 0, 1, 0, 1, 0, ... which has no limit.

63. (a) $\dfrac{x^3}{3} - \dfrac{x^7}{7(3!)} + \dfrac{x^{11}}{11(5!)} + \cdots$
$+ \dfrac{(-1)^n x^{4n+3}}{(4n+3)(2n+1)!} + \cdots$

(b) The first two nonzero terms suffice (through degree 7).

(c) 0.31026830   **(d)** Within 1.5×10^{-7}

64. (a) 0.88566

(b) $\dfrac{41}{60} \approx 0.68333$

(c) Since f is concave up, the trapezoids used to estimate the area lie above the curve, and the estimate is too large.

(d) Since all the derivatives are positive (and $x > 0$), the remainder, $R_n(x)$, must be positive. This means that $P_n(x)$ is smaller than $f(x)$.

(e) $e - 2 \approx 0.71828$

65. (a) Because $[\$1000(1.08)^{-n}](1.08)^n = \$1000$ will be available after n years.

(b) Assume that the first payment goes to the charity at the end of the first year.
$1000(1.08)^{-1} + 1000(1.08)^{-2}$
$+ 1000(1.08)^{-3} + \cdots$

(c) This is a geometric series with sum equal to \$12,500. This represents the amount which must be invested today in order to completely fund the perpetuity forever.

66. \$16,666.67 [Again, assuming first payment at end of year.]

67. (a) $0\left(\dfrac{1}{2}\right) + 1\left(\dfrac{1}{2}\right)^2 + 2\left(\dfrac{1}{2}\right)^3 + 3\left(\dfrac{1}{2}\right)^4 + \cdots$

(b) $1 + 2x + 3x^2 + 4x^3 + \cdots$

(c) $x^2 + 2x^3 + 3x^4 + 4x^5 + \cdots$

(d) The expected payoff of the game is \$1.

68. (a) $\dfrac{b^2 \sqrt{3}}{4} + \dfrac{3b^2 \sqrt{3}}{4^2} + \dfrac{3^2 b^2 \sqrt{3}}{4^3} + \cdots$

(b) $b^2 \sqrt{3}$

(c) No, not every point is removed. But the remaining points are "isolated" enough that there are no regions and hence no area remaining.

69. $\dfrac{1}{(1-x)^2} = 1 + 2x + 3x^2 + 4x^3 + 5x^4 + \cdots$
Substitute $x = \dfrac{1}{2}$ to get the desired result.

70. (b) Solve $x = \dfrac{2x^2}{(x-1)^3}$. $x \approx 2.769$.

Chapter 10
Parametric, Vector, and Polar Functions

10.1 Parametric Functions
(pp. 513–520)

Quick Review 10.1

1. $(1, 0)$ 2. $(0, -1)$
3. $x^2 + y^2 = 1$
4. The portion in the first three quadrants
5. $x = t, y = t^2 + 1, -1 \le t \le 3$
6. $x = 2 \cos t + 2, y = 2 \sin t + 3, 0 \le t \le 2\pi$
7. $\dfrac{3}{2}$ 8. $y = \dfrac{3}{2}x + 3\sqrt{2}$
9. $y = -\dfrac{2}{3}x + \dfrac{5\sqrt{2}}{6}$ 10. $\dfrac{31^{3/2} - 8}{27}$

Section 10.1 Exercises

1. (a) $-\dfrac{1}{2} \tan t$ (b) $-\dfrac{1}{8} \sec^3 t$

2. (a) $\sqrt{3}$ (b) 0

3. (a) $-\sqrt{3 + \dfrac{3}{t}}$ (b) $-\dfrac{\sqrt{3}}{t^{3/2}}$

4. (a) $-t$ (b) t^2

5. (a) $\dfrac{3t^2}{2t - 3}$ (b) $\dfrac{6t^2 - 18t}{(2t - 3)^3}$

6. (a) $\dfrac{2t - 1}{2t + 1}$ (b) $\dfrac{4}{(2t + 1)^3}$

7. (a) $(2, 0)$ and $(2, -2)$
   (b) $(1, -1)$ and $(3, -1)$
8. (a) Nowhere
   (b) $(1, 0)$ and $(-1, 0)$

9. (a) At $t = \pm\dfrac{2}{\sqrt{3}}$, or $\approx (0.845, -3.079)$ and
     $(3.155, 3.079)$

   (b) Nowhere
10. (a) $(-2, 4)$ and $(-2, -2)$
   (b) $(1, 1)$ and $(-5, 1)$

11. 4 12. $\dfrac{21}{2}$

13. $\dfrac{2\sqrt{2} - 1}{3} \approx 0.609$ 14. π^2

15. $\ln 2$ 16. ≈ 4.497
17. $8\pi^2$ 18. ≈ 14.214
19. ≈ 178.561 20. π
21. (a) $x(t) = 2t, y(t) = t + 1, 0 \le t \le 1$
   (b) $3\pi\sqrt{5}$
   (c) $3\pi\sqrt{5}$

22. (a) Because these values for $x(t)$ and $y(t)$ satisfy
    $y = \dfrac{r}{h}x$, which is the equation for the line
    through the origin and (h, r), and this range of
    t-values gives the correct initial and terminal
    points.

   (b) $\pi r \sqrt{r^2 + h^2}$ (c) $\pi r \sqrt{r^2 + h^2}$
23. (a) π (b) π
24. ≈ 22.103

25. Just substitute x for t and note that $\dfrac{dx}{dx} = 1$.

26. Use the parametrization $x = g(y), y = y$,
    $c \le y \le d$, substitute y for t and note $\dfrac{dy}{dy} = 1$.

27. At $t = \sqrt{13} - 1$, or $\approx (3.394, 5.160)$
28. ≈ 159.485 29. ≈ 144.513
30. $\dfrac{64\pi a^2}{3}$
31. $3\pi a^2$
32. $5\pi^2 a^3$
33. (a) $x = \cos t + t \sin t, y = \sin t - t \cos t$
   (b) $2\pi^2$
34. (a) $x = a(\cos t + t \sin t), y = a(\sin t - t \cos t)$
   (b) $2a\pi^2$
35. (a) ≈ 461.749 ft   (b) ≈ 41.125 ft
36. (a) ≈ 641.236 ft
   (b) $\dfrac{5625}{64} \approx 87.891$ ft
37. (a) ≈ 840.421 ft
   (b) $\dfrac{16{,}875}{64} \approx 263.672$ ft

38. (a) 703.125 ft

   (b) $\dfrac{5625}{16} = 351.5625$ ft

39. Just substitute x for t and note that $\dfrac{dx}{dx} = 1$.
40. ≈ 1273.371
41. ≈ 9.417
42. ≈ 116.687

10.2 Vectors in the Plane
(pp. 520–529)

Quick Review 10.2

1. $\sqrt{17}$ 2. $\dfrac{1}{4}$
3. $b = 11$ 4. $a = 4$
5. $b = 6$

6. (a) $120°$ (b) $\dfrac{2\pi}{3}$

7. (a) $-30°$ (b) $-\dfrac{\pi}{6}$

8. (a) $-45°$ **(b)** $-\dfrac{\pi}{4}$

9. $c \approx 2.832$

10. $\theta \approx 1.046$ radians or $59.935°$

Section 10.2 Exercises

1. (a) $\langle 9, -6 \rangle$ **(b)** $3\sqrt{13}$

2. (a) $\langle 4, -10 \rangle$ **(b)** $2\sqrt{29}$

3. (a) $\langle 1, 3 \rangle$ **(b)** $\sqrt{10}$

4. (a) $\langle 5, -7 \rangle$ **(b)** $\sqrt{74}$

5. (a) $\langle 12, -19 \rangle$ **(b)** $\sqrt{505}$

6. (a) $\langle -16, 29 \rangle$ **(b)** $\sqrt{1097}$

7. (a) $\left\langle \dfrac{1}{5}, \dfrac{14}{5} \right\rangle$ **(b)** $\dfrac{\sqrt{197}}{5}$

8. (a) $\left\langle -3, \dfrac{70}{13} \right\rangle$ **(b)** $\dfrac{\sqrt{6421}}{13}$

9. $\langle 1, -4 \rangle$ **10.** $\langle -1, 1 \rangle$

11. $\langle -2, -3 \rangle$ **12.** $\langle 0, 0 \rangle$

13. $\left\langle -\dfrac{1}{2}, \dfrac{\sqrt{3}}{2} \right\rangle$ **14.** $\left\langle -\dfrac{1}{\sqrt{2}}, -\dfrac{1}{\sqrt{2}} \right\rangle$

15. $\left\langle -\dfrac{\sqrt{3}}{2}, -\dfrac{1}{2} \right\rangle$ **16.** $\left\langle -\dfrac{1}{\sqrt{2}}, \dfrac{1}{\sqrt{2}} \right\rangle$

17. (a)

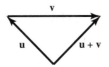

(b)

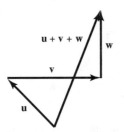

(c)

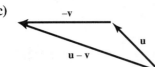

(d)

18. (a)

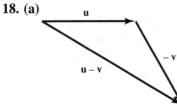

(b)

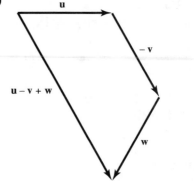

(c)

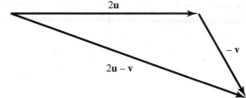

(d)

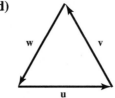

$\mathbf{u} + \mathbf{v} + \mathbf{w} = 0$

19. $\left\langle \dfrac{3}{5}, \dfrac{4}{5} \right\rangle$ **20.** $\left\langle \dfrac{4}{5}, -\dfrac{3}{5} \right\rangle$

21. $\left\langle -\dfrac{15}{17}, \dfrac{8}{17} \right\rangle$ **22.** $\left\langle -\dfrac{5}{\sqrt{29}}, -\dfrac{2}{\sqrt{29}} \right\rangle$

23. Tangent: $\pm\left\langle \dfrac{1}{\sqrt{17}}, \dfrac{4}{\sqrt{17}} \right\rangle$

     Normal: $\pm\left\langle \dfrac{4}{\sqrt{17}}, -\dfrac{1}{\sqrt{17}} \right\rangle$

24. Tangent: $\pm\left\langle \dfrac{1}{\sqrt{5}}, \dfrac{2}{\sqrt{5}} \right\rangle$

     Normal: $\pm\left\langle \dfrac{2}{\sqrt{5}}, -\dfrac{1}{\sqrt{5}} \right\rangle$

25. Tangent: $\pm\left\langle -\dfrac{12}{\sqrt{219}}, \dfrac{5}{\sqrt{73}} \right\rangle \approx \pm\langle -0.811, 0.585 \rangle$

     Normal: $\pm\left\langle \dfrac{5}{\sqrt{73}}, \dfrac{12}{\sqrt{219}} \right\rangle \approx \pm\langle 0.585, 0.811 \rangle$

26. Tangent: $\pm\left\langle \dfrac{1}{\sqrt{2}}, \dfrac{1}{\sqrt{2}} \right\rangle$

     Normal: $\pm\left\langle \dfrac{1}{\sqrt{2}}, -\dfrac{1}{\sqrt{2}} \right\rangle$

27. Angle at $A = \cos^{-1}\left(\dfrac{1}{\sqrt{5}} \right) \approx 63.435°$

     Angle at $B = \cos^{-1}\left(\dfrac{3}{5} \right) \approx 53.130°$

     Angle at $C = \cos^{-1}\left(\dfrac{1}{\sqrt{5}} \right) \approx 63.435°$

28. $90°$

29. (a) Both equal $u_1(v_1 + w_1) + u_2(v_2 + w_2)$.
   (b) Both equal $(u_1 + v_1)w_1 + (u_2 + v_2)w_2$.
30. Both equal $u_1{}^2 + u_2{}^2$.
31. $(\mathbf{u} + \mathbf{v}) \cdot (\mathbf{u} - \mathbf{v})$
$$= (u_1 + v_1)(u_1 - v_1) + (u_2 + v_2)(u_2 - v_2)$$
$$= u_1{}^2 - v_1{}^2 + u_2{}^2 - v_2{}^2$$
$$= (u_1{}^2 + u_2{}^2) - (v_1{}^2 + v_2{}^2)$$
$$= |\mathbf{u}|^2 - |\mathbf{v}|^2$$
32. This comes immediately from $\cos\left(\dfrac{\pi}{2}\right) = 0$.
33.

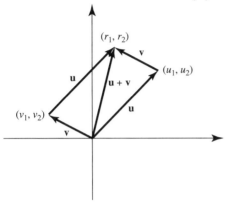

$r_1 - v_1 = u_1$ so $r_1 = u_1 + v_1$
$r_2 - v_2 = u_2$ so $r_2 = u_2 + v_2$
34. (a) To find $\mathbf{u} - \mathbf{v}$, place both vectors with their initial points at the origin. The vector drawn from the terminal point of $\mathbf{v}$ to the terminal point of $\mathbf{u}$ is $\mathbf{u} - \mathbf{v}$. Or, add $\mathbf{u}$ and $-\mathbf{v}$ according to the parallelogram law.
   (b)

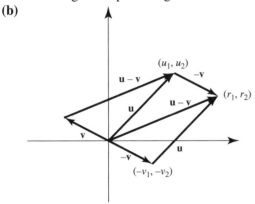

$r_1 - (-v_1) = u_1$ so $r_1 = u_1 - v_1$
$r_2 - (-v_2) = u_2$ so $r_2 = u_2 - v_2$

35. (a) Let $P = (a, b)$ and $Q = (c, d)$. Then
$$\left(\frac{1}{2}\right)\overrightarrow{OP} + \left(\frac{1}{2}\right)\overrightarrow{OQ} = \left(\frac{1}{2}\right)\langle a, b\rangle + \left(\frac{1}{2}\right)\langle c, d\rangle$$
$$= \left\langle \frac{(a+c)}{2}, \frac{(b+d)}{2}\right\rangle = \overrightarrow{OM}$$
   (b) $\overrightarrow{OM} = \left(\dfrac{2}{3}\right)\overrightarrow{OP} + \left(\dfrac{1}{3}\right)\overrightarrow{OQ}$
   (c) $\overrightarrow{OM} = \left(\dfrac{1}{3}\right)\overrightarrow{OP} + \left(\dfrac{2}{3}\right)\overrightarrow{OQ}$
   (d) Possible answer:
   M is a fraction of the way from P to Q. Let d be this fraction. Then
$$\overrightarrow{OM} = d\overrightarrow{OQ} + (1 - d)\overrightarrow{OP}.$$
36. $\overrightarrow{CA} = -\mathbf{u} - \mathbf{v}$ and $\overrightarrow{CB} = \mathbf{u} - \mathbf{v}$. Since $|\mathbf{v}| = |\mathbf{u}|$, these vectors are orthogonal, as $(-\mathbf{u} - \mathbf{v}) \cdot (\mathbf{u} - \mathbf{v}) = |\mathbf{v}|^2 - |\mathbf{u}|^2 = 0$.
37. Two adjacent sides of the rhombus can be given by two vectors of the same length, $\mathbf{u}$ and $\mathbf{v}$. Then the diagonals of the rhombus are $(\mathbf{u} + \mathbf{v})$ and $(\mathbf{u} - \mathbf{v})$. These two vectors are orthogonal since $(\mathbf{u} + \mathbf{v}) \cdot (\mathbf{u} - \mathbf{v}) = |\mathbf{u}|^2 - |\mathbf{v}|^2 = 0$.
38. Two adjacent sides of a rectangle can be given by two vectors $\mathbf{u}$ and $\mathbf{v}$. The diagonals are then $(\mathbf{u} + \mathbf{v})$ and $(\mathbf{u} - \mathbf{v})$. These two vectors will be orthogonal if and only if $\mathbf{u}$ and $\mathbf{v}$ are the same length, since $(\mathbf{u} + \mathbf{v}) \cdot (\mathbf{u} - \mathbf{v}) = |\mathbf{u}|^2 - |\mathbf{v}|^2$.
39. Let two adjacent sides of the parallelogram be given by two vectors $\mathbf{u}$ and $\mathbf{v}$. The diagonals are then $(\mathbf{u} + \mathbf{v})$ and $(\mathbf{u} - \mathbf{v})$. So the lengths of the diagonals satisfy
$$|\mathbf{u} + \mathbf{v}|^2 = (\mathbf{u} + \mathbf{v}) \cdot (\mathbf{u} + \mathbf{v})$$
$$= |\mathbf{u}|^2 + 2\mathbf{u} \cdot \mathbf{v} + |\mathbf{v}|^2$$
and $|\mathbf{u} - \mathbf{v}|^2 = (\mathbf{u} - \mathbf{v}) \cdot (\mathbf{u} - \mathbf{v})$
$$= |\mathbf{u}|^2 - 2\mathbf{u} \cdot \mathbf{v} + |\mathbf{v}|^2.$$
The two lengths will be the same if and only if $\mathbf{u} \cdot \mathbf{v} = 0$, which means that $\mathbf{u}$ and $\mathbf{v}$ are perpendicular and the parallelogram is a rectangle.

40. The indicated diagonal is $(\mathbf{u} + \mathbf{v})$. The cosine of

the angle between the diagonal and $\mathbf{u}$ is

$$\frac{(\mathbf{u} + \mathbf{v}) \cdot \mathbf{u}}{|\mathbf{u} + \mathbf{v}| \, |\mathbf{u}|} = \frac{|\mathbf{u}|^2 + \mathbf{v} \cdot \mathbf{u}}{|\mathbf{u} + \mathbf{v}| \, |\mathbf{u}|}.$$

But the cosine of the angle between the diagonal

and $\mathbf{v}$ is

$$\frac{[(\mathbf{u} + \mathbf{v}) \cdot \mathbf{v}]}{[|\mathbf{u} + \mathbf{v}| \, |\mathbf{v}|]} = \frac{[\mathbf{u} \cdot \mathbf{v} + |\mathbf{v}|^2]}{[|\mathbf{u} + \mathbf{v}| \, |\mathbf{v}|]}.$$

If $\mathbf{u}$ and $\mathbf{v}$ are the same length then these two

quantities are equal, and the diagonal makes the

same angle with both sides.

41. The slopes are the same.
42. $\mathbf{v} = \mathbf{0}$
43. $\approx \langle -338.095, 725.046 \rangle$
44. $\approx \langle 104.189, -590.885 \rangle$
45. Speed ≈ 346.735 mph
  direction $\approx 14.266°$ east of north
46. $\mathbf{w} \approx \langle 2.205, 1.432 \rangle$
47. ≈ 39.337 lb
48. (a) $\approx (4.950, 4.950)$
  (b) $\approx (-1.978, 0.950)$
49. $\overrightarrow{AB} = \langle -3, 4 \rangle = \overrightarrow{CD}$

50. $\overrightarrow{AB} = \langle 2, -5 \rangle = \overrightarrow{CD}$

51. $\mathbf{u} = \langle u_1, u_2 \rangle$, $\mathbf{v} = \langle v_1, v_2 \rangle$, $\mathbf{w} = \langle w_1, w_2 \rangle$
  (i) $\mathbf{u} + \mathbf{v} = \langle u_1 + v_1, u_2 + v_2 \rangle$
    $= \langle v_1 + u_1, v_2 + u_2 \rangle = \mathbf{v} + \mathbf{u}$
  (ii) $(\mathbf{u} + \mathbf{v}) + \mathbf{w}$
    $= \langle u_1 + v_1, u_2 + v_2 \rangle + \langle w_1, w_2 \rangle$
    $= \langle (u_1 + v_1) + w_1, (u_2 + v_2) + w_2 \rangle$
    $= \langle u_1 + (v_1 + w_1), u_2 + (v_2 + w_2) \rangle$
    $= \mathbf{u} + (\mathbf{v} + \mathbf{w})$
  (iii) $\mathbf{u} + \mathbf{0} = \langle u_1, u_2 \rangle + \langle 0, 0 \rangle = \langle u_1 + 0, u_2 + 0 \rangle$
    $= \langle u_1, u_2 \rangle = \mathbf{u}$
  (iv) $\mathbf{u} + (-\mathbf{u}) = \langle u_1, u_2 \rangle + \langle -u_1, -u_2 \rangle$
    $= \langle u_1 - u_1, u_2 - u_2 \rangle = \langle 0, 0 \rangle = \mathbf{0}$
  (v) $0\mathbf{u} = 0\langle u_1, u_2 \rangle = \langle 0u_1, 0u_2 \rangle = \langle 0, 0 \rangle = \mathbf{0}$
  (vi) $1\mathbf{u} = 1\langle u_1, u_2 \rangle = \langle 1u_1, 1u_2 \rangle = \langle u_1, u_2 \rangle = \mathbf{u}$
  (vii) $a(b\mathbf{u}) = a(b\langle u_1, u_2 \rangle) = a\langle bu_1, bu_2 \rangle$
    $= \langle abu_1, abu_2 \rangle = ab\langle u_1, u_2 \rangle = (ab)\mathbf{u}$
  (viii) $a(\mathbf{u} + \mathbf{v}) = a\langle u_1 + v_1, u_2 + v_2 \rangle$
    $= \langle au_1 + av_1, au_2 + av_2 \rangle$
    $= \langle au_1, au_2 \rangle + \langle av_1, av_2 \rangle$
    $= a\langle u_1, u_2 \rangle + a\langle v_1, v_2 \rangle$
    $= a\mathbf{u} + a\mathbf{v}$
  (ix) $(a + b)\mathbf{u} = (a + b)\langle u_1, u_2 \rangle$
    $= \langle (a + b)u_1, (a + b)u_2 \rangle$
    $= \langle au_1 + bu_1, au_2 + bu_2 \rangle$
    $= \langle au_1, au_2 \rangle + \langle bu_1, bu_2 \rangle = a\mathbf{u} + b\mathbf{u}$

52. $\langle 3, 4 \rangle = \left\langle \dfrac{7}{2}, \dfrac{7}{2} \right\rangle + \left\langle -\dfrac{1}{2}, \dfrac{1}{2} \right\rangle$
53. (a) $y = -x - 1$
  (b) $y = x + 3$
54. $\cos^{-1}\left(\dfrac{7\sqrt{2}}{10} \right) \approx 8.130°$

10.3 Vector-valued Functions (pp. 529–539)

Quick Review 10.3

1. $y = \left(-\dfrac{1}{\sqrt{3}} \right)x + \dfrac{4}{\sqrt{3}}$, or approximately
  $y = -0.577x + 2.309$
2. $y = \sqrt{3}x$
3. 0
4. Undefined; vertical tangent
5. $y = \left(-\dfrac{5\sqrt{3}}{4} \right)x + 10$

6. $y = \left(\dfrac{4\sqrt{3}}{15} \right)x + \dfrac{9}{10}$

7. $\dfrac{1}{4}$

8. ≈ 3.400
9. ≈ 2.958
10. $y = xe^x - e^x + 3$

Section 10.3 Exercises

1. $6\mathbf{i} - 3\mathbf{j}$ **2.** $-3\mathbf{i} + 4\mathbf{j}$
3. (a) $-\mathbf{i} - \mathbf{j}$ (b) $7\mathbf{i} + 5\mathbf{j}$
4. (a) $8\mathbf{i} + 2\mathbf{j}$ (b) $2\mathbf{i} - 6\mathbf{j}$
  (c) $15\mathbf{i} - 6\mathbf{j}$ (d) $\mathbf{i} - 16\mathbf{j}$
5. (a)

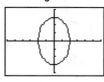

[−6, 6] by [−4, 4]
  (b) $\mathbf{v}(t) = (-2 \sin t)\mathbf{i} + (3 \cos t)\mathbf{j}$
    $\mathbf{a}(t) = (-2 \cos t)\mathbf{i} + (-3 \sin t)\mathbf{j}$
  (c) Speed $= 2$; direction $= \langle -1, 0 \rangle$
  (d) Velocity $= 2\langle -1, 0 \rangle$
6. (a)

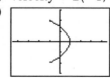

[−4.5, 4.5] by [−3, 3]
  (b) $\mathbf{v}(t) = (-2 \sin 2t)\mathbf{i} + (2 \cos t)\mathbf{j}$
    $\mathbf{a}(t) = (-4 \cos 2t)\mathbf{i} - (2 \sin t)\mathbf{j}$
  (c) Speed $= 2$; direction $= \langle 0, 1 \rangle$
  (d) Velocity $= 2\langle 0, 1 \rangle$

7. (a)

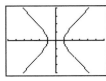

[−6, 6] by [−4, 4]

(b) $\mathbf{v}(t) = (\sec t \tan t)\mathbf{i} + (\sec^2 t)\mathbf{j}$
$\mathbf{a}(t) = (\sec t \tan^2 t + \sec^3 t)\mathbf{i} + (2 \sec^2 t \tan t)\mathbf{j}$

(c) Speed $= \dfrac{2\sqrt{5}}{3}$; direction $= \left\langle \dfrac{1}{\sqrt{5}}, \dfrac{2}{\sqrt{5}} \right\rangle$

(d) Velocity $= \dfrac{2\sqrt{5}}{3} \left\langle \dfrac{1}{\sqrt{5}}, \dfrac{2}{\sqrt{5}} \right\rangle$

8. (a)

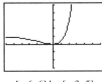

[−6, 6] by [−3, 5]

(b) $\mathbf{v}(t) = \left(\dfrac{2}{t+1}\right)\mathbf{i} + (2t)\mathbf{j}$

$\mathbf{a}(t) = \left(-\dfrac{2}{(t+1)^2}\right)\mathbf{i} + 2\mathbf{j}$

(c) Speed $= \sqrt{5}$; direction $= \left\langle \dfrac{1}{\sqrt{5}}, \dfrac{2}{\sqrt{5}} \right\rangle$

(d) Velocity $= \sqrt{5} \left\langle \dfrac{1}{\sqrt{5}}, \dfrac{2}{\sqrt{5}} \right\rangle$

9. (a) $y = -1$ **(b)** $x = 0$

10. (a) $y = -\dfrac{3}{2}x + \dfrac{6\sqrt{2} - 7}{2}$

(b) $y = \dfrac{2}{3}x + \dfrac{5\sqrt{2} + 18}{6}$

11. $-3\mathbf{i} + (4\sqrt{2} - 2)\mathbf{j}$

12. $\left(\sqrt{2} + \dfrac{\pi}{2}\right)\mathbf{j}$

13. $(\sec t)\mathbf{i} + (\ln |\sec t|)\,\mathbf{j} + \mathbf{C}$

14. $(\ln |t|)\mathbf{i} - (\ln |5 - t|)\mathbf{j} + \mathbf{C}$

15. $\mathbf{r}(t) = ((t+1)^{3/2} - 1)\mathbf{i} - (e^{-t} - 1)\mathbf{j}$

16. $\mathbf{r}(t) = \left(\dfrac{t^4}{4} + 2t^2 + 1\right)\mathbf{i} + \left(\dfrac{t^2}{2} + 1\right)\mathbf{j}$

17. $\mathbf{r}(t) = (8t + 100)\mathbf{i} + (-16t^2 + 8t)\mathbf{j}$

18. $\mathbf{r}(t) = \left(-\dfrac{t^2}{2} + 10\right)\mathbf{i} + \left(-\dfrac{t^2}{2} + 10\right)\mathbf{j}$

19. $t = 0, \pi, 2\pi$

20. $t = \dfrac{k\pi}{2}$, k any nonnegative integer

21. $t = \dfrac{k\pi}{2}$, k any nonnegative integer

22. For all values of t

23. $\cos^{-1}\left(\dfrac{3}{5}\right) \approx 53.130°$

24. $90°$

25. (a) $3\mathbf{i}$ **(b)** $t \neq 0, -3$
(c) $t = 0, -3$

26. (a) $2\mathbf{i}$ **(b)** $(-1, 0) \cup (0, \infty)$
(c) $(-\infty, -1] \cup \{0\}$

27. 2

28. (a) Initial $= \left(\dfrac{1}{4}, 1\right)$; terminal $= \left(\dfrac{e^8}{4} - 2, e^4\right)$

(b) $\dfrac{e^8 + 7}{4} \approx 746.989$

(c) $\pi\left(\dfrac{e^{16} - 12e^8 - 69}{16}\right) \approx 1{,}737{,}746.456$

29. (a) $\mathbf{v}(t) = (\cos t)\mathbf{i} - (2 \sin 2t)\mathbf{j}$

(b) $t = \dfrac{\pi}{2}, \dfrac{3\pi}{2}$

(c) $y = 1 - 2x^2$, $-1 \le x \le 1$. The particle starts at $(0, 1)$, goes to $(1, -1)$, then goes to $(-1, -1)$, and then goes to $(0, 1)$, tracing the curve twice.

30. (a) $\dfrac{t^2 - 4}{2t^2 - 2t}$

(b) $t = -2$: horizontal tangent at $(-28, 16)$
$t = 0$: vertical tangent at $(0, 0)$
$t = 1$: vertical tangent at $(-1, -11)$
$t = 2$: horizontal tangent $(4, -16)$

31. $\mathbf{r}(t) = \left(\dfrac{3}{2}t^2 + \dfrac{3\sqrt{10}}{5}t + 1\right)\mathbf{i}$
$\qquad + \left(-\dfrac{1}{2}t^2 - \dfrac{\sqrt{10}}{5}t + 2\right)\mathbf{j}$

32. (a) $(2\sqrt{2}, 6)$ **(b)** -6
(c) -24

33. (a) 160 seconds **(b)** 225 meters

(c) $\dfrac{15}{4}$ meters per second

(d) At $t = 80$ seconds

34. (a) $t = 2$

(b) First particle: $\left\langle \dfrac{1}{\sqrt{5}}, -\dfrac{2}{\sqrt{5}} \right\rangle$

Second particle: $\left\langle \dfrac{1}{\sqrt{2}}, \dfrac{1}{\sqrt{2}} \right\rangle$

35. (a) Referring to the figure, look at the circular arc from the point where $t = 0$ to the point "m". On one hand, this arc has length given by $r_0\theta$, but it also has length given by vt. Setting those two quantities equal gives the result.

(b) $\mathbf{a}(t) = -\dfrac{v^2}{r_0}\left[\left(\cos \dfrac{vt}{r_0}\right)\mathbf{i} + \left(\sin \dfrac{vt}{r_0}\right)\mathbf{j}\right]$

(c) From part (b) above, $\mathbf{a}(t) = -\left(\dfrac{v}{r_0}\right)^2 \mathbf{r}(t)$.

So, by Newton's second law, $\mathbf{F} = -m\left(\dfrac{v}{r_0}\right)^2 \mathbf{r}$.

Substituting for $\mathbf{F}$ in the law of gravitation gives the result.

(d) Set $\dfrac{vT}{r_0} = 2\pi$ and solve for vT.

(e) Substitute $\dfrac{2\pi r_0}{T}$ for v in $v^2 = \dfrac{GM}{r_0}$ and solve for T^2.

36. $y = (e^x - 1)^2 - 1$ or $y = e^{2x} - 2e^x$, for $x \ge 0$

37. (a) Apply Corollary 3 to each component separately.

(b) Follows immediately from (a) since any two anti-derivatives of $\mathbf{r}(t)$ must have identical derivatives, namely $\mathbf{r}(t)$.

38. $\dfrac{d}{dt}|\mathbf{v}|^2 = \dfrac{d}{dt}(\mathbf{v} \cdot \mathbf{v}) = \mathbf{v}' \cdot \mathbf{v} + \mathbf{v} \cdot \mathbf{v}' = 2\mathbf{v} \cdot \mathbf{v}' = 0.$
Therefore, $|\mathbf{v}|$ is constant.

39. Let $\mathbf{C} = \langle C_1, C_2 \rangle$. $\dfrac{d\mathbf{C}}{dt} = \left| \dfrac{dC_1}{dt}, \dfrac{dC_2}{dt} \right| = \langle 0, 0 \rangle$.

40. (a) Suppose $\mathbf{u} = \langle u_1(t), u_2(t) \rangle$.

$$\frac{d}{dt}(c\mathbf{u}) = \frac{d}{dt}\langle cu_1(t), cu_2(t) \rangle$$
$$= \left\langle \frac{d}{dt}(cu_1(t)), \frac{d}{dt}(cu_2(t)) \right\rangle$$
$$= \left\langle c\frac{du_1}{dt}, c\frac{du_2}{dt} \right\rangle = c\left\langle \frac{du_1}{dt}, \frac{du_2}{dt} \right\rangle = c\frac{d\mathbf{u}}{dt}$$

(b) $\dfrac{d}{dt}(f\mathbf{u}) = \dfrac{d}{dt}\langle fu_1, fu_2 \rangle$

$= \langle fu_1' + f'u_1, fu_2' + f'u_2 \rangle$

$= \langle fu_1', fu_2' \rangle + \langle f'u_1, f'u_2 \rangle$

$= f\mathbf{u}' + f'\mathbf{u}$

41. $\mathbf{u} = \langle u_1, u_2 \rangle$, $\mathbf{v} = \langle v_1, v_2 \rangle$

(a) $\dfrac{d}{dt}(\mathbf{u} + \mathbf{v}) = \dfrac{d}{dt}(\langle u_1 + v_1, u_2 + v_2 \rangle)$

$= \left\langle \dfrac{d}{dt}(u_1 + v_1), \dfrac{d}{dt}(u_2 + v_2) \right\rangle$

$= \langle u_1' + v_1', u_2' + v_2' \rangle$

$= \langle u_1', u_2' \rangle + \langle v_1', v_2' \rangle = \dfrac{d\mathbf{u}}{dt} + \dfrac{d\mathbf{v}}{dt}$

(b) $\dfrac{d}{dt}(\mathbf{u} - \mathbf{v}) = \dfrac{d}{dt}(\langle u_1 - v_1, u_2 - v_2 \rangle)$

$= \left\langle \dfrac{d}{dt}(u_1 - v_1), \dfrac{d}{dt}(u_2 - v_2) \right\rangle$

$= \langle u_1' - v_1', u_2' - v_2' \rangle$

$= \langle u_1', u_2' \rangle - \langle v_1', v_2' \rangle$

$= \dfrac{d\mathbf{u}}{dt} - \dfrac{d\mathbf{v}}{dt}$

42. $\dfrac{d\mathbf{r}}{dt} = \dfrac{df}{dt}\mathbf{i} + \dfrac{dg}{dt}\mathbf{j}$

$\left(\dfrac{d\mathbf{r}}{dt}\right)\left(\dfrac{dt}{ds}\right) = \left(\dfrac{df}{dt}\mathbf{i} + \dfrac{dg}{dt}\mathbf{j}\right)\left(\dfrac{dt}{ds}\right)$

$= \left(\dfrac{df}{dt} \cdot \dfrac{dt}{ds}\right)\mathbf{i} + \left(\dfrac{dg}{dt} \cdot \dfrac{dt}{ds}\right)\mathbf{j}$

$= \dfrac{df}{ds}\mathbf{i} + \dfrac{dg}{ds}\mathbf{j}$

$= \dfrac{d\mathbf{r}}{ds}$

43. $f(t)$ and $g(t)$ differentiable at $c \Rightarrow f(t)$ and $g(t)$ continuous at $c \Rightarrow \mathbf{r}(t) = f(t)\mathbf{i} + g(t)\mathbf{j}$ is continuous at c.

44. (a) Let $\mathbf{r}(t) = \langle x(t), y(t) \rangle$.

$$\int_a^b k\mathbf{r}(t)\, dt = \int_a^b \langle kx(t), ky(t) \rangle\, dt$$
$$= \left\langle \int_a^b kx(t)\, dt, \int_a^b ky(t)\, dt \right\rangle$$
$$= \left\langle k\int_a^b x(t)\, dt, k\int_a^b y(t)\, dt \right\rangle$$
$$= k\left\langle \int_a^b x(t)\, dt, \int_a^b y(t)\, dt \right\rangle = k\int_a^b \langle x(t), y(t) \rangle\, dt$$
$$= k\int_a^b \mathbf{r}(t)\, dt$$

(b) Let $\mathbf{r}_1(t) = \langle x_1(t), y_1(t) \rangle$ and $\mathbf{r}_2(t) = \langle x_2(t), y_2(t) \rangle$.

$$\int_a^b (\mathbf{r}_1(t) \pm \mathbf{r}_2(t))\, dt$$
$$= \int_a^b (\langle x_1(t), y_1(t) \rangle \pm \langle x_2(t), y_2(t) \rangle)\, dt$$
$$= \int_a^b \langle x_1(t) \pm x_2(t), y_1(t) \pm y_2(t) \rangle\, dt$$
$$= \left\langle \int_a^b (x_1(t) \pm x_2(t))\, dt, \int_a^b (y_1(t) \pm y_2(t))\, dt \right\rangle$$
$$= \left\langle \int_a^b x_1(t)\, dt \pm \int_a^b x_2(t)\, dt, \int_a^b y_1(t)\, dt \pm \int_a^b y_2(t)\, dt \right\rangle$$
$$= \left\langle \int_a^b x_1(t)\, dt, \int_a^b y_1(t)\, dt \right\rangle \pm \left\langle \int_a^b x_2(t)\, dt, \int_a^b y_2(t)\, dt \right\rangle$$
$$= \int_a^b \mathbf{r}_1(t)\, dt \pm \int_a^b \mathbf{r}_2(t)\, dt$$

(c) Let $\mathbf{C} = \langle C_1, C_2 \rangle$, $\mathbf{r}(t) = \langle x(t), y(t) \rangle$.

$$\int_a^b \mathbf{C} \cdot \mathbf{r}(t)\, dt = \int_a^b (C_1 xt + C_2 yt)\, dt$$
$$= C_1 \int_a^b xt\, dt + C_2 \int_a^b yt\, dt$$
$$= \langle C_1, C_2 \rangle \cdot \left\langle \int_a^b xt\, dt, \int_a^b yt\, dt \right\rangle$$
$$= \mathbf{C} \cdot \int_a^b \mathbf{r}(t)\, dt$$

45. (a) Let $\mathbf{r}(t) = f(t)\mathbf{i} + g(t)\mathbf{j}$. Then

$$\frac{d}{dt}\int_a^t \mathbf{r}(q)\, dq = \frac{d}{dt}\int_a^t [f(q)\mathbf{i} + g(q)\mathbf{j}]\, dq$$
$$= \frac{d}{dt}\left[\left(\int_a^t f(q)\, dq\right)\mathbf{i} + \left(\int_a^t g(q)\, dq\right)\mathbf{j} \right]$$
$$= \left(\frac{d}{dt}\int_a^t f(q)\, dq\right)\mathbf{i} + \left(\frac{d}{dt}\int_a^t g(q)\, dq\right)\mathbf{j}$$
$$= f(t)\mathbf{i} + g(t)\mathbf{j} = \mathbf{r}(t).$$

(b) Let $\mathbf{S}(t) = \displaystyle\int_a^t \mathbf{r}(q)\, dq$. Then part (a) shows that $\mathbf{S}(t)$ is an antiderivative of $\mathbf{r}(t)$. Let $\mathbf{R}(t)$ be any antiderivative of $\mathbf{r}(t)$. Then according to 37(b), $\mathbf{S}(t) = \mathbf{R}(t) + \mathbf{C}$. Letting $t = a$, we have $0 = \mathbf{S}(a) = \mathbf{R}(a) + \mathbf{C}$. Therefore, $\mathbf{C} = -\mathbf{R}(a)$ and $\mathbf{S}(t) = \mathbf{R}(t) - \mathbf{R}(a)$. The result follows by letting $t = b$.

10.4 Modeling Projectile Motion (pp. 539–552)

Quick Review 10.4

1. $\langle 50 \cos 25°, 50 \sin 25° \rangle \approx \langle 45.315, 21.131 \rangle$
2. $\langle -40, 40\sqrt{3} \rangle$
3. x-intercepts: $\left(\frac{5}{2}, 0\right)$ and $(-8, 0)$
   y-intercept: $(0, -40)$
4. $\left(-\frac{11}{4}, -\frac{441}{8}\right)$
5. x-intercepts: $(0, 0)$ and $(20, 0)$
   y-intercept: $(0, 0)$
6. $(10, 100)$
7. $y = -\cos x + 2$
8. $y = \frac{t^3}{3} + 3t + \frac{25}{3}$
9. $y = 16 + 4e^{-t}$
10. $y = 2 - e^{-x^2}$

Section 10.4 Exercises

1. 50 seconds
2. 490 m/sec
3. (a) After ≈ 72.154 seconds,
       ≈ 25.510 km downrange
   (b) 4020 m
   (c) ≈ 6377.55 m
4. After 2 seconds, $32\sqrt{3} \approx 55.426$ feet away (horizontally)
5. After ≈ 2.135 seconds, ≈ 66.421 feet from the stopboard
6. ≈ 1.184 inches
7. (a) $7\sqrt{2} \approx 9.899$ m/sec
   (b) $\approx 18.435°$ or $71.565°$
8. $\approx 3.136 \times 10^{-14}$ meters, or $\approx 3.136 \times 10^{-12}$ cm
9. ≈ 278.016 ft/sec, or ≈ 189.556 mph
10. Yes, $\approx 32.079°$
11. No. When it has travelled 135 ft in the horizontal direction, it is only about 29.942 feet above the ground.
12. ≈ 0.255 feet beyond the pin
13. (a) ≈ 149.307 ft/sec
    (b) ≈ 2.245 seconds
14. In the formula for range, $\sin 2\alpha = \sin 2(90 - \alpha)$.
15. $\approx 39.261°$ and $50.739°$
16. (a) Substitute $2v_0$ for v_0 in the formula for range.
    (b) 41%
17. ≈ 46.597 ft/sec

18. $y(t) = v_0(\sin \alpha)t - \frac{1}{2}gt^2$, and we know the maximum height is $\frac{(v_0 \sin \alpha)^2}{2g}$ and it occurs when $t = \frac{v_0 \sin \alpha}{g}$. Substituting $t = \frac{v_0 \sin \alpha}{2g}$ into the equation for $y(t)$ gives a height of $\frac{3(v_0 \sin \alpha)^2}{8g}$, which is three-fourths of the maximum height.

19. Integrating, $\frac{d}{dt}\mathbf{r}(t) = c_1\mathbf{i} + (-gt + c_2)\mathbf{j}$. The initial condition on the velocity gives $c_1 = v_0 \cos \alpha$ and $c_2 = v_0 \sin \alpha$. Integrating again,
    $$\mathbf{r}(t) = ((v_0 \cos \alpha)t + c_3)\mathbf{i} + \left(-\frac{gt^2}{2} + (v_0 \sin \alpha)t + c_4\right)\mathbf{j}.$$
    The initial condition on the position gives
    $c_3 = x_0$ and $c_4 = y_0$.

20. ≈ 79.107 ft/sec
21. It takes about 1.924 seconds. The arrow passes about 3.698 feet above the rim. (It's 73.698 feet above the ground.)
22. The projectile rises straight up and then falls straight down, returning to the firing point.
23. Angle $\approx 62°$
    Maximum height $= 4$ feet (independent of the measured angle)
    Speed of engine ≈ 8.507 ft/sec (changes with the angle)

24. The height of A is given by $y_A = (v \sin \alpha)t - \frac{1}{2}gt^2$ and the height of B is given by $y_B = R \tan \alpha - \frac{1}{2}gt^2$. The second terms in y_A and y_B $\left(-\frac{gt^2}{2}\right)$ are equal for any value of t. But A moves R units horizontally to B's line of fall in $\frac{R}{v \cos \alpha}$ time units, and the first terms in y_A and y_B are also equal at that time:
    $$(v \sin \alpha)\left(\frac{R}{v \cos \alpha}\right) = R \tan \alpha.$$ Therefore, A and B will always be at the same height when A reaches B's line of fall.

25. (a)

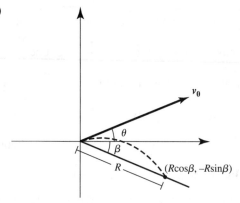

$$x = (v_0 \cos \theta)t$$

$$y = (v_0 \sin \theta)t - \frac{1}{2}gt^2$$

$$x = R \cos \beta \Rightarrow R \cos \beta = (v_0 \cos \theta)t$$

$$\Rightarrow t = \frac{R \cos \beta}{v_0 \cos \theta}. \text{ Then } y = -R \sin \beta$$

$$\Rightarrow -R \sin \beta = \frac{(v_0 \sin \theta) R \cos \beta}{v_0 \cos \theta} - \frac{g}{2} \frac{R^2 \cos^2 \beta}{v_0^2 \cos^2 \theta}$$

$$\Rightarrow R = \frac{2v_0^2}{g \cos^2 \beta} \cos \theta \sin (\theta + \beta).$$

Let $f(\theta) = \cos \theta \sin (\theta + \beta)$.

$$f'(\theta) = \cos \theta \cos (\theta + \beta) - \sin \theta \sin (\theta + \beta)$$

$$f'(\theta) = 0 \Rightarrow \tan \theta \tan (\theta + \beta) = 1$$

$$\Rightarrow \tan \theta = \cot (\theta + \beta)$$

$$\Rightarrow \theta + \beta = 90° - \theta. \text{ Note that } f''(\theta) < 0, \text{ so } R$$

is maximum when $\theta + \beta = 90° - \theta$.

(b)

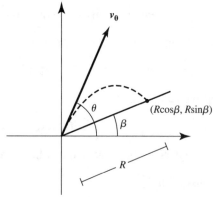

$R = \dfrac{2v_0^2}{g \cos^2 \beta} \cos \theta \sin (\theta - \beta)$ is maximum

when $\tan \theta = \cot (\theta - \beta)$,

so $\theta - \beta = 90° - \theta$.

The initial velocity vector bisects the angle

between the hill and the vertical for max

range.

26. (a) $\mathbf{r}(t) = (x(t))\mathbf{i} + (y(t))\mathbf{j}$, where
$x(t) = (145 \cos 23° - 14)t$ and
$y(t) = 2.5 + (145 \sin 23°)t - 16t^2$.

(b) At $t \approx 1.771$ seconds, it reaches a maximum height of about 52.655 feet.

(c) Range ≈ 428.262 feet
flight time ≈ 3.585 seconds

(d) At $t \approx 0.342$ and $t \approx 3.199$ seconds, and it is 40.847 and 382.208 feet from home plate at those times.

(e) Yes. According to part (d), the ball is still 20 feet above the ground when it is 382 feet from home plate.

27. (a) (Assuming that "x" is zero at the point of impact.)
$\mathbf{r}(t) = (x(t))\mathbf{i} + (y(t))\mathbf{j}$, where
$x(t) = (35 \cos 27°)t$ and
$y(t) = 4 + (35 \sin 27°)t - 16t^2$.

(b) At $t \approx 0.497$ seconds, it reaches its maximum height of about 7.945 feet.

(c) Range ≈ 37.460 feet
flight time ≈ 1.201 seconds

(d) At $t \approx 0.254$ and $t \approx 0.740$ seconds, when it is ≈ 29.554 and ≈ 14.396 feet from where it will land.

(e) Yes. It changes things because the ball won't clear the net.

28. (a) $\mathbf{r}(t) = (x(t))\mathbf{i} + (y(t))\mathbf{j}$, where

$$x(t) = \left(\frac{152}{0.12}\right)(1 - e^{-0.12t})(\cos 20°) \text{ and}$$

$$y(t) = 3 + \left(\frac{152}{0.12}\right)(1 - e^{-0.12t})(\sin 20°)$$
$$+ \left(\frac{32}{0.12^2}\right)(1 - 0.12t - e^{-0.12t})$$

(b) At $t \approx 1.484$ seconds it reaches its maximum height of about 40.435 feet.

(c) Range ≈ 372.323 feet
flight time ≈ 3.126 seconds

(d) At $t \approx 0.689$ and $t \approx 2.305$ seconds, when it is about 94.513 and 287.628 feet from home plate.

(e) Yes, the batter has hit a home run since the ball is more than 15 feet above the ground when it passes over the fence.

29. (a) $\mathbf{r}(t) = (x(t))\mathbf{i} + (y(t))\mathbf{j}$, where

$$x(t) = \left(\frac{1}{0.08}\right)(1 - e^{-0.08t})(152 \cos 20° - 17.6)$$

and

$$y(t) = 3 + \left(\frac{152}{0.08}\right)(1 - e^{-0.08t})(\sin 20°)$$
$$+ \left(\frac{32}{0.08^2}\right)(1 - 0.08t - e^{-0.08t})$$

(b) At $t \approx 1.527$ seconds it reaches its maximum height of about 41.893 feet.

(c) Range ≈ 351.734 feet
Flight time ≈ 3.181 seconds

(d) At $t \approx 0.877$ and $t \approx 2.190$ seconds, when it is about 106.028 and 251.530 feet from home plate.

(e) No. The wind gust would need to be greater than 12.846 ft/sec in the direction of the hit in order for the ball to clear the fence for a home run.

30. (a)

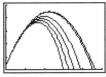

[0, 500] by [0, 50]

(b)

drag coeff	time at max ht	max ht
$k = 0.01$	$t \approx 1.612$	44.777
$k = 0.02$	$t \approx 1.599$	44.336
$k = 0.10$	$t \approx 1.505$	41.149
$k = 0.15$	$t \approx 1.454$	39.419
$k = 0.20$	$t \approx 1.407$	37.854
$k = 0.25$	$t \approx 1.363$	36.431

(c)

drag coeff	flight time	range
$k = 0.01$	$t \approx 3.289$	462.152
$k = 0.02$	$t \approx 3.273$	452.478
$k = 0.10$	$t \approx 3.153$	386.274
$k = 0.15$	$t \approx 3.088$	352.983
$k = 0.20$	$t \approx 3.028$	324.410
$k = 0.25$	$t \approx 2.974$	299.661

(d) This follows from the following two limits (as $k \to 0$):

$$\lim_{k \to 0} \frac{1 - e^{-kt}}{k} = t, \text{ and}$$
$$\lim_{k \to 0} \frac{1 - kt - e^{-kt}}{k^2} = -\frac{t^2}{2}.$$

As $k \to 0$, the air resistance approaches 0.

31. The points in question are $(x, y) = \left(\dfrac{R}{2}, y_{\max}\right)$. So,

$$x = \frac{v_0^2 \sin \alpha \cos \alpha}{g}, \text{ and } y = \frac{(v_0 \sin \alpha)^2}{2g}. \text{ Substituting}$$

these into the given equation for the ellipse yields

an identity.

32. From Equation (10), find $\left(\dfrac{d\mathbf{r}}{dt}\right)$ and $\left(\dfrac{d^2\mathbf{r}}{dt^2}\right)$, and then show that they satisfy both the equation and the initial conditions.

10.5 Polar Coordinates and Polar Graphs (pp. 552–559)

Quick Review 10.5

1. $y = -x + 2$　　　　**2.** $x^2 + y^2 = 9$

3. $(x + 2)^2 + (y - 4)^2 = 4$

4. (a) No
　(b) No
　(c) Yes

5. (a) No
　(b) No
　(c) No

6. (a) No
　(b) Yes
　(c) No

7. (a) Yes
　(b) Yes
　(c) Yes

8. Graph $y = (x - 2)^{1/2}$ and $y = -(x - 2)^{1/2}$

9. Graph $y = \left(\dfrac{4 - x^2}{3}\right)^{1/2}$ and $y = -\left(\dfrac{4 - x^2}{3}\right)^{1/2}$

10. $(x - 2)^2 + (y + 3)^2 = 4$, center $= (2, -3)$, radius $= 2$

Section 10.5 Exercises

1. (a) and (e) are the same.
　(b) and (g) are the same.
　(c) and (h) are the same.
　(d) and (f) are the same.

2. (a) and (f) are the same.
　(b) and (h) are the same.
　(c) and (g) are the same.
　(d) and (e) are the same.

3.

[−3, 3] by [−2, 2]

(a) $(1, 1)$
(b) $(1, 0)$
(c) $(0, 0)$
(d) $(-1, -1)$

4.

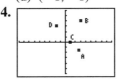

[−9, 9] by [−6, 6]

(a) $\left(\dfrac{3\sqrt{3}}{2}, -\dfrac{3}{2}\right)$

(b) $(3, 4)$

(c) $(1, 0)$

(d) $(-\sqrt{3}, 3)$

5.

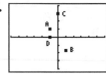

$[-6, 6]$ by $[-4, 4]$

(a) $\left(\sqrt{2}, \dfrac{3\pi}{4}\right)$ or $\left(\sqrt{2}, -\dfrac{5\pi}{4}\right)$

(b) $\left(2, -\dfrac{\pi}{3}\right)$ or $\left(-2, \dfrac{2\pi}{3}\right)$

(c) $\left(3, \dfrac{\pi}{2}\right)$ or $\left(3, \dfrac{5\pi}{2}\right)$

(d) $(1, \pi)$ or $(-1, 0)$

6.

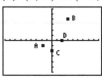

$[-9, 9]$ by $[-6, 6]$

(a) $\left(2, \dfrac{7\pi}{6}\right)$ or $\left(-2, \dfrac{\pi}{6}\right)$

(b) $\left(5, \tan^{-1}\dfrac{4}{3}\right)$ or $\left(-5, \pi + \tan^{-1}\dfrac{4}{3}\right)$

(c) $\left(2, \dfrac{3\pi}{2}\right)$ or $\left(2, -\dfrac{\pi}{2}\right)$

(d) $(2, 0)$ or $(2, 2\pi)$

7.

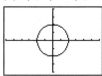

$[-6, 6]$ by $[-4, 4]$

8.

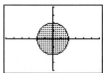

$[-6, 6]$ by $[-4, 4]$

9.

$[-3, 3]$ by $[-2, 2]$

10.

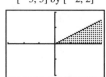

$[-3, 3]$ by $[-2, 2]$

11.

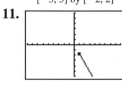

$[-9, 9]$ by $[-6, 6]$

12.

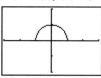

$[-6, 6]$ by $[-4, 4]$

13.

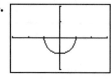

$[-3, 3]$ by $[-2, 2]$

14.

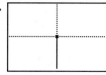

$[-3, 3]$ by $[-2, 2]$

15.

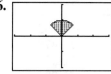

$[-3, 3]$ by $[-2, 2]$

16.

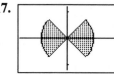

$[-3, 3]$ by $[-2, 2]$

17.

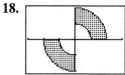

$[-1.8, 1.8]$ by $[-1.2, 1.2]$

18.

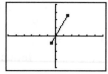

$[-3, 3]$ by $[-2, 2]$

19. $y = 0$, the x-axis

20. $x = 0$, the y-axis

21. $y = 4$, a horizontal line

22. $x = -3$, a vertical line

23. $x + y = 1$, a line (slope $= -1$, y-intercept $= 1$)

24. $x^2 + y^2 = 1$, a circle (center $= (0, 0)$, radius $= 1$)

25. $x^2 + y^2 = 4y$, a circle (center $= (0, 2)$, radius $= 2$)

26. $y - 2x = 5$, a line (slope $= 2$, y-intercept $= 5$)

27. $xy = 1$, a hyperbola

28. $y^2 = x$, a parabola

29. $y = e^x$, the exponential curve

30. $x^2 = y^2$, the union of two lines: $y = \pm x$

31. $y = \ln x$, the logarithmic curve

32. $(x + y)^2 = 1$,
the union of two lines: $x + y = \pm 1$

33. $(x + 2)^2 + y^2 = 4$, a circle (center = $(-2, 0)$, radius = 2)

34. $x^2 + (y - 4)^2 = 16$, a circle (center = $(0, 4)$, radius = 4)

35. $(x - 1)^2 + (y - 1)^2 = 2$, a circle (center = $(1, 1)$, radius = $\sqrt{2}$)

36. $x + \sqrt{3}y = 4$,

a line $\left(\text{slope} = -\dfrac{1}{\sqrt{3}},\ y\text{-intercept} = \dfrac{4}{\sqrt{3}}\right)$

37. $r \cos \theta = 7$

38. $r \sin \theta = 1$

39. $\theta = \dfrac{\pi}{4}$

40. $r \cos \theta - r \sin \theta = 3$

41. $r^2 = 4$ or $r = 2$

42. $r^2(\cos^2 \theta - \sin^2 \theta) = 1$

43. $r^2(4 \cos^2 \theta + 9 \sin^2 \theta) = 36$

44. $r^2 \cos \theta \sin \theta = 2$ or $r^2 \sin 2\theta = 4$

45. $r \sin^2 \theta = 4 \cos \theta$

46. $r^2(1 + \cos \theta \sin \theta) = 1$

47. $r = 4 \sin \theta$

48. $r^2 - 6r \cos \theta + 2r \sin \theta + 6 = 0$

49. (a)

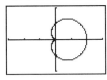

$[-3, 3]$ by $[-2, 2]$

(b) Length of interval = 2π

50. (a)

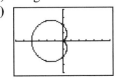

$[-6, 6]$ by $[-4, 4]$

(b) Length of interval = 2π

51. (a)

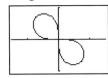

$[-1.5, 1.5]$ by $[-1, 1]$

(b) Length of interval = $\dfrac{\pi}{2}$

52. (a)

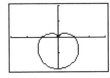

$[-3, 3]$ by $[-2, 2]$

(b) Length of interval = 2π

53. (a)

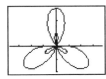

$[-3.75, 3.75]$ by $[-2, 3]$

(b) Length of interval = 2π

54. (a)

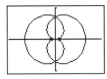

$[-1.5, 1.5]$ by $[-1, 1]$

(b) Length of interval = 4π

55. (a)

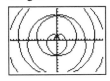

$[-15, 15]$ by $[-10, 10]$

(b) Required interval = $(-\infty, \infty)$

56. (a)

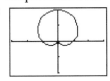

$[-3, 3]$ by $[-2, 2]$

(b) Length of interval = 2π

57. (a)

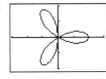

$[-3, 3]$ by $[-2, 2]$

(b) Length of interval = π

58. (a)

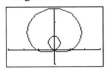

$[-3, 3]$ by $[-1, 3]$

(b) Length of interval = 2π

59. x-axis, y-axis, origin

60. Origin

61. y-axis

62. x-axis, y-axis, origin

63. (a) Because $r = a \sec \theta$ is equivalent to $r \cos \theta = a$, which is equivalent to the Cartesian equation $x = a$.

(b) $r = a \csc \theta$ is equivalent to $y = a$.

64. (a) The graph is the same for $n = 2$ and $n = -2$, and in general, it's the same for $n = 2k$ and $n = -2k$. The graphs for $n = 2, 4$, and 6 are roses with 4, 8, and 12 "petals" respectively. The graphs for $n = \pm 2$ and $n = \pm 6$ are shown below.

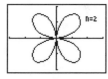

$[-3, 3]$ by $[-2, 2]$

$[-3, 3]$ by $[-2, 2]$

(b) 2π

(c) The graph is a rose with $2|n|$ "petals".

(d) The graphs are roses with 3, 5, and 7 "petals" respectively. The "center leaf" points upward if $n = -3, +5,$ or -7. The graphs for $n = 3$ and $n = -3$ are shown below.

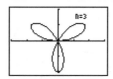

$[-3, 3]$ by $[-2, 2]$

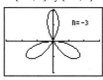

$[-3, 3]$ by $[-2, 2]$

(e) π

(f) The graph is a rose with $|n|$ "petals".

65. (a) We have $x = r \cos \theta$ and $y = r \sin \theta$. By taking $t = \theta$, we have $r = f(t)$, so $x = f(t) \cos t$ and $y = f(t) \sin t$.

(b) $x = 3 \cos t, y = 3 \sin t$

(c) $x = (1 - \cos t) \cos t, y = (1 - \cos t) \sin t$

(d) $x = (3 \sin 2t) \cos t, y = (3 \sin 2t) \sin t$

66. (a)

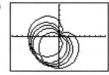

$[-9, 9]$ by $[-6, 6]$

(b)

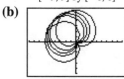

$[-9, 9]$ by $[-6, 6]$

(c) The graph of r_2 is the graph of r_1 rotated counterclockwise about the origin by the angle α.

67. $d = [(x_2 - x_1)^2 + (y_2 + y_1)^2]^{1/2}$
$= [(r_2 \cos \theta_2 - r_1 \cos \theta_1)^2$
$\quad + (r_2 \sin \theta_2 - r_1 \sin \theta_1)^2]^{1/2}$

and then simplify using trigonometric identities.

68. (a)

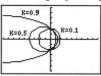

$[-9, 9]$ by $[-6, 6]$

The graphs are ellipses.

(b) As $k \to 0^+$, the graph approaches the circle of radius 2 centered at the origin.

69. (a)

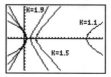

$[-5, 25]$ by $[-10, 10]$

The graphs are hyperbolas.

(b) As $k \to 1^+$, the right branch of the hyperbola goes to infinity and "disappears". The left branch approaches the parabola $y^2 = 4 - 4x$.

70. (a)

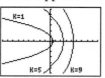

$[-9, 9]$ by $[-6, 6]$

The graphs are parabolas.

(b) As $k \to 0^+$, the limit of the graph is the negative x-axis.

10.6 Calculus of Polar Curves
(pp. 559–568)

Quick Review 10.6

1. $-\dfrac{5}{3} \cot t$

2. $-\dfrac{5}{3} \cot 2 \approx 0.763$

3. $(0, 5)$ and $(0, -5)$

4. $(3, 0)$ and $(-3, 0)$

5. ≈ 12.763

6. The upper half of the outer loop

7. The inner loop

8. The lower half of the outer loop

9. 36

10. ≈ 2.403

Section 10.6 Exercises

1. At $\theta = 0$: -1
At $\theta = \pi$: 1

2. At $\theta = 0$: undefined
At $\theta = -\dfrac{\pi}{2}$: 0
At $\theta = \dfrac{\pi}{2}$: 0
At $\theta = \pi$: undefined

3. At $(2, 0)$: $-\dfrac{2}{3}$

At $\left(-1, \dfrac{\pi}{2}\right)$: 0

At $(2, \pi)$: $\dfrac{2}{3}$

At $\left(5, \dfrac{3\pi}{2}\right)$: 0

4. At $\left(1.5, \dfrac{\pi}{3}\right)$: undefined

At $\left(4.5, \dfrac{2\pi}{3}\right)$: 0

At $(6, \pi)$: undefined

At $\left(3, \dfrac{3\pi}{2}\right)$: 1

5. $\theta = \dfrac{\pi}{2}$ $[x = 0]$

6. $\theta = \dfrac{\pi}{6}$ $\left[y = \dfrac{1}{\sqrt{3}}x\right]$

$\theta = \dfrac{\pi}{2}$ $[x = 0]$

$\theta = \dfrac{5\pi}{6}$ $\left[y = -\dfrac{1}{\sqrt{3}}x\right]$

7. $\theta = 0$ $[y = 0]$

$\theta = \dfrac{\pi}{5}$ $\left[y = \left(\tan\dfrac{\pi}{5}\right)x\right]$

$\theta = \dfrac{2\pi}{5}$ $\left[y = \left(\tan\dfrac{2\pi}{5}\right)x\right]$

$\theta = \dfrac{3\pi}{5}$ $\left[y = \left(\tan\dfrac{3\pi}{5}\right)x\right]$

$\theta = \dfrac{4\pi}{5}$ $\left[y = \left(\tan\dfrac{4\pi}{5}\right)x\right]$

8. $\theta = 0$ $[y = 0]$

$\theta = \dfrac{\pi}{2}$ $[x = 0]$

9. Horizontal at: $\left(-\dfrac{1}{2}, \dfrac{\pi}{6}\right)$ $\left[y = -\dfrac{1}{4}\right]$,

$\left(-\dfrac{1}{2}, \dfrac{5\pi}{6}\right)$ $\left[y = -\dfrac{1}{4}\right]$,

$\left(-2, \dfrac{3\pi}{2}\right)$ $[y = 2]$

Vertical at: $\left(0, \dfrac{\pi}{2}\right)$ $[x = 0]$,

$\left(-\dfrac{3}{2}, \dfrac{7\pi}{6}\right)$ $\left[x = \dfrac{3\sqrt{3}}{4}\right]$,

$\left(-\dfrac{3}{2}, \dfrac{11\pi}{6}\right)$ $\left[x = -\dfrac{3\sqrt{3}}{4}\right]$

10. Horizontal at: $\left(\dfrac{3}{2}, \dfrac{\pi}{3}\right)$ $\left[y = \dfrac{3\sqrt{3}}{4}\right]$,

$(0, \pi)$ $[y = 0]$,

$\left(\dfrac{3}{2}, \dfrac{5\pi}{3}\right)$ $\left[y = -\dfrac{3\sqrt{3}}{4}\right]$

Vertical at: $(2, 0)$ $[x = 2]$,

$\left(\dfrac{1}{2}, \dfrac{2\pi}{3}\right)$ $\left[x = -\dfrac{1}{4}\right]$,

$\left(\dfrac{1}{2}, \dfrac{4\pi}{3}\right)$ $\left[x = -\dfrac{1}{4}\right]$,

$(2, 2\pi)$ $[x = 2]$

11. Horizontal at: $(0, 0)$ $[y = 0]$,

$\left(2, \dfrac{\pi}{2}\right)$ $[y = 2]$,

$(0, \pi)$ $[y = 0]$

Vertical at: $\left(\sqrt{2}, \dfrac{\pi}{4}\right)$ $[x = 1]$,

$\left(\sqrt{2}, \dfrac{3\pi}{4}\right)$ $[x = -1]$

12. Horizontal at: $(-0.676, 0.405)$ $[y \approx -0.267]$,

$(5.176, 2.146)$ $[y \approx 4.343]$,

$(5.176, 4.137)$ $[y \approx -4.343]$,

$(-0.676, 5.878)$ $[y \approx 0.267]$

Vertical at: $(-1, 0)$ $[x = -1]$,

$(1.5, 1.186)$ $\left[x = \dfrac{9}{16}\right]$,

$(7, \pi)$ $[x = -7]$,

$(1.5, 5.097)$ $\left[x = \dfrac{9}{16}\right]$,

$(-1, 2\pi)$ $[x = -1]$

13. 18π

14. $\dfrac{3}{2}\pi a^2$

15. $2a^2$

16. $\dfrac{\pi}{8}$

17. 2

18. 4

19. $\dfrac{\pi}{2} - 1$

20. $\dfrac{2\pi}{3} - \dfrac{\sqrt{3}}{2}$

21. $5\pi - 8$

22. $6\pi - 16$

23. $a^2\pi$

24. $3\sqrt{3} - \pi$

25. $8 - \pi$

26. (a) $\dfrac{3\sqrt{3}}{2} + 2\pi$ **(b)** $3\sqrt{3} + \pi$

27. $12\pi - 9\sqrt{3}$

28. $\dfrac{3\sqrt{3}}{4}$

29. (a) $\dfrac{3}{2} - \dfrac{\pi}{4}$

(b) Yes. $x = \tan \theta \cos \theta \Rightarrow x = \sin \theta$

$$y = \tan \theta \sin \theta \Rightarrow y = \frac{\sin^2 \theta}{\cos \theta}$$

$$\lim_{\theta \to -\pi/2^+} x = -1, \quad \lim_{\theta \to -\pi/2^+} y = \infty$$

$$\lim_{\theta \to \pi/2^-} x = 1, \quad \lim_{\theta \to \pi/2^-} y = \infty$$

30. The integral given is incorrect because $r = \cos \theta$ sweeps out the circle twice as θ goes from 0 to 2π. You can't use equation (2) from the text on the interval $[0, 2\pi]$ because $r = \cos \theta$ is negative for $\dfrac{\pi}{2} < \theta < \dfrac{3\pi}{2}$. The correct area is $\dfrac{5\pi}{4}$, which can be found by computing the areas of the cardioid $\dfrac{3\pi}{2}$ and the circle $\dfrac{\pi}{4}$ separately and subtracting.

31. $\dfrac{19}{3}$

32. $e^{\pi} - 1$

33. 8

34. $2a$

35. ≈ 6.887

36. ≈ 2.296

37. $\dfrac{\pi + 3}{8}$

38. 2π

39. $\pi\sqrt{2} \approx 4.443$

40. $\sqrt{5}\pi(e^{\pi/2} + 1) \approx 40.818$

41. $(4 - 2\sqrt{2})\pi \approx 3.681$

42. $4a^2\pi^2$

43. $\left(\dfrac{dx}{d\theta}\right)^2 + \left(\dfrac{dy}{d\theta}\right)^2$

$\quad = (f'(\theta) \cos \theta - f(\theta) \sin \theta)^2$

$\qquad + (f'(\theta) \sin \theta + f(\theta) \cos \theta)^2$

$\quad = (f'(\theta) \cos \theta)^2 + (f(\theta) \sin \theta)^2 + (f'(\theta) \sin \theta)^2$

$\qquad + (f(\theta) \cos \theta)^2$

$\quad = (f(\theta))^2 (\sin^2 \theta + \cos^2 \theta)$

$\qquad + (f'(\theta))^2 (\cos^2 \theta + \sin^2 \theta)$

$\quad = (f(\theta))^2 + (f'(\theta))^2 = r^2 + \left(\dfrac{dr}{d\theta}\right)^2$

44. (a) a

(b) a

(c) $\dfrac{2a}{\pi}$

45. If $g(\theta) = 2f(\theta)$, then
$\sqrt{g(\theta)^2 + g'(\theta)^2} = 2\sqrt{f(\theta)^2 + f'(\theta)^2}$, so the length of g is 2 times the length of f.

46. If $g(\theta) = 2f(\theta)$, then
$2\pi\, g(\theta) \sin \theta \sqrt{g(\theta)^2 + g'(\theta)^2}$
$= 4[2\pi f(\theta) \sin \theta \sqrt{f(\theta)^2 + f'(\theta)^2}]$,
so the area generated by g is 4 times that of f.

47. (a) Let $r = 1.75 + \dfrac{0.06\theta}{2\pi}$.

(b) Since $\dfrac{dr}{d\theta} = \dfrac{b}{2\pi}$, this is just Equation 4 for the length of the curve.

(c) ≈ 741.420 cm, or ≈ 7.414 m

(d) $\left(r^2 + \left(\dfrac{b}{2\pi}\right)^2\right)^{1/2} = r\left(1 + \left(\dfrac{b}{2\pi r}\right)^2\right)^{1/2} \approx r$ since $\left(\dfrac{b}{2\pi r}\right)^2$ is a very small quantity squared.

(e) $L \approx 741.420$ cm (from part (c)),
$L_a \approx 741.416$ cm

48. (a) Use the approximation, L_a, from 47(e). If the reel has made n complete turns, then the angle is $2\pi n$. So from the integral,

$L_a = \pi b n^2 + 2\pi r_0 n$. Solving for n gives

$$n = \left(\frac{r_0}{b}\right)\left(\sqrt{\frac{bL}{r_0^2 \pi} + 1} - 1\right).$$

(b) The take up reel slows down as time progresses.

(c) Since L is proportional to time, the formula in part (a) shows that n will grow roughly as the square root of time.

49. $\left(\dfrac{5a}{6}, 0\right)$

50. $\left(0, \dfrac{4a}{3\pi}\right)$

▮ Chapter 10 Review Exercises (pp. 569–572)

1. (a) $\langle -17, 32 \rangle$

(b) $\sqrt{1313}$

2. (a) $\langle -1, -1 \rangle$

(b) $\sqrt{2}$

3. (a) $\langle 6, -8 \rangle$

(b) 10

4. (a) $\langle 10, -25 \rangle$

(b) $\sqrt{725} = 5\sqrt{29}$

5. $\left(-\dfrac{\sqrt{3}}{2}, -\dfrac{1}{2}\right)$ [assuming counterclockwise]

6. $\left\langle \dfrac{\sqrt{3}}{2}, \dfrac{1}{2}\right\rangle$

7. $\left\langle \dfrac{8}{\sqrt{17}}, -\dfrac{2}{\sqrt{17}}\right\rangle$

8. $\langle -3, -4 \rangle$

9. (a) $y = \dfrac{\sqrt{3}}{2}x + \dfrac{1}{4}$

(b) $\dfrac{1}{4}$

10. (a) $y = -3x + \dfrac{13}{4}$

(b) 6

11. (a) $\left(0, \dfrac{1}{2}\right)$ and $\left(0, -\dfrac{1}{2}\right)$

(b) Nowhere

12. (a) $(0, 2)$ and $(0, -2)$

(b) $(-2, 0)$ and $(2, 0)$

13. (a) $(0, 0)$

(b) Nowhere

14. (a) $(0, 9)$ and $(0, -9)$

(b) $(-4, 0)$ and $(4, 0)$

15.

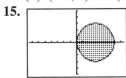

[−7.5, 7.5] by [−5, 5]

16.

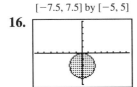

[−7.5, 7.5] by [−5, 5]

17. (a)

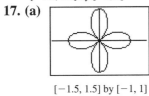

[−1.5, 1.5] by [−1, 1]

(b) 2π

18. (a)

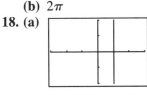

[−3, 3] by [−2, 2]

(b) π

19. (a)

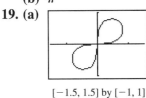

[−1.5, 1.5] by [−1, 1]

(b) $\dfrac{\pi}{2}$

20. (a)

[−1.5, 1.5] by [−1, 1]

(b) π

21. Tangent lines at $\theta = \dfrac{\pi}{4}, \dfrac{3\pi}{4}, \dfrac{5\pi}{4}$, and $\dfrac{7\pi}{4}$

Cartesian equations are $y = \pm x$.

22. Tangent lines at $\theta = \dfrac{\pi}{2}$ and $\dfrac{3\pi}{2}$

Cartesian equation is $x = 0$.

23. Horizontal: $y = 0$, $y \approx \pm 0.443$, $y \approx \pm 1.739$

Vertical: $x = 2$, $x \approx 0.067$, $x \approx -1.104$

24. Horizontal: $y = \dfrac{1}{2}$, $y = -4$

Vertical: $x = 0$, $x \approx \pm 2.598$

25. $y = \pm x + \sqrt{2}$ and $y = \pm x - \sqrt{2}$

26. $y = x - 1$ and $y = -x - 1$

27. $x = y$, a line

28. $x^2 + y^2 = 3x$,

a circle $\left(\text{center} = \left(\dfrac{3}{2}, 0\right), \text{radius} = \dfrac{3}{2}\right)$

29. $x^2 = 4y$, a parabola

30. $x - \sqrt{3}y = 4\sqrt{3}$ or $y = \dfrac{x}{\sqrt{3}} - 4$, a line

31. $r = -5 \sin \theta$ **32.** $r = 2 \sin \theta$

33. $r^2 \cos^2 \theta + 4r^2 \sin^2 \theta = 16$, or

$r^2 = \dfrac{16}{\cos^2 \theta + 4 \sin^2 \theta}$

34. $(r \cos \theta + 2)^2 + (r \sin \theta - 5)^2 = 16$

35. $\dfrac{\ln 2 + 24}{8} \approx 3.087$

36. $4\sqrt{3}$

37. 8

38. $\pi\sqrt{2}$

39. $\pi - 3$

40. $\pi\sqrt{2}$

41. ≈ 3.183

42. ≈ 12.363

43. $\dfrac{9\pi}{2}$

44. $\dfrac{\pi}{12}$

45. $\dfrac{\pi}{4} + 2$

46. 5π

47. $\dfrac{76\pi}{3}$

48. ≈ 10.110

49. $\pi(2 - \sqrt{2}) \approx 1.840$

50. $4\pi \approx 12.566$

51. (a) $\mathbf{v}(t) = (-4 \sin t)\mathbf{i} + (\sqrt{2} \cos t)\mathbf{j}$

$\mathbf{a}(t) = (-4 \cos t)\mathbf{i} + (-\sqrt{2} \sin t)\mathbf{j}$

(b) 3

(c) $\cos^{-1}\dfrac{7}{9} \approx 38.942°$

52. (a) $\mathbf{v}(t) = (\sqrt{3} \sec t \tan t)\mathbf{i} + (\sqrt{3} \sec^2 t)\mathbf{j}$

$\mathbf{a}(t) = \sqrt{3}(\sec t \tan^2 t + \sec^3 t)\mathbf{i}$
$+ (2\sqrt{3} \sec^2 t \tan t)\mathbf{j}$

(b) $\sqrt{3}$

(c) $90°$

53. 1

54. $\mathbf{a}(t) = (-2 e^t \sin t)\mathbf{i} + (2 e^t \cos t)\mathbf{j}$, and $\mathbf{r}(t) \cdot \mathbf{a}(t) = 0$ for all t. The angle between $\mathbf{r}$ and $\mathbf{a}$ is always $90°$.

55. $6\mathbf{i}$

56. $3\mathbf{i} + (\ln 2)\mathbf{j}$

57. $\mathbf{r}(t) = (\cos t - 1)\mathbf{i} + (\sin t + 1)\mathbf{j}$

58. $\mathbf{r}(t) = (\tan^{-1} t + 1)\mathbf{i} + \sqrt{t^2 + 1}\,\mathbf{j}$

59. $\mathbf{r}(t) = \mathbf{i} + t^2\mathbf{j}$

60. $\mathbf{r}(t) = (-t^2 + 6t - 2)\mathbf{i} + (-t^2 + 2t + 2)\mathbf{j}$

61. **(a)** $\dfrac{\pi\sqrt{17}}{4} \approx 3.238$

 (b) x-component: $\dfrac{3\pi^2}{16\sqrt{2}}$

  y-component: $-\dfrac{5\pi^2}{16\sqrt{2}}$

 (c) $\dfrac{x^2}{9} + \dfrac{y^2}{25} = 1$

62. **(a)** ≈ 25.874

 (b) $\dfrac{1250\pi}{3}$

 (c) ≈ 1040.728

63. **(a)** 1

 (b) $e^3\sqrt{2}$

 (c) $(e^3 - 1)\sqrt{2}$

64. **(a)** $\dfrac{104}{5}$

 (b) $\dfrac{4144}{135}$

 (c) $\dfrac{dy}{dx} = \dfrac{3}{5}\sqrt{x + 2}$

65. Speed ≈ 591.982 mph
 Direction $\approx 8.179°$ north of east

66. Direction $\approx 2.073°$
 Length ≈ 411.891 lbs

67. It hits the ground ≈ 2.135 seconds later, approximately 66.421 horizontal feet from where it left the thrower's hand. Assuming it doesn't bounce or roll, it will still be there 3 seconds after it was thrown.

68. 57 feet

69. **(a)**

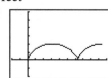

  [−2, 10] by [−2, 6]

 (b) $\mathbf{v}(0) = \langle 0, 0 \rangle$ $\mathbf{v}(1) = \langle 2\pi, 0 \rangle$
  $\mathbf{a}(0) = \langle 0, \pi^2 \rangle$ $\mathbf{a}(1) = \langle 0, -\pi^2 \rangle$

  $\mathbf{v}(2) = \langle 0, 0 \rangle$ $\mathbf{v}(3) = \langle 2\pi, 0 \rangle$
  $\mathbf{a}(2) = \langle 0, \pi^2 \rangle$ $\mathbf{a}(3) = \langle 0, -\pi^2 \rangle$

 (c) Topmost point: 2π ft/sec
  center of wheel: π ft/sec
  Reasons: Since the wheel rolls half a circumference, or π feet every second, the center of the wheel will move π feet every second. Since the rim of the wheel is turning at a rate of π ft/sec about the center, the velocity of the topmost point relative to the center is π ft/sec, giving it a total velocity of 2π ft/sec.

70. For 4325 yds: $v_0 \approx 644.360$ ft/sec
 For 4752 yds: $v_0 \approx 675.420$ ft/sec

71. **(a)** ≈ 59.195 ft/sec
 (b) ≈ 74.584 ft/sec

72. **(a)** ≈ 91.008 ft/sec
 (b) 59.97 ft

73. We have $x = (v_0 t) \cos \alpha$ and
 $y + \dfrac{gt^2}{2} = (v_0 t) \sin \alpha$. Squaring and adding gives
 $x^2 + \left(y + \dfrac{gt^2}{2}\right)^2 = (v_0 t)^2(\cos^2 \alpha + \sin^2 \alpha) = v_0^2 t^2.$

74. **(a)** $\mathbf{r}(t) = (155 \cos 18° - 11.7)t\mathbf{i}$
   $+ (4 + 155 \sin 18° t - 16t^2)\mathbf{j}$
  $x(t) = (155 \cos 18° - 11.7)t$
  $y(t) = 4 + 155 \sin 18° t - 16t^2$

 (b) At ≈ 1.497 seconds, it reaches a maximum height of ≈ 39.847 ft.

 (c) Range ≈ 417.307 ft
  Flight time ≈ 3.075 sec

 (d) At times $t \approx 0.534$ and $t \approx 2.460$ seconds, when it is ≈ 72.406 and ≈ 333.867 feet from home plate.

 (e) Yes, the batter has hit a home run. When the ball is 380 feet from home plate (at $t \approx 2.800$ seconds), it is approximately 12.673 feet off the ground and therefore clears the fence by at least two feet.

75. **(a)**
$$\mathbf{r}(t) = \left[(155 \cos 18° - 11.7)\left(\frac{1}{0.09}\right)(1 - e^{-0.09t})\right]\mathbf{i}$$
$$+ \left[4 + \left(\frac{155 \sin 18°}{0.09}\right)(1 - e^{-0.09t})\right.$$
$$\left. + \frac{32}{0.09^2}(1 - 0.09t - e^{-0.09t})\right]\mathbf{j}$$
$$x(t) = (155 \cos 18° - 11.7)\left(\frac{1}{0.09}\right)(1 - e^{-0.09t})$$
$$y(t) = 4 + \left(\frac{155 \sin 18°}{0.09}\right)(1 - e^{-0.09t})$$
$$+ \frac{32}{0.09^2}(1 - 0.09t - e^{-0.09t})$$

 (b) At ≈ 1.404 seconds, it reaches a maximum height of ≈ 36.921 feet.

 (c) Range ≈ 352.520 ft
  Flight time ≈ 2.959 secs

 (d) At times $t \approx 0.753$ and $t \approx 2.068$ seconds, when it is ≈ 98.799 and ≈ 256.138 feet from home plate

 (e) No, the batter has not hit a home run. If the drag coefficient k is less than ≈ 0.011, the hit will be a home run.

76. **(a)** $\overrightarrow{BD} = \overrightarrow{AD} - \overrightarrow{AB}$

 (b) $\overrightarrow{AP} = \overrightarrow{AB} + \dfrac{1}{2}\overrightarrow{BD} = \dfrac{1}{2}\overrightarrow{AB} + \dfrac{1}{2}\overrightarrow{AD}$

 (c) $\overrightarrow{AC} = \overrightarrow{AB} + \overrightarrow{AD}$, so by part (b), $\overrightarrow{AP} = \dfrac{1}{2}\overrightarrow{AC}$.

77. The widths between the successive turns are constant and are given by $2\pi a$.

Cumulative Review Exercises (pp. 573–576)

1. 0

2. $\dfrac{3}{4}$

3. -1

4. -1

5. 3

6. 1

7. e^2

8. 3

9. (a) 1 (b) 1
   (c) 1 (d) Yes
   (e) No

10. All $x \le -2$ and $x \ge 2$

11. Horizontal: $y = 0$
    vertical: $x = 0$, $x = \dfrac{1}{2}$

12. One possible answer:

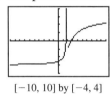

[−10, 10] by [−4, 4]

13. $\dfrac{1}{5}$

14. $-\dfrac{3}{(x-2)^2}$

15. $\dfrac{3 \sin (\sqrt{1-3x})}{2\sqrt{1-3x}}$

16. $\sin x \sec^2 x + \tan x \cos x = \dfrac{(\sin x)(1 + \cos^2 x)}{\cos^2 x}$

17. $\dfrac{2x}{x^2 + 1}$

18. $(2x - 1)e^{x^2 - x}$

19. $2x \tan^{-1} x + \dfrac{x^2}{1 + x^2}$

20. $(x^{-3} - 3x^{-4})e^x$

21. $\dfrac{3 \csc^2 x}{(1 + \cos x)^4}(1 - \csc x \cot x - \cos x \csc x \cot x)$
    $= \dfrac{3(1 - 2\cos x)}{(\sin^4 x)(1 + \cos x)^3}$

22. $-\dfrac{1}{\sqrt{1 - x^2}} + \dfrac{1}{1 + x^2}$

23. $\dfrac{1 + xy \sin (xy)}{2xy - x^2 \sin (xy)}$

24. $\dfrac{|x|}{2x\sqrt{|x|}}$

25. $\cot t = \dfrac{x - 1}{1 - y}$

26. $(\cos x)^{x-1}[\cos x \ln (\cos x) - x \sin x]$

27. $\sqrt{1 + x^3}$

28. $2x \sin (x^2) - 2 \sin (2x)$

29. $\dfrac{(2y + 2)^2(\sec^3 x + \sec x \tan^2 x) - 2 \sec^2 x \tan^2 x}{(2y + 2)^3}$

30. -1

31. (a) $v = 3t^2 - 12t + 9$, $a = 6t - 12$
    (b) $t = 1$ or $t = 3$
    (c) Right: $0 \le t < 1$, $3 < t \le 5$
        Left: $1 < t < 3$
    (d) -3 m/sec

32. (a) $y = -2x + 1$ (b) $y = \dfrac{1}{2}x - \dfrac{3}{2}$

33. (a) $y = \left(\dfrac{3 - \pi\sqrt{3}}{6}\right)\left(x - \dfrac{\pi}{3}\right) + \dfrac{\pi}{6}$
    $\approx -0.407x + 0.950$

(b) $y = \left(\dfrac{6}{\pi\sqrt{3} - 3}\right)\left(x - \dfrac{\pi}{3}\right) + \dfrac{\pi}{6}$
    $\approx 2.458x - 2.050$

34. (a) $y = -\dfrac{\sqrt{3}}{2}x + 2\sqrt{3} \approx -0.866x + 3.464$
    (b) $y = \dfrac{2}{\sqrt{3}}x + \dfrac{5}{2\sqrt{3}} \approx 1.155x + 1.443$

35. (a) $y = -\dfrac{\sqrt{3}}{2}x + 2\sqrt{3} \approx -0.866x + 3.464$
    (b) $y = \dfrac{2}{\sqrt{3}}x + \dfrac{5}{2\sqrt{3}} \approx 1.155x + 1.443$

36. (a) $y = \sqrt{2}x - 1 \approx 1.414x - 1$
    (b) $y = -\dfrac{1}{\sqrt{2}}x + 2 \approx -0.707x + 2$

37. $f(x) = \begin{cases} -x + 4, & x \le 3 \\ 2x - 5, & x > 3 \end{cases}$

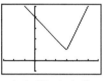

[−3, 6] by [−1, 5]

38. (a) $x \ne 0, 2$ (b) $x = 0$
    (c) $x = 2$
    (d) Absolute maximum of 2 at $x = 0$
        Absolute minimum of 0 at $x = -2, 2, 3$

39. According to the Mean Value Theorem the driver's speed at some time was $\dfrac{111}{1.5} = 74$ mph.

40. (a) Increasing in $[-0.7, 2]$, decreasing in $[-2, -0.7]$, and has a local minimum at $x \approx -0.7$.
    (b) $y \approx -2x^2 + 3x + 3$

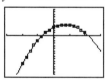

[−3, 3] by [−15, 10]

    (c) $f(x) = -\dfrac{2}{3}x^3 + \dfrac{3}{2}x^2 + 3x + 1$

41. $f(x) = x^2 - 3x - \cos x - 1$

42. (a) $\left[-2, -\dfrac{2\sqrt{6}}{3}\right], \left[0, \dfrac{2\sqrt{6}}{3}\right]$
    (b) $\left[-\dfrac{2\sqrt{6}}{3}, 0\right], \left[\dfrac{2\sqrt{6}}{3}, 2\right]$
    (c) Approximately $(-1.042, 1.042)$
    (d) Approximately $(-2, -1.042), (1.042, 2)$
    (e) Local max of approximately 3.079 at
        $x = -\dfrac{2\sqrt{6}}{3}$ and $x = \dfrac{2\sqrt{6}}{3}$;
        local min of 0 at $x = 0$
    (f) $\approx (\pm 1.042, 1.853)$

43. (a) *f* has an absolute maximum at $x = 1$ and an absolute minimum at $x = 3$.
(b) *f* has a point of inflection at $x = 2$.
(c) One possible answer:

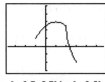

[−3.7, 5.7] by [−3,5]

44. Dimensions: $4\sqrt{2}$ by $\sqrt{2}$, area: 8

45. $y = \sqrt{2}\left(x - \dfrac{\pi}{4}\right) + \sqrt{2} \approx 1.414x + 0.303$

46. 3%

47. (a) About 1.9 ft/sec
(b) About 0.15 rad/sec

48. (a) $\dfrac{9}{16\pi} \approx 0.179$ in./min

(b) $\dfrac{36}{25\pi} \approx 0.458$ in./min

49. (a) 165 in.   **(b)** 165 in.
50. 2.5   **51.** 2π

52. $\ln 3 + \dfrac{26}{3} \approx 9.765$ **53.** 1

54. 7   **55.** $\dfrac{\ln 2}{1 + \ln 2} \approx 0.409$

56. $-2\mathbf{i} + (\ln 3)\mathbf{j}$

57. $-\cot(e^x + 1) - e^x + C$

58. $\dfrac{1}{2} \tan^{-1}\left(\dfrac{s}{2}\right) + C$

59. $\dfrac{1}{2 \cos^2(x - 3)} + C$

60. $\dfrac{e^{-x}}{5}(2 \sin 2x - \cos 2x) + C$

61. $\dfrac{8}{7} \ln|x - 6| - \dfrac{1}{7} \ln|x + 1| + C$

$= \dfrac{1}{7} \ln \dfrac{(x - 6)^8}{|x + 1|} + C$

62. 8975 ft^3

63. $y = -\dfrac{1}{t + 1} - \dfrac{1}{2}e^{-2t} + \dfrac{7}{2}$

64. $y = -\dfrac{1}{4} \sin 2\theta + \cos \theta + \dfrac{1}{2}\theta - \dfrac{\pi}{4}$

65. $\displaystyle\int x^2 \sin x \, dx = (2 - x^2) \cos x + 2x \sin x + C$

The graph of the slope field of the differential equation $\dfrac{dy}{dx} = x^2 \sin x$ and the antiderivative $y = (2 - x^2) \cos x + 2x \sin x$ is shown below.

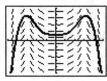

[−5, 5] by [−10, 10]

66. $e^x(x - 1) + C$

67. (a) $y = 4268e^{kt}$, $k = \dfrac{\ln(5/3)}{3} \approx 0.170$
(b) About 4268

68. (a) About 6.13°C
(b) About 2 hours and 27 minutes after it was 65°C above room temperature, or about 2 hours and 12 minutes after it was 50°C above room temperature.

69. $y = \dfrac{500}{1 + Ce^{-0.08x}}$

70. $y = Ce^{x^2/2 + 3x} + 4$

71.

x	y
0	0
0.1	0.1
0.2	0.2095
0.3	0.3285
0.4	0.4568
0.5	0.5946
0.6	0.7418
0.7	0.8986
0.8	1.0649
0.9	1.2411
1.0	1.4273

72. 4   **73.** $\dfrac{64}{3}$

74. ≈ 16.039 **75.** $\dfrac{27\pi}{2} \approx 42.412$

76. $\dfrac{\pi}{14} \approx 0.224$ **77.** $\dfrac{128\pi}{3} \approx 134.041$

78. ≈ 0.763 **79.** ≈ 2.556
80. 4   **81.** ≈ 6.110
82. ≈ 8.423 **83.** ≈ 3.470

84. ≈ 32.683 **85.** $\dfrac{9\pi}{280} \approx 0.101$

86. $8\pi - 2\pi^2 \approx 5.394$
87. (a) 1.2 m   **(b)** 180 J
88. (a) 70,686 ft-lb   **(b)** 4 min, 17 sec
89. ≈ 12.166 ft^3
90. $f(x) = \ln x$ grows slower than $g(x) = \sqrt{x}$.
91. Converges   **92.** Diverges
93. Converges   **94.** Converges
95. Diverges   **96.** Converges

97. $1 - 2x + 4x^2 - 8x^3 + \cdots + (-1)^n 2^n x^n + \cdots$;
$-\dfrac{1}{2} < x < \dfrac{1}{2}$

98. (a) $x - \dfrac{x^5}{5 \cdot 2!} + \dfrac{x^9}{9 \cdot 4!} - \dfrac{x^{13}}{13 \cdot 6!} + \cdots$

$+ (-1)^n \dfrac{x^{4n+1}}{(4n + 1) \cdot (2n)!} + \cdots$

(b) $-\infty < x < \infty$; Since the cosine series converges for all real numbers, so does the integrated series, by the term-by-term integration theorem (Section 9.1, Theorem 2).

99. $\ln 2 + x - \dfrac{x^2}{2} + \dfrac{x^3}{3} - \dfrac{x^4}{4} + \cdots + (-1)^{n-1}\dfrac{x^n}{n}$
$+ \cdots; -1 < x \le 1.$

100. $(x - 2\pi) - \dfrac{(x - 2\pi)^3}{3!} + \dfrac{(x - 2\pi)^5}{5!} - \cdots$
$+ (-1)^n\dfrac{(x - 2\pi)^{2n+1}}{(2n + 1)!} + \cdots$

101. $P_6(x) = 1 - x + \dfrac{x^2}{2!} - \dfrac{x^3}{3!} + \dfrac{x^4}{4!} - \dfrac{x^5}{5!} + \dfrac{x^6}{6!}$

By the Alternating Series Estimation Theorem,
$\left|\text{error}\right| \le \left|\dfrac{x^7}{7!}\right| \le \dfrac{1}{7!} < 0.001.$

102. $1 + \dfrac{1}{3}x - \dfrac{2}{2! \cdot 3^2}x^2 + \dfrac{2 \cdot 5}{3! \cdot 3^3}x^3 - \dfrac{2 \cdot 5 \cdot 8}{4! \cdot 3^4}x^4 + \cdots$
$+ (-1)^{n-1}\dfrac{2 \cdot 5 \cdot \cdots \cdot (3n - 4)}{n! \cdot 3^n}x^n + \cdots$

$R = 1$

103. Converges
104. Diverges
105. Converges
106. Converges
107. (a) $R = 1; -3 < x \le -1$
    (b) $-3 < x < -1$
    (c) At $x = -1$
108. (a) $R = 1; -1 \le x \le 1$
    (b) $-1 \le x \le 1$
    (c) Nowhere
109. $\left\langle \dfrac{2}{\sqrt{13}}, -\dfrac{3}{\sqrt{13}} \right\rangle$
110. $\left\langle \dfrac{1}{2}, \dfrac{\sqrt{3}}{2} \right\rangle$

111. Tangent: $\left\langle -\dfrac{4}{5}, -\dfrac{3}{5} \right\rangle, \left\langle \dfrac{4}{5}, \dfrac{3}{5} \right\rangle$

normal: $\left\langle \dfrac{3}{5}, -\dfrac{4}{5} \right\rangle, \left\langle -\dfrac{3}{5}, \dfrac{4}{5} \right\rangle$
112. (a) $\mathbf{v}(t) = (-\cos t)\mathbf{i} + (1 + \sin t)\mathbf{j}$
    $\mathbf{a}(t) = (\sin t)\mathbf{i} + (\cos t)\mathbf{j}$
    (b) 4

113. Yes. When $x = 130$ ft,
$t = \dfrac{130}{100}\cos 45° \approx 1.838$ sec and $y \approx 75.9$ ft, high
enough to easily clear the 35-ft tree.
114. $x - y = 2$; line with slope 1 and y-intercept -2
115.

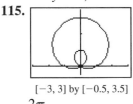

$[-3, 3]$ by $[-0.5, 3.5]$
2π

116. Horizontal tangent lines: $y = 0, y = \pm\dfrac{3\sqrt{3}}{4}$
vertical tangent lines: $x = -2, x = \dfrac{1}{4}$

Appendix A3 (pp. 584–592)

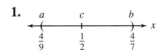

1.

$\delta = \dfrac{1}{18}$

2.

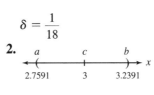

$\delta = 0.2391$
3. $\delta = 0.39$
4. $\delta = 0.36$
5. $(-2.01, -1.99); \delta = 0.01$
6. $(-0.19, 0.21); \delta = 0.19$
7. $(3, 15); \delta = 5$
8. $(-\sqrt{4.5}, -\sqrt{3.5}); \delta = \sqrt{4.5} - 2 \approx 0.121$
9. (a) -4
    (b) $\delta = 0.05$
10. (a) 2
    (b) $\delta = \dfrac{1}{12}$
11. (a) $\sin 1 \approx 0.841$
    (b) $\delta = 0.018$
12. (a) $\dfrac{1}{3}$
    (b) $\delta = 0.155$
13. $\delta = \min \{1 - \sqrt{1 - \epsilon}, \sqrt{1 + \epsilon} - 1\}$
14. $\delta = \min \left\{ \sqrt{3} - \sqrt{\dfrac{3}{1 + 3\epsilon}}, \sqrt{\dfrac{3}{1 - 3\epsilon}} - \sqrt{3} \right\}$
15. (a) $I = (5, 5 + \epsilon^2)$
    (b) $\lim\limits_{x \to 5^+} \sqrt{x - 5} = 0$
16. (a) $I = (4 - \epsilon^2, 4)$
    (b) $\lim\limits_{x \to 4^-} \sqrt{4 - x} = 0$

Appendix A5.1 (pp. 593–606)

1. $x^2 + (y - 2)^2 = 4$

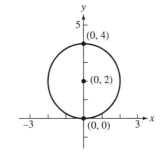

2. $(x + 1)^2 + (y - 5)^2 = 10$

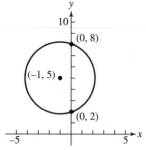

3. Center $= (-2, 2)$; radius $= 2$

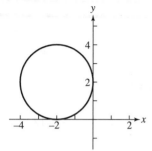

4. Center $= (2, -2)$; radius $= 2\sqrt{2}$

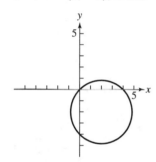

5. The circle with center at $(1, 0)$ and radius 2 plus its interior.

6. The region exterior to the unit circle and interior to the circle with center at $(0, 0)$ and radius 2.

7. $y^2 = 8x$; focus is $(2, 0)$; directrix is $x = -2$

8. $y^2 = -4x$; focus is $(-1, 0)$; directrix is $x = 1$

9. $x^2 = -6y$; focus is $\left(0, -\dfrac{3}{2}\right)$; directrix is $y = \dfrac{3}{2}$

10. $x^2 = 2y$; focus is $\left(0, \dfrac{1}{2}\right)$; directrix is $y = -\dfrac{1}{2}$

11. $\dfrac{x^2}{4} - \dfrac{y^2}{9} = 1$; foci are $(\pm\sqrt{13}, 0)$; vertices are $(\pm 2, 0)$; asymptotes are $y = \pm\dfrac{3}{2}x$

12. $\dfrac{x^2}{4} + \dfrac{y^2}{9} = 1$; foci are $(0, \pm\sqrt{5})$; vertices are $(0, \pm 3)$

13. $\dfrac{x^2}{2} + y^2 = 1$; foci are $(\pm 1, 0)$; vertices are $(\pm\sqrt{2}, 0)$

14. $\dfrac{y^2}{4} - x^2 = 1$; foci are $(0, \pm\sqrt{5})$; vertices are $(0, \pm 2)$; asymptotes are $y = \pm 2x$

15. Focus is $(3, 0)$; directrix is $x = -3$

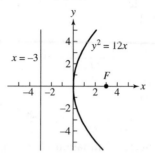

16. Focus is $\left(0, \dfrac{1}{16}\right)$; directrix is $y = -\dfrac{1}{16}$

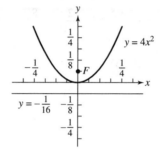

17. $\dfrac{x^2}{25} + \dfrac{y^2}{16} = 1$; foci are $(\pm 3, 0)$

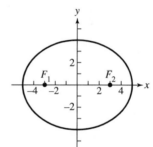

18. $\dfrac{x^2}{2} + \dfrac{y^2}{3} = 1$; foci are $(0, \pm 1)$

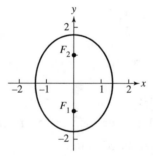

19. $\dfrac{x^2}{4} + \dfrac{y^2}{2} = 1$

20. $\dfrac{x^2}{9} + \dfrac{y^2}{25} = 1$

21. $x^2 - y^2 = 1$; asymptotes are $y = \pm x$; foci are $(\pm\sqrt{2}, 0)$

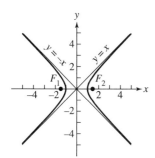

22. $\dfrac{y^2}{2} - \dfrac{x^2}{8} = 1$; asymptotes are $y = \pm\dfrac{x}{2}$; foci are $(0, \pm\sqrt{10})$

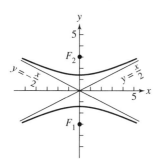

23. $y^2 - x^2 = 1$

24. $\dfrac{x^2}{9} - \dfrac{y^2}{16} = 1$

25. (a) Vertex is $(1, -2)$; focus is $(3, -2)$; directrix is $x = -1$

   (b)

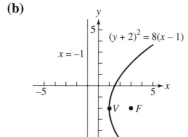

26. (a) Foci are $(4 \pm \sqrt{7}, 3)$; vertices are $(0, 3)$ and $(8, 3)$; center is $(4, 3)$

   (b)

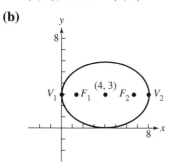

27. (a) Center is $(2, 0)$; foci are $(-3, 0)$ and $(7, 0)$; asymptotes are $y = \pm\dfrac{3(x - 2)}{4}$; vertices are $(-2, 0)$ and $(6, 0)$

   (b)

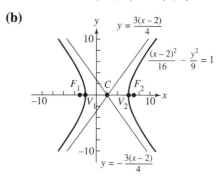

28. $(y + 3)^2 = 4(x + 2)$; vertex is $(-2, -3)$; focus is $(-1, -3)$; directrix is $x = -3$

29. $\dfrac{(x + 2)^2}{6} + \dfrac{(y + 1)^2}{9} = 1$; vertices are $(-2, 2)$ and $(-2, -4)$; foci are $(-2, -1 \pm \sqrt{3})$; center is $(-2, -1)$

30. $\dfrac{(x - 2)^2}{4} - \dfrac{(y - 2)^2}{5} = 1$; vertices are $(4, 2)$ and $(0, 2)$; foci are $(5, 2)$ and $(-1, 2)$; center is $(2, 2)$; asymptotes are $y = \pm\dfrac{\sqrt{5}}{2}(x - 2) + 2$

31. $(y - 1)^2 - (x + 1)^2 = 1$; vertices are $(-1, 2)$ and $(-1, 0)$; foci are $(-1, 1 \pm \sqrt{2})$; center is $(-1, 1)$; asymptotes are $y = \pm(x + 1) + 1$

32. Circle; center is $(-2, 0)$; radius is 4

33. Circle; center is $(7, -3)$, radius is 1

34. Parabola; focus is $(-1, 0)$; vertex is $(-1, 1)$

35. Ellipse; center is $(-2, 0)$; foci are $(-4, 0)$ and $(0, 0)$; vertices are $(-2 \pm \sqrt{5}, 0)$

36. Hyperbola; center is $(1, 2)$; foci are $(1 \pm \sqrt{2}, 2)$; vertices are $(2, 2)$ and $(0, 2)$; asymptotes are $y = \pm(x - 1) + 2$

37. Volume of the parabolic solid is $V_1 = \dfrac{\pi h b^2}{8}$; volume of the cone is $V_2 = \dfrac{\pi h b^2}{12}$; $\dfrac{V_1}{V_2} = \dfrac{3}{2}$

38. (a) Volume of the solid formed by revolving A about the y-axis is $V_1 = \dfrac{\pi x^2\sqrt{kx}}{5}$; volume of the solid formed by revolving B about the y-axis is $V_3 = V_2 - V_1 = \dfrac{4\pi x^2\sqrt{kx}}{5}$; $\dfrac{V_3}{V_1} = \dfrac{4}{1} = 4$

   (b) 1:1 $\left(\text{both equal to } \dfrac{\pi k x^2}{2}.\right)$

39. The slopes of the two tangents to $y^2 = 4px$ from the point $(-p, a)$ are $m_1 = \dfrac{2p}{a + \sqrt{a^2 + 4p^2}}$ and

$m_2 = \dfrac{2p}{a - \sqrt{a^2 + 4p^2}}$, and $m_1 m_2 = -1$.

40. $2\sqrt{2}$ by $\sqrt{2}$; area $= 4$

41. (a) 24π

    (b) 16π

42. 24π

43. 24π

44. $y = \dfrac{wx^2}{2H}$

45. $\dfrac{dr_A}{dt} = \dfrac{dr_B}{dt} \Rightarrow \dfrac{d}{dt}(r_A - r_B) = 0$

    $\Rightarrow r_A - r_B = $ a constant

46. *PF* will always equal *PB* because the string has constant length $AB = FP + PA = AP + PB$.

Appendix A5.2 (pp. 606–611)

1. $e = \dfrac{3}{5}$; foci are $(\pm 3, 0)$; directrices are $x = \pm \dfrac{25}{3}$

2. $e = \dfrac{1}{\sqrt{2}}$; foci are $(0, \pm 1)$; directrices are $y = \pm 2$

3. $e = \dfrac{1}{\sqrt{3}}$; foci are $(0, \pm 1)$; directrices are $y = \pm 3$

4. $e = \dfrac{1}{\sqrt{3}}$; foci are $(\pm\sqrt{3}, 0)$; directrices are $x = \pm 3\sqrt{3}$

5. $\dfrac{x^2}{27} + \dfrac{y^2}{36} = 1$

6. $\dfrac{x^2}{1600} + \dfrac{y^2}{1536} = 1$

7. $\dfrac{x^2}{100} + \dfrac{y^2}{94.24} = 1$

8. $\dfrac{x^2}{4851} + \dfrac{y^2}{4900} = 1$

9. $e = \dfrac{\sqrt{5}}{3}$; $\dfrac{x^2}{9} + \dfrac{y^2}{4} = 1$

10. $e = \dfrac{1}{2}$; $\dfrac{x^2}{64} + \dfrac{y^2}{48} = 1$

11. Take $c = 4$ and $a = 5$, then $e = \dfrac{c}{a} = \dfrac{4}{5}$ and $b = 3$. The equation is $\dfrac{x^2}{25} + \dfrac{y^2}{9} = 1$.

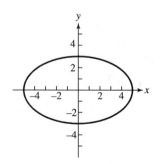

12. Take $c = 1$ and $a = 4$, then $e = \dfrac{c}{a} = \dfrac{1}{4}$ and $b = \sqrt{15}$. Therefore, $\dfrac{x^2}{16} + \dfrac{y^2}{15} = 1$ is a model of Pluto's orbit.

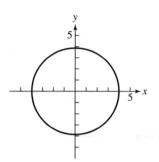

13. $\dfrac{(x-1)^2}{4} + \dfrac{(y-4)^2}{9} = 1$; foci are $(1, 4 \pm \sqrt{5})$; $e = \dfrac{\sqrt{5}}{3}$; directrices are $y = 4 \pm \dfrac{9\sqrt{5}}{5}$.

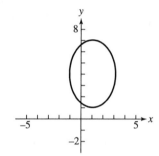

14. $\dfrac{x^2}{36} + \dfrac{y^2}{20} = 1$

15. $e = \dfrac{5}{4}$; foci are $(\pm 5, 0)$; directrices are $x = \pm \dfrac{16}{5}$

16. $e = \sqrt{2}$; foci are $(0, \pm 4)$; directrices are $y = \pm 2$

17. $e = \sqrt{5}$; foci are $(\pm\sqrt{10}, 0)$; directrices are $x = \pm \dfrac{\sqrt{10}}{5}$

18. $e = \sqrt{5}$; foci are $(0, \pm\sqrt{10})$; directrices are $y = \pm \dfrac{2}{\sqrt{10}}$

19. $y^2 - \dfrac{x^2}{8} = 1$ **20.** $x^2 - \dfrac{y^2}{8} = 1$

21. $e = \sqrt{2}$; $\dfrac{x^2}{8} - \dfrac{y^2}{8} = 1$

22. $e = 2$; $x^2 - \dfrac{y^2}{3} = 1$

23. $\dfrac{(y-6)^2}{36} - \dfrac{(x-1)^2}{45} = 1$

24. $\dfrac{x^2}{a^2} - \dfrac{y^2}{a^2(e^2 - 1)} = 1$

25. $a = 0, b = -4, c = 0$; $e = \dfrac{\sqrt{3}}{2}$

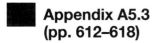

Appendix A5.3
(pp. 612–618)

1. Hyperbola
2. Parabola
3. Ellipse
4. Ellipse
5. Parabola
6. Hyperbola
7. Parabola
8. Ellipse (circle)
9. Hyperbola
10. Parabola
11. Hyperbola
12. Hyperbola
13. Ellipse
14. Hyperbola
15. Ellipse
16. Parabola
17. $(x')^2 - (y')^2 = 4$; hyperbola
18. $3(x')^2 + (y')^2 = 2$; ellipse
19. $4(x')^2 + 16y' = 0$; parabola
20. $(x')^2 + 5(y')^2 = 2$; ellipse
21. $(y')^2 = 1$; parallel horizontal lines
22. $4(y')^2 = 1$; parallel horizontal lines
23. $(x')^2 + 4y' = 0$; parabola
24. $(x')^2 - (y')^2 - 2\sqrt{2}x' + 2 = 0$; hyperbola
25. $4(x')^2 + 2(y')^2 = 19$; ellipse
26. $5(x')^2 - 3(y')^2 = 7$; hyperbola

27. $\sin \alpha = \dfrac{1}{\sqrt{5}}$, $\cos \alpha = \dfrac{2}{\sqrt{5}}$; or $\sin \alpha = -\dfrac{2}{\sqrt{5}}$,
    $\cos \alpha = \dfrac{1}{\sqrt{5}}$

28. $\sin \alpha = \dfrac{2}{\sqrt{5}}$, $\cos \alpha = \dfrac{1}{\sqrt{5}}$;
    or $\sin \alpha = -\dfrac{1}{\sqrt{5}}$, $\cos \alpha = \dfrac{2}{\sqrt{5}}$

29. $\sin \alpha \approx 0.23$, $\cos \alpha \approx 0.97$;
    $A' \approx 0.88$, $B' \approx 0.00$, $C' \approx 3.12$, $D' \approx 0.74$,
    $E' \approx -1.20$, $F' = -3$;
    $0.88(x')^2 + 3.12(y')^2 + 0.74x' - 1.20y' - 3 = 0$;
    ellipse

30. $\sin \alpha \approx 0.10$, $\cos \alpha \approx 0.995$;
    $A' \approx 2.05$, $B' \approx 0.00$, $C' \approx -3.05$, $D' \approx 2.99$,
    $E' \approx -0.30$, $F' = -7$;
    $2.05(x')^2 - 3.05(y')^2 + 2.99x' - 0.30y' - 7 = 0$;
    hyperbola

31. $\sin \alpha \approx 0.45$, $\cos \alpha \approx 0.89$;
    $A' \approx 0.00$, $B' \approx 0.00$, $C' \approx 5.00$, $D' = 0$,
    $E' = 0$, $F' = -5$;
    $5.00(y')^2 - 5 = 0$ or $y' = \pm 1.00$; parallel lines

32. $\sin \alpha \approx 0.32$, $\cos \alpha \approx 0.95$;
    $A' \approx 0.00$, $B' \approx 0.00$, $C' \approx 20.00$, $D' = 0$,
    $E' = 0$, $F' = -49$;
    $20.00(y')^2 - 49 = 0$; parallel lines

33. $\sin \alpha \approx 0.63$, $\cos \alpha \approx 0.77$;
    $A' \approx 5.05$, $B' \approx 0.00$, $C' \approx -0.05$, $D' \approx -5.07$,
    $E' \approx -6.19$, $F' = -1$;
    $5.05(x')^2 - 0.05(y')^2 - 5.07x' - 6.19y' - 1 = 0$;
    hyperbola

34. $\sin \alpha \approx -0.38$, $\cos \alpha \approx 0.92$;
    $A' \approx 0.55$, $B' \approx 0.00$, $C' \approx 10.45$, $D' \approx 18.48$,
    $E' \approx -7.65$, $F' = -86$;
    $0.55(x')^2 + 10.45(y')^2 + 18.48x'$
    $\quad - 7.65y' - 86 = 0$; ellipse

35. (a) $(x')^2 - (y')^2 = 2$
    (b) $(x')^2 - (y')^2 = 2a$
36. Yes, the graph is a hyperbola: with $AC < 0$ we have $-4AC > 0$ and $B^2 - 4AC > 0$.
37. Yes, $x^2 + 4xy + 5y^2 - 1 = 0$
38. $B' = B \cos 2\alpha = 0$
39. (a) $\dfrac{(x')^2}{b^2} + \dfrac{(y')^2}{a^2} = 1$

    (b) $\dfrac{(y')^2}{a^2} - \dfrac{(x')^2}{b^2} = 1$

    (c) $(x')^2 + (y')^2 = a^2$

    (d) $y' = -\dfrac{1}{m}x'$

    (e) $y' = -\dfrac{1}{m}x' + \dfrac{b}{m}$

40. (a) $\dfrac{(x')^2}{a^2} + \dfrac{(y')^2}{b^2} = 1$

    (b) $\dfrac{(x')^2}{a^2} - \dfrac{(y')^2}{b^2} = 1$

    (c) $(x')^2 + (y')^2 = a^2$

    (d) $y' = mx'$

    (e) $y' = mx' + b$

41. (a) Hyperbola

    (b) $y = -\dfrac{2x}{x - 1}$

    (c) At $(3, -3)$: $y = -2x + 3$;
        At $(-1, -1)$: $y = -2x - 3$

$[-9.4, 9.4]$ by $[-6.2, 6.2]$

42. (a) False. If $A = C = 1$, $B = 2$, the graph is a parabola.
    (b) False. If $A = C = 1$, $B = 2$, the graph is a parabola.
    (c) True. $B^2 - 4AC > 0$, the graph is a hyperbola.
43. (a) Parabola
    (b) The equation can be written in the form $(x + 2y + 3)^2 = 0$.
44. (a) Parabola
    (b) The equation can be written in the form $(3x + y - 2)^2 = 0$.

Appendix A6
(pp. 618–627)

1. $\cosh x = \dfrac{5}{4}$; $\tanh x = -\dfrac{3}{5}$; $\coth x = -\dfrac{5}{3}$;
   $\text{sech } x = \dfrac{4}{5}$; $\text{csch } x = -\dfrac{4}{3}$

2. $\cosh x = \dfrac{5}{3}$; $\tanh x = \dfrac{4}{5}$; $\coth x = \dfrac{5}{4}$;
   $\text{sech } x = \dfrac{3}{5}$; $\text{csch } x = \dfrac{3}{4}$

3. $\sinh x = \dfrac{8}{15}; \tanh x = \dfrac{8}{17}; \coth x \dfrac{17}{8};$

   $\text{sech } x = \dfrac{15}{17}; \text{csch } x = \dfrac{15}{8}$

4. $\sinh x = \dfrac{12}{5}; \tanh x = \dfrac{12}{13}; \coth x \dfrac{13}{12};$

   $\text{sech } x = \dfrac{5}{13}; \text{csch } x = \dfrac{5}{12}$

5. $x + \dfrac{1}{x}$

6. $\dfrac{x^4 - 1}{2x^2}$

7. e^{5x}

8. e^{-3x}

9. e^{4x}

10. 0

13. $\dfrac{dy}{dx} = 2 \cosh \dfrac{x}{3}$

14. $\dfrac{dy}{dx} = \cosh (2x + 1)$

15. $\dfrac{dy}{dt} = \text{sech}^2 \sqrt{t} + \dfrac{\tanh \sqrt{t}}{\sqrt{t}}$

16. $\dfrac{dy}{dt} = -\text{sech}^2 \dfrac{1}{t} + 2t \tanh \dfrac{1}{t}$

17. $\dfrac{dy}{dz} = \coth z$

18. $\dfrac{dy}{dz} = \tanh z$

19. $\dfrac{dy}{d\theta} = (\text{sech } \theta \tanh \theta)(\ln \text{sech } \theta)$

20. $\dfrac{dy}{d\theta} = (\text{csch } \theta \coth \theta)(\ln \text{csch } \theta)$

21. $\dfrac{dy}{dx} = \tanh^3 x$

22. $\dfrac{dy}{dx} = \coth^3 x$

23. $y = 2x; \dfrac{dy}{dx} = 2$

24. $y = 4x; \dfrac{dy}{dx} = 4$

25. $\dfrac{dy}{dx} = \dfrac{1}{2\sqrt{x(1 + x)}}$

26. $\dfrac{dy}{dx} = \dfrac{1}{\sqrt{4x^2 + 7x + 3}}$

27. $\dfrac{dy}{d\theta} = \dfrac{1}{1 + \theta} - \tanh^{-1} \theta$

28. $\dfrac{dy}{d\theta} = (2\theta + 2) \tanh^{-1} (\theta + 1) - 1$

29. $\dfrac{dy}{dt} = \dfrac{1}{2\sqrt{t}} - \coth^{-1} \sqrt{t}$

30. $\dfrac{dy}{dt} = 1 - 2t \coth^{-1} t$

31. $\dfrac{dy}{dx} = -\text{sech}^{-1} x$

32. $\dfrac{dy}{dx} = -\dfrac{x}{\sqrt{1 - x^2}} \text{sech}^{-1} x$

33. $\dfrac{dy}{d\theta} = \dfrac{\ln 2}{\sqrt{1 + \left(\frac{1}{2}\right)^{2\theta}}}$

34. $\dfrac{dy}{d\theta} = -\dfrac{\ln 2}{\sqrt{1 + 2^{2\theta}}}$

35. $\dfrac{dy}{dx} = |\sec x|$

36. $\dfrac{dy}{dx} = \sec x, 0 < x < \dfrac{\pi}{2}$

37. (a) $\dfrac{d}{dx}(\tan^{-1} (\sinh x) + C) = \text{sech } x$

   (b) $\dfrac{d}{dx}(\sin^{-1} (\tanh x) + C) = \text{sech } x$

38. $\dfrac{d}{dx}\left(\dfrac{x^2}{2} \text{sech}^{-1} x - \dfrac{1}{2}\sqrt{1 - x^2} + C\right) = x \, \text{sech}^{-1} x$

39. $\dfrac{d}{dx}\left(\dfrac{x^2 - 1}{2} \coth^{-1} x + \dfrac{x}{2} + C\right) = x \coth^{-1} x$

40. $\dfrac{d}{dx}\left(x \tanh^{-1}x + \dfrac{1}{2} \ln (1 - x^2) + C\right) = \tanh^{-1} x$

41. $\dfrac{\cosh 2x}{2} + C$

42. $5 \cosh \dfrac{x}{5} + C$

43. $12 \sinh \left(\dfrac{x}{2} - \ln 3\right) + C$

44. $\dfrac{4}{3} \sinh (3x - \ln 2) + C$

45. $7 \ln \left|\cosh \dfrac{x}{7}\right| + C$

46. $\sqrt{3} \ln \left|\sinh \dfrac{\theta}{\sqrt{3}}\right| + C$

47. $\tanh \left(x - \dfrac{1}{2}\right) + C$

48. $\coth (5 - x) + C$

49. $-2 \, \text{sech } \sqrt{t} + C$

50. $-\text{csch } (\ln t) + C$

51. $\ln \left(\dfrac{5}{2}\right) \approx 0.916$

52. $\dfrac{1}{2} \ln \left(\dfrac{17}{8}\right) \approx 0.377$

53. $\dfrac{3}{32} + \ln 2 \approx 0.787$

54. $\ln 4 - \dfrac{3}{4} \approx 0.636$

55. $e - e^{-1} \approx 2.350$

56. $e - e^{-1} - 2 \approx 1.086$

57. $\dfrac{3}{4}$

58. $8(e^2 - e^{-2} - e + e^{-1}) \approx 39.227$

59. $\dfrac{3}{8} + \ln \sqrt{2} \approx 0.722$

60. $\dfrac{99}{10} - 2 \ln 10 \approx 5.295$

61. 2π

62. π

63. $\left(2 \ln \dfrac{199}{100} - \dfrac{99}{100}\right)\pi \approx 1.214$

64. (a) $\dfrac{6}{5}$

    (b) $\dfrac{\sinh ab}{a}$

65. (a) If $g(x) = \dfrac{f(x) + f(-x)}{2}$, then

    $g(-x) = \dfrac{f(-x) + f(x)}{2} = g(x).$ Thus,

    $\dfrac{f(x) + f(-x)}{2}$ is even. If $h(x) = \dfrac{f(x) - f(-x)}{2}$,

    then $h(-x) = \dfrac{f(-x) - f(x)}{2} = -\dfrac{f(x) - f(-x)}{2} =$

    $-h(x).$ Thus $\dfrac{f(x) - f(-x)}{2}$ is odd.

    (b) Even part: $\dfrac{e^x + e^{-x}}{2} = \cosh x$

    Odd part: $\dfrac{e^x - e^{-x}}{2} = \sinh x$

66. (a) If f is even, then

    $\dfrac{f(x) + f(-x)}{2} + \dfrac{f(x) - f(-x)}{2}$

    $= \dfrac{2f(x)}{2} + \dfrac{f(x) - f(x)}{2} = f(x) + 0$

    (b) If f is odd, then

    $\dfrac{f(x) + f(-x)}{2} + \dfrac{f(x) - f(-x)}{2}$

    $= \dfrac{f(x) - f(x)}{2} + \dfrac{f(x) + f(x)}{2} = 0 + f(x)$

68. (a) $a = \dfrac{d^2s}{dt^2} = -k^2s$ is directed toward the origin.

    (b) $a = \dfrac{d^2s}{dt^2} = k^2s$ is directed away from the

    origin.

69. $y = \operatorname{sech}^{-1}(x) - \sqrt{1 - x^2}$

70. $16\pi \ln 6 + \dfrac{455\pi}{9} \approx 248.889$

72. (c) $A(0) = 0, C = 0, u = 2A(u)$